C000177661

Procurement Routes for Partnering
A Practical Guide

Procurement Routes for Partnering
A Practical Guide

By
Jon Broome BEng, PhD, MAPM

ThomasTelford

Published by Thomas Telford Publishing, Thomas Telford Ltd,
1 Heron Quay, London E14 4JD.

URL: http://www.thomastelford.com

Distributors for Thomas Telford books are

USA: ASCE Press, 1801 Alexander Bell Drive, Reston,
VA 20191-4400, USA
Japan: Maruzen Co. Ltd, Book Department, 3–10 Nihonbashi 2-
chome, Chuo-ku, Tokyo 103
Australia: DA Books and Journals, 648 Whitehorse Road, Mitcham
3132, Victoria

First published 2002

Also available from Thomas Telford Books
Enterprise focused management, Ted Hutchin. ISBN 07277 2979 9

NEC and Partnering: a guide to building winning teams,
John Bennett & Andrew Baird. ISBN 07277 2955 1

Partnering in Europe: incentives based alliancing for projects,
Bob Scott. ISBN 07277 2965 9

Unconstrained organisations: managing sustainable change,
Ted Hutchin. ISBN 07277 3016 9

A catalogue record for this book is available from the British Library

ISBN: 0 7277 3136 X

© JB Project Consulting and Thomas Telford Limited 2002

All rights, including translation, reserved. Except as permitted by the
Copyright, Designs and Patents Act 1988, no part of this publication
may be reproduced, stored in a retrieval system or transmitted in
any form or by any means, electronic, mechanical, photocopying
or otherwise, without the prior written permission of the Publishing
Director, Thomas Telford Publishing, Thomas Telford Ltd, 1 Heron
Quay, London E14 4JD.

This book is published on the understanding that the author is solely
responsible for the statements made and opinions expressed in it and
that its publication does not necessarily imply that such statements
and/or opinions are or reflect the views or opinions of the publishers.
While every effort has been made to ensure that the statements made
and the opinions expressed in this publication provide a safe and
accurate guide, no liability or responsibility can be accepted in this
respect by the author or publishers.

Typeset by Prepress Projects Ltd, Perth, Scotland
Printed and bound in Great Britain by MPG Books Ltd, Bodmin, Cornwall

This book is dedicated to my niece and nephew:
Abigail, at the time of finishing this book aged 3¾,
and Edward, aged 1¾

Contents

Acknowledgements

I would first like to thank the sponsors of the original research: London Underground Ltd, National Power plc (now Innogy plc), Anglian Water Services plc and UKAEA (the United Kingdom Atomic Energy Authority). I would also like to thank:

- all interviewees who participated in the original research, from which many lessons have been drawn
- all the individuals and organizations that I have worked with as a consultant and trainer for their insights and for allowing me to 'test run' models to check their usefulness to practitioners.

For their active participation in this book, I would like to thank:

- Sir Michael Latham for writing the Foreword
- Professor Perry of the University of Birmingham specifically for his input into Chapter 8 and, more generally, for being my academic mentor, role model, supporter and friend for some 8½ years now
- Norman Kerfoot, of the *Advance* consultancy, for co-authoring Chapter 9 and allowing me the pleasure of working with *Advance*
- Bob Soames FCIPS, of Contracts Consultancy, for giving detailed comments, particularly from a Chartered Institute of Purchasing and Supply perspective
- Malcolm Gibbins, of Amec, for his comments on Chapter 4
- Jeremy Brinton, the commissioning editor of Thomas Telford, for his (almost) ever-present enthusiasm for the book and patience with me.

Finally, I would like to thank my friends for their ongoing support, both while I have been writing this book and, more generally, for their understanding and patience. This especially means (in no particular order): Phil and Saha, Steve and Kate, Tim and Sarah, Mike, Mojo, Jane and Chris, my brother, Nick, and his wife, Paula, and my girlfriend, Claire.

Foreword

There has been a tremendous surge of interest and involvement in partnering in recent years. I suppose that my report *Constructing the team* helped by placing heavy emphasis on teamwork and co-operation rather than the adversarialism and conflict to which the whole construction industry was very prone when I began my work in 1993. Partnering received further major emphasis from the Egan report (*Rethinking construction*) in 1998, and it has received very substantial backing for public sector work in guidance documents and reports from the Treasury, the National Audit Office and the Office of Government Commerce. It is now the preferred procurement route for many major clients. Since it was almost entirely unknown in Britain even 9 years ago, that is a remarkable development.

However, there is still a great deal to learn. Plenty of so-called 'partnering' is not really partnering at all, leading to disappointment and reinforcing the inherent cynicism of many in the construction process. That is why this book is so valuable. It rightly seeks to ground the entire approach of partnering in commercial reality by genuinely aligning the motivations and aspirations of all involved in the project. A partnering agreement that ignores commercial pressures and incentives will break down at the first hint of trouble. Equally, one that is not rooted in real commitment by all to working in a genuine spirit of finding 'win–win' solutions will fail because support for the ideal of partnering is not even skin deep. The participants need to understand what partnering really involves and what responses it requires from all in the team, whether they be client, consultant, main or specialist contractor or anyone else throughout the supply chain. Achieving this balanced approach of real understanding, genuine commitment and the opportunity to fulfil desired commercial objectives is not easy, and certainly not cosy. It requires real training and genuine culture change by all involved at every level of the project.

This book will help them a lot. As the author says, readers do not need to read every word (although I would encourage them to do so). Busy people can pick out the core messages and implementation proposals and use them as a checklist for action. I am sure all readers will benefit from this serious and practical study and I commend it to a wide audience.

Sir Michael Latham
Author of *Constructing the team,* Chairman of Willmott Dixon Ltd,
Knowles Management Ltd and Partnership Sourcing Ltd

Glossary

This glossary is presented so that the reader can quickly become familiar with the terminology used in this book. The definitions are approximate, as there is often variation in how each term is put into practice. These issues are discussed in more detail in the book.

Banked award	An incentive payment that has been earned by the contractor or consultant but is 'banked' by the client until the end of the project.
Benchmark	A performance measure taken to measure how well you do what you do. Benchmarks can be used to compare performance either internally over time or with other organizations. High-level benchmarks are often referred to as key performance indicators (KPIs).
Benchmarking	The use of benchmarks to compare organizations' performance (see above). If a difference in the benchmark measure is identified it is desirable to look behind the figures to find out why this is and then to apply the best ideas that are applicable to your own organization, with modification if necessary.
CapEx	Capital expenditure: the costs of developing, designing and constructing a facility or asset up to the point at which it enters use.
Conditional award/incentive	An incentive that has been earned but which is 'conditional' upon achieving another measure of performance.
Cost-based contract	A contract in which the basis of payment is to reimburse the contractor his costs plus an allowance for profit and indirect overheads. An incentive mechanism of some sort is normally added to increase the contractor's motivation to perform.

Cost-reimbursable contract	A cost-based contract between a client and a contractor with no incentive mechanism to motivate the contractor to minimize costs.
ECC	The NEC Engineering and Construction Contract: the construction contract of the NEC family of contracts.
Fee-at-risk	'Fee-at-risk' contracts are those in which the consultant or contractor is paid on a fee basis. However, the fee is divided into two parts: a guaranteed base fee and a 'fee-at-risk'. The amount of fee-at-risk that is paid is graduated according to the achievement of project objectives and/or other aspects of performance.
Gatepost incentive	An incentive paid for achieving a set level of performance, for example a lump sum payment for completing by a set date. If this performance is not attained, no incentive is paid.
Graduated incentive	An incentive paid per unit of performance, for example an amount per day added or subtracted for early or late completion.
Incentive	An inducement to motivate an organization (in this book) or individual to place greater emphasis on achieving an objective or to act in a certain way. An incentive can take many forms but is usually based around money. A positive incentive, such as a bonus, provides a 'moving towards' motivation, whereas a negative incentive, such as a damage, provides a 'moving away from' motivation.
(Balanced) incentive plan	A contractual mechanism whereby incentives are stated against particular aspects of the consultant's or contractor's performance. The 'balanced' refers to the importance of designing the incentive plan so that the consultant or contractor is motivated to pursue the project's objectives, putting the same emphasis as the client on each objective.
Key performance indicators	Often abbreviated to KPIs; see benchmarks.
NEC	New Engineering Contract: a very flexible family of conditions of contract suitable for use in many circumstances in the construction and heavy engineering industries.

OpEx	Operating expenditure: the cost of operating a facility or asset once the construction phase is complete.
Partnering	The concept of collaborative working in the construction and heavy engineering industries which has many definitions and ways of being implemented. It is not a procurement method.
Performance incentive	An incentive, usually monetary in form, placed against a pre-stated measurable unit of end of project performance for the completed asset, for example time.
Price-based contract	A contract in which the basis of payment is what the contractor tendered per unit or item of output, irrespective of what it has actually cost.
Procurement	In construction terms, how you go about buying and maintaining a construction asset.
Project alliance	An alliance formed for a specific project. Although the various consultants, contractors and suppliers may have individual contracts with the client, there is usually an overarching incentive mechanism that ties the fortunes of the participants to the overall success of the project rather than to just their individual contracts.
Process incentive	An incentive based on a measure of how a consultant or contractor delivers the project, for example the level of programming.
Risk	The literature on risk gives many definitions. In this book risk is defined as a source of uncertainty in achieving defined objectives, the level of uncertainty associated with an individual risk being a combination of the likelihood and impact of its occurrence.
Risk management	A structured process for identifying and evaluating risks before developing and implementing actions to reduce the likelihood and/or impact of their occurrence.
Strategic alliance	An agreement between client and contractor(s) to carry out projects of a similar type over a number of years. However, the client is unable to define its exact requirements at the start of the alliance. Each project is usually let as a separate contract but partially governed by the terms of the alliance agreement.

Target cost contract	A cost-reimbursable contract in which a target cost is agreed and any under- or over-run of costs, compared with this target, split in pre-agreed proportions between the parties.
Term partnering	A partnering arrangement in which organizations partner under a term maintenance arrangement. It is therefore a longer-term arrangement.
Traditional route	A procurement route in which the client or its consultant does all the design before putting the project out to tender and selecting a contractor, normally on the lowest price, to construct the design.
Value	Used in a value management sense, whereby 'value' equals functionality divided by whole-life cost.
Value management	Value management can be divided into three stages/sets of sub-processes:

- value planning, which helps stakeholders to define what value means to them and then select the best outline scheme for maximizing it
- value engineering, which increases the value of the selected outline scheme, focusing more on reducing whole-life costs than on increasing functionality
- value analysis, which is the review of an existing project or process to determine what lessons can be learned and applied to future projects.

1. Introduction

This chapter outlines what you will gain from reading this book and how to use it. It is broken down into the following sections:

1.1 Why read this book? An overview.
1.2 The background to this book.
1.3 The style of this book and how to use it.

1.1   Why read this book?

This book is based on **two premises**:

(*a*) The introduction to the engineering and construction industries of the various collaborative processes that come under the label of 'partnering' can and has produced real benefits for clients, contractors, subcontractors and consultants, but

(*b*) How the parties to a contract act in practice is heavily influenced by what they perceive to be in their best interests — partnering workshops aimed at changing behaviour and implementing good process have their part to play. However, if we expect organizations and their people to behave in one way, for example collaboratively, proactively and in the client's best interests, yet reward them commercially for behaving in another, for example taking the traditional confrontational and contractual approach, then we are deluding ourselves that the desired results will be achieved consistently.

If you, the reader, fundamentally disagree with either of these statements, then this is not the book for you. However, this book is for you if:

- you wish to adopt or increase the effectiveness of partnering arrangements
- you want to decrease your construction costs and timescales, increase the performance and enhance the functionality of the asset resulting from the construction, and have greater certainty in achieving these objectives
- you are responsible for, advise on or just have an interest in different procurement paths.

As such, this book will be of interest (with the intention that it becomes essential reading) to lawyers and contract advisers on both sides of the contractual fence. It is also intended to be suitable for academic use because, although it is not written in an academic style, it cites existing literature and provides references at the end of each chapter.

This book is predominantly about the second of the two opening premises — essentially, how to align motivations so that it is in all parties' interests to embrace the collaborative processes and behaviours associated with partnering. It is relevant for those who have to partner on a project-specific, term maintenance or strategic basis, the last referring to a series of projects in which the opportunity of profitable repeat order business is the main motivator for the contractor. Those with project-specific requirements include:

- organizations that are regular clients of the construction industry but have a large one-off project
- public sector clients whose actions are to some extent constrained by the desire for public accountability
- construction clients that do not have sufficient supply-chain leverage — in plain English, this means that they are not able to offer the 'carrot' of repeat business to a contractor (this applies to about 80% of UK construction clients).

In all of these circumstances, a contractor may be more motivated to display opportunistic contractual behaviour in order to maximize the return. Despite this, there is remarkably little literature that addresses the motivational aspects of project-specific partnering. Indeed, little is written in any detail on how to motivate strategic or term partnerships other than by using the prospect of repeat order business. This book aims to fill that void. It does not go into the detail of how to write clauses but instead concentrates on the broad contractual frameworks and incentives. If the 'big picture' is wrong, then the detail will rarely save it. The detail can, however, undermine it, but the 'big picture' — the procurement or contract strategy — should be well thought through before the detail is dived into. Various studies have shown that choice of strategy can easily affect out-turn costs by plus or minus 10% on a one-off project basis, and there are a few examples of savings of 30% as a result of partnering.

This book starts from the viewpoint of the high-level principles, concepts and processes of partnering and procurement strategy and works down to their detailed application, especially of the more innovative routes. **It aims to give you, the reader, both the big picture and detailed useable guidance in an accessible form.** More specifically, this book will give you the following:

- A brief, practical, logical and integrated overview of partnering and when it is appropriate to take the partnering approach is given in Chapter 2.

- Clear guidance on the concepts and processes of developing a procurement strategy, providing much of the theory on which the practicalities in subsequent chapters are hung, is presented in Chapter 3. In addition, this chapter references common methodologies or tools that feed into the procurement process, for example value and risk management, selecting contractors on quality, benchmarks and benchmarking (Appendices 1–6).
- Knowledge of what the different mainstream, conventional procurement routes and traditional price-based payment mechanisms are, their advantages and disadvantages, when to use them and their suitability for partnering will be gained from Chapter 4.
- An understanding of the principles and considerations behind developing a balanced incentive plan, so that a contractor or consultant is motivated to pursue the project objectives in a balanced way, with the same emphasis on each as desired by the client, is pursued in Chapter 5. These same principles and considerations apply whether an incentive plan is being developed for a price-based contract, target cost contract or alliance.
- Knowledge of the different incentive mechanisms for motivating the consultant or contractor to pursue a specific objective of the client, including reduced capital cost under price-based contracts, reduced whole-life costs, increased functionality (which is not described as a measure against a specific objective), performance incentives (which are described as measures against specific objectives), improved process, and health and safety, will be acquired in Chapter 6.
- An understanding of cost-reimbursable contracts and their seven key implementation points and detailed advice on when to use such contracts will be gained in Chapter 7, which includes a detailed section on their financial administration.
- Building on the previous chapter, Chapter 8 gives insight into when to use target cost contracts and provides an additional[1] key implementation point,[2] including specific advice on how to agree the target, what risks to include or exclude from it and how to set the share profile, which governs the pain/gain share. This chapter also includes sections on guaranteed maximum price contracts and prime contracting.
- The characteristics of an 'alliance', both project specific and strategic, when it is appropriate to use these procurement routes and their key implementation points, with a focus on the procurement aspects, are covered in Chapter 9.
- Models for combining the incentive mechanisms for individual objectives, outlined in Chapter 6, and adding them to procurement routes, whether price-based, cost-reimbursable, target cost or an alliance, are presented in Chapter 10. This chapter builds on the previous ones and, as well as giving some additional principles and concepts, gives specific models on which multiple-incentive plans can be based.

- The final chapter (Chapter 11) summarizes the key themes and lessons that emerge from this book. In essence these are:
  - The contractual framework in which the parties work substantially defines their motivations, particularly in a one-off project in which there is little likelihood of repeat business for the contractor.
  - If motivations are aligned through the contract, then the parties are much more likely to work together, instigating the collaborative processes that come under the 'partnering' label, and much less likely to resort to traditional confrontational behaviour.
  - All parties are therefore more likely to achieve their objectives and a 'win–win' situation is achieved, but
  - The broad contractual framework, the type of incentives used and the details have to be fine tuned to the project; there is no universal answer or 'right' way to set up the contract.

The level of detail and its specificity (in terms of application) in Chapters 3, 5–8 and 10 is to my knowledge greater than anything previously published in this country. This book is one that enables practitioners to develop the framework, incentives and details, up to the point of writing the contract clauses, to put the contract/procurement route into operation.

1.2   Background to this book

This book originates from a combination of four circumstances:

- My research for my PhD on the NEC Engineering and Construction Contract (ECC). One of the aims of this contract is to give a stimulus — or motivation — to good project management, both through the procedures of the contract and through the flexibility it has in selecting the procurement routes. The latter stimulated my interest in target cost contracts.
- I was encouraged and supported to develop this interest by my then research supervisor and now friend Professor John Perry of the University of Birmingham, who has had long-term research interest in target cost contracts and incentives.
- At that time the literature was — and, to a lesser extent, still is — thin on the commercial aspects of partnering, in terms of both motivations and how open book financial administration works.
- I was also motivated by my own and others' cynicism that partnering was not just about 'being nice', but had to be founded on a strong commercial base, so that it could flourish in good times and survive in bad.

As a result, a research proposal was written and submitted to the Engineering and Physical Sciences Research Council, which, on account of one of the five referees' views, did not obtain funding on the grounds that it was not needed. This was despite the industry being willing to partly fund the study. However, thanks to this industry support, the research proceeded on a part-time basis for 2 years from March 1998. I would like to express my gratitude to those companies that funded the work; they were (in order of financial contribution): London Underground Ltd, National Power plc (now Innogy plc), Anglian Water Services Ltd and United Kingdom Atomic Energy Authority (UKAEA). Their involvement gave me access to various projects for research, although it could be argued that the study was ahead of its time in that there were not too many innovative arrangements in the UK at that time. However, it enabled me to access literature not only from the UK but also from Europe, the USA, Japan and Australia. The output of this research was numerous briefing papers to the industrial sponsors and a number of academic papers.

At the same time as this research was starting, I was also setting up my own training, consultancy and facilitation firm. Consequently, I have been involved in the development of numerous contract/procurement strategies, both as a specialist consultant and as a facilitator. I have also provided many days' training on the ECC, contract strategy and partnering. These three perspectives — research, consultancy/facilitation and training — have been instrumental in the development of this book.

The research approach has developed the high-level concepts and principles, taken examples from around the world and provided access to a breadth of projects in the UK and to the people who implement them. My gratitude is extended to all who gave their time for the research. The consultancy and facilitation has allowed me to be party to the 'nitty gritty' of the process and influences that affect the development of contract strategy. The training has provided further insight from participants' experiences and contributions, which I have learned from. It has also allowed me to develop this approach to putting material across.

However, a potential drawback of this approach is that too many of the examples in this book come from using the NEC family of contracts to put the procurement/contract strategy into effect. This is partly because it is almost certainly the most flexible standard form of contract in use today worldwide and partly because this is where the majority of my contacts have come from.

1.3   Style of this book and how to use it

As a result of giving training on contract strategy, the ECC, partnering, value management and 'soft skills', I have explored 'accelerated learning' techniques (see the bibliography at the end of this chapter if you are interested in finding out more about these techniques). I now apply these techniques to my own learning. Many of these techniques are incorporated into this book. Therefore, the reader will find the following features.

Highlighting of key statements is in **bold**. This means that **this statement is important**. It also allows the reader **to skim through this book or a chapter and gain a 'big picture' overview of the key principles and implementation**

points. I know that only the most dedicated student of procurement strategy is likely to read this book through from cover to cover. However, readers can quickly obtain the flavour of the book or chapter and the important points by skimming through them, **before referring to the detail when it is relevant to them to do so**, that is when actually implementing something specific, for instance when setting up a financial management system or setting the share profile.

> **Preview questions** These are located at the start of each chapter or section, asking readers to preview and reflect on what they want to learn from each chapter. So, having read so far and skimmed through this book to gain an overview, what specifically do you want to gain from reading it? (Note that purpose is extremely important for effective learning!)

> Boxes with a background tint like this contain case studies. These illustrate how the concept or principle has been applied in practice. This both promotes understanding and allows the reader to turn the abstract into the concrete, which helps memory.

Sections written in slightly smaller text and indented like this are designed specifically to engage the reader by asking questions while working through the logic. Reflect on why I would want to do this.

Could it be that by asking a question, I am both forcing you to think and raising curiosity about the answer! What are the benefits of this?

Perhaps it increases your understanding and retention.

> Boxes like this, with a single line surrounding the text, contain quotes from what other researchers and authors have said on the same or related points. This both reinforces what I have said and says it in a different way, which might give the reader a different insight, as well as satisfying the reader looking for academic rigour and/or other references.

Additionally, I have provided diagrams wherever possible to appeal to the visual sense and have aimed to write in a clear, accessible style. **Most importantly, the content is intended to be relevant and practical so that the reader can apply what is in the book!**

The intention is that you can either read through the book from cover to cover or dip into it for detailed advice as appropriate. If you are to do the second, I suggest that you skim through the book, slowing down to read and absorb the bold statements, mini-summaries and illustrations in order to understand main concepts, key principles and implementation points.

This will also expose you to the structure and relevance of the book. Then, **when a specific occasion occurs, refer to the relevant part for the detail.**

> **Review questions** At the end of each section or chapter, there are questions and/or scenarios for the reader to reflect on, or work through, and apply what has been learnt. While this book gives you information, it is only by thinking and applying what has been read that real understanding is gained. The boxes and questions prompt you to do this. You can, of course, scan the material at the start of the chapter, make up your own questions that you want answered, and then see if you can answer them having read the chapter. So, briefly reviewing what has been said in this section so far, how do you most effectively learn from a book?
>
> [Prompts: is it through discussing the content with others, teaching it to others, summarizing in your own words what have you learnt so far, reorganizing and sequencing the material, applying it in practice, making time to reflect on the content, doing regular reviews, even listening to music while learning, etc.?] And having done this reflection, how are you going to apply the learning technique that works for you to this book?

At the end of each chapter, I suggest that the reader converts the material into a mind or learning map to provide a visual summary of what has been discussed. Space has been left for you to do this. The exception is this chapter, where I have provided a learning map as an example to illustrate the principles. Learning maps are one of the most important discoveries in accelerated learning because by constructing them learners are reviewing the material and making their own connections. Consequently, such maps increase understanding and retention, both through their construction and by giving the learner a one-page summary of key points to refer back to.

However you use this book, I hope that it stimulates thought and allows you to apply partnering and alliancing concepts in a practical way. As a result, I hope that it aids the delivery of projects with greater certainty of and/or improved outcomes, as well as enabling the participants to work together in a much more enjoyable and rewarding atmosphere.

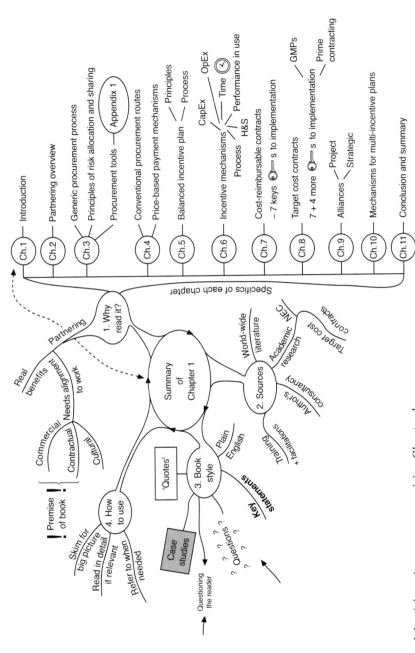

Fig. 1.1 A learning map summarizing Chapter 1

References

1. Buzan T. with Buzan B. *The mind map book: radiant thinking*. BBC Books, London, 1995.
2. Scheele P. R. *The photoreading whole mind system*, 3rd edn. Learning Strategies Corporation, Wayzata, Minnesota, 1999.

Bibliography

DePorter B. with Hernacki M. *Quantum learning: unleash the genius within you*. Piatkus, London, 1993.

McKergow M. and Jackson P. Z. *Accelerated learning training for trainers* (course notes). Mark McKergow Associates, Cheltenham, UK, 15–17 October 2001.

Ostrander S., Schroeder L. and Ostrander N. *Superlearning 2000*. Souvenir Press, London, 1995.

Rose C. *MASTER it faster: how to learn faster, make good decisions and think creatively*. Accelerated Learning Systems, Aylesbury, UK, 1999.

Rose C. and Tracy B. *Accelerated learning* (tape and guide). Nightingale Conant, Niles, Illinois, 1995.

2. Partnering

2.1 Introduction

The main purpose of this chapter is to give the reader a practical, logical and integrated framework for implementing partnering. In it I briefly review relevant partnering literature and practice before presenting my own framework for partnering. In presenting this framework, I will concentrate on the subject of 'aligned objectives' as this is most relevant to procurement.

Another objective of this chapter is to illustrate that partnering is not a utopia and that it is not always appropriate to partner. The corollary of this is to define the circumstances when it is appropriate to partner.

Preview   Quickly scan through this chapter now. Having done this, write down, as specifically as possible, what you expect to gain from reading it.

( )

( )

2.2   What is partnering? A quick review of partnering literature

The purpose of this section is to give readers a feel for the development of partnering in the UK, as well as enabling them to reference other partnering literature that takes their interest.

It is a generalization to say that most of the processes for partnering came from the construction industry of Japan, and that they are, in turn, the application of total quality management and lean manufacturing concepts, taken from the manufacturing industries (see, for example, reference 1). However, the motivation for partnering and its popularization came from the USA (see, for example, reference 2).

Sir Michael Latham, in his joint industry- and government-sponsored report of 1994,[3] drew attention to the benefits of partnering. In it, he stated his committee's confidence that partnering 'can bring significant benefits by improving quality and timeliness of completion while reducing costs' and that 'it includes the concepts of teamwork between supplier and client, and of total continuous improvement. It requires openness between the parties, ready acceptance of new ideas, trust and perceived mutual benefit.' The following year, the Reading University-based Centre for Strategic Studies in Construction published its guide *Trusting the team: the best practice guide to partnering in construction*[4] (referred to as the first Reading report). It included an illustration that quite neatly summed up the Centre's thinking on partnering at the time (Fig. 2.1).

In this diagram, the continuous improvement aspect relates to measuring the efficiency of what you are doing and finding ways to improve it. The problem resolution aspect relates to having an established disputes ladder, whereby an attempt is made to solve any disagreement at the lowest possible level within a fixed timescale, for example between site-based staff doing the work within a day. If no resolution can be achieved, it is referred up a level for resolution, again within a fixed timescale — say a week — and so on. The idea is that disagreements do not turn into disputes that fester for the duration of construction and result in a disputed claim at the end of the contract.

Other literature, such as the Construction Industry Board's *Partnering in the team*[5] and the European Construction Institute's *Partnering in the public sector: a toolkit for post award, project specific partnering on construction projects*,[6] refined or expanded on the main themes of the first Reading report.

In April 1998, Bennett and Jayes, with the Reading Construction Forum, published *The seven pillars of partnering — a guide to second generation partnering*[7] (known as the second Reading report), which focused primarily on strategic/term partnering arrangements stretching over multiple projects. They stated that there are seven components to successful partnering (Fig. 2.2), which can be defined as follows:

*   strategy: establishing the client's objectives and the broad framework for achieving them

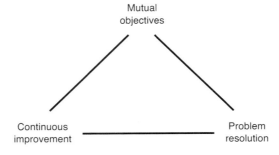

Fig. 2.1. Centre for Strategic Studies in Construction model of partnering in 1995

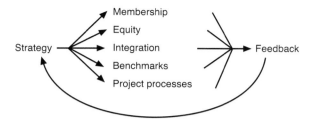

Fig. 2.2. Bennett and Jayes' Seven pillars of partnering

- membership: identification and assessment of suitable partners to implement the strategy
- equity: ensuring that the partners are rewarded on the basis of fair prices and fair profits
- integration: achieving greater efficiency by using co-operation and building trust
- benchmarks: setting measured targets for continuous improvement
- project processes: establishing best-practice processes based on process engineering
- feedback: capturing lessons and feeding them back into future projects.

Another report that has had a major impact is Sir John Egan's Construction Task Force's *Rethinking construction*.[8] Egan was the chairman of one of the UK's most progressive construction clients — BAA, the airport operator. Prior to this, he had been chairman of the car manufacturer Jaguar, and his report emphasizes the need for many of the principles and production processes used in the car industry to be taken up by the construction industry: for instance, total quality management techniques, 'lean' production principles, integrated supply chains, greater standardization and prefabrication, increased use of information technology, etc. The cynic may dismiss these, saying that construction is different, with each project being a unique 'one-off' at a different location, subject to different ground and weather conditions, rather than a production-line process. Although there is some truth in this view, there is also a lot of truth in the opposing view that, if you are a repeat order client, you may have a requirement for many projects of a similar type, in which the same processes, components, contractor, subcontractors and suppliers can be used. Evidence from clients such as BAA, J. Sainsbury Ltd, McDonalds and many other repeat order clients provides irrefutable proof that these techniques can be applied and do produce significant savings in time and cost and improved quality compared with the competitive tendering process. My main criticism of this report is that, apart from 'wait and see', it provided little guidance on how these principles and processes might be applied to the one-off or occasional client.

2.3 The development of partnering in practice

When facilitating both project and strategic partnering workshops, I am often asked to 'tell us how to partner', to which my response is 'you make it up as you go along!' This is because, **in reality, there are so many concepts and techniques that can be used under the banner of partnering. Which ones are used depends on your company's circumstances, business drivers, culture, attitude to risk, existing relationships with contractors and suppliers, length of time partnering, etc.** However, I and a fellow consultant, Lynn Margett, have observed a general spectrum of partnering, which is illustrated in Fig. 2.3.

As you look across the spectrum from left to right, you will see that each phase tends to build on the previous one. For instance:

- You may initially select a partner on a competitive bid price and against weighted quality criteria.
- For the next project you may ask fewer contractors to tender and pick a preferred contractor to negotiate with to finalize the details of the contract and price.
- Following this, you may do the same but under a target cost contract.
- On the next contract you may ask a contractor to work with your consultant to develop the design, and then develop a target price on an open book basis (in which the contractor reveals all the subcontract quotes and cost make-up).

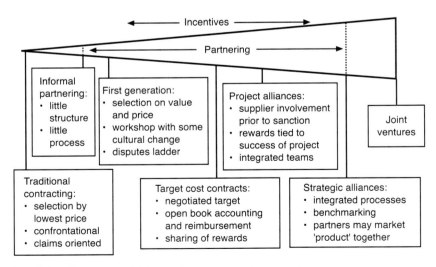

Fig. 2.3. Broome and Margett's spectrum of partnering

- Following this, depending on the project type, you may invite your mechanical, electrical and civil engineering contractors to work with your consultants under a project alliance in which each of the main parties' fortunes are tied to the success of the project, not to their individual contract.
- You may then form a strategic alliance with a contractor or contractors for work of a certain type or with a number of contractors, which will be brought together to form a project alliance when a suitable project arises.

Some clients will not have enough or sufficiently complex projects to develop across this spectrum. However, the point is that **the 'ing' in partnering suggests a dynamic approach and**, as the literature in the previous section points out, **continuous improvement, which implies continually trying to do things differently and better than before**.

2.4 A model *for* partnering

2.4.1 Overview

An overview of my own model for partnering is explained and illustrated below (see Fig. 2.4):

- *Aligned objectives.* People and companies act in a certain way because they perceive it to be in their interests. So if you want them to change how they behave, you need to change their motivations. This is the role of procurement.
- *Changing culture and skills.* Both client and contractor organizations have benefited in the past from acting in certain ways. Consequently, people and groups within those organizations have been rewarded with

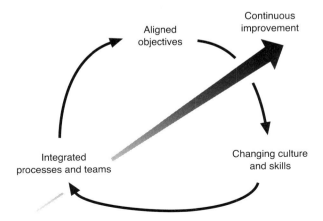

Fig. 2.4. A model for *partnering*

praise, pay rises, promotions, etc. for acting in ways congruent with their organizations' objectives and culture. This behaviour becomes ingrained at an individual level (attitude) and company or industry level (culture). To expect people to change overnight from, at worst, say, aggressively confrontational to trusting and collaborative is unrealistic but a change in culture is necessary for the next step.

Likewise, they will have learnt certain skills, both hard and soft, which reflect how the industry has worked. New skills may need to be learnt or the focus for applying existing skills changed. For instance, rather than a quantity surveyor reactively measuring what has been done, the same financial management skills can be applied in a more proactive way to forecast costs and help clients save money. Hard negotiating skills may be replaced with joint problem-solving skills.

- *Integrated processes and teams.* As trust and collaboration develop, organizations can lower their barriers to some extent and allow their processes and teams to become more integrated. This not only makes for greater efficiency, meaning that work is done faster and at lower cost than before, but also for more effective work, so that each party achieves its objectives to a greater extent.
- *Continuous improvement.* Because better outcomes are achieved, organizations and individuals can see the benefits of working together, so they perhaps adjust commercial terms to be less defensive and tie their fortunes together more, that is align objectives, and so the cycle of continuous improvement is repeated.

This model fits in with other models of business change in which business objectives, processes and organization and behaviour all have to be addressed to achieve long-lasting and sustainable change. The reason why it is called a model *for* partnering is because it can be used as the basis for partnering workshops by asking questions such as:

- What are the project teams' different objectives?
- Do we need to alter the commercial terms to further align our objectives?
- What can or could stop us from achieving these objectives?
- How do we wish to work together, in terms of values and behaviour?
- What additional skills do we need to access in order to achieve these objectives?
- What processes do we need to put in place to achieve our objectives?
- How can we integrate our processes with each other's to increase efficiency and effectiveness?
- How are we going to measure how well we are doing and continually improve our performance?

This model seems to make sense to people in terms of both training and facilitations. It will be explored in greater detail below although, as already stated, the 'aligned objectives' aspect will be considered in greatest detail because that is the subject of this book.

2.4.2 The case for aligned objectives

This subsection explores the case both for aligning the commercial objectives of the organizations intending to partner and for replacing the term 'mutual objectives', used in early partnering literature, with 'aligned objectives'.

The mutual objectives aspect of previous partnering models (see Fig. 2.1) relates to identifying the mutual objectives of the parties to a project — and there are many, for instance:

- zero health and safety incidents
- no environmental law, ethical or social transgressions
- completion within the contract period (note, I do not say the *original* contract period)
- minimum costs of administration
- minimum 'hassle' generally
- ultimately, a functional, fit-for-purpose end asset, within the client's timescale and budget, which suggests
- a desire for a degree of certainty over the outcome, which may be at the expense of minimum possible time or, particularly, cost.

The contractor also wants to achieve these outcomes, as they are likely to result in a satisfied client, which in turn will result in repeat order business and/or an enhanced reputation, leading to work from other clients. These objectives are therefore mutual. The first Reading report[4] suggested that these mutual objectives are identified and discussed at the start of the project. A typical partnering workshop, as well as defining a disputes ladder and processes for continuous improvement, will do this and solidify them into a mission statement for the project which the participants sign. Although this has benefits, in that there is a common focus and understanding, this 'partnering charter' very rarely has legal status.

However, although the client might want to incur minimum cost, the contractor — and subcontractors — want cash flow and ultimately profit. Contractors do not want repeat order *loss*-making work. Traditionally, the way to increase profit has been for the contractor to use the conditions of contract to make up for low bids by punishing the client for any mistakes and changes in the contract documents and project administration. Clients and their consultants naturally fight these claims. **Under traditional procurement routes not only are the minimum cost (to the client) and maximum profit (to the contractor) objectives often not mutual, but the client, contractor and subcontractors are unlikely to put the same emphasis on achieving each of the mutual objectives.**

The first Reading report[4] to some extent recognized this, stating that 'there must be a genuine alignment of interests in which everyone can win.' It reported that case studies — largely from the USA — found that:

- project teams' 'mutual objectives' are 'reinforced by well-thought-out incentive schemes'
- it is 'more efficient for the whole project team to have a real incentive to work hard when problems arise and to solve them at lowest possible cost. Profit sharing is one effective way of achieving this change in attitude.'

However, it did not address how this could be achieved.

Barlow *et al.* published a study of the practice of partnering in 1997, entitled *Towards positive partnering: revealing the realities for the construction industry.*[9] It found wide variations in how partnering was implemented — which matches the wide and varied number of definitions of partnering — and concluded that 'partnering is essentially a generic term embracing a range of practices designed to promote co-operation ...' From a business point of view, greater collaboration is not a project objective: it is a means to an end if you believe, as I and other authors do, that improved co-operation will generally increase the chances of a project being a commercial success.

Barlow *et al.* also looked at the contractual and commercial framework in their five detailed case studies. They found that in four of the cases clients used supply-chain leverage to motivate their partners, and this often took the form of threatening not to give repeat order business to a contractor that tried to enforce its contractual rights. This will come as no surprise to many contractors! Indeed, some authors appear to encourage this practice.[10] My view is that the 'carrot' of repeat order business should be used, but not abused, as in the long term the better contractors will not want to work for these clients and/or will include hidden premiums in their prices. I have had various conversations with contractors that confirm this premise.

One of Barlow *et al.*'s[9] case studies was a single project: the development of the Andrews oilfield in the North Sea (see Chapter 9 for a detailed account). In this case, the client, by way of its construction manager, developed an alliance approach in which risk and reward were shared among the partners. This project came in £39 million below its agreed alliance delivery cost of £373 million, which, in turn, was £77 million below the client's original estimate. It also came in 6 months ahead of its original 3-year programme. Barlow *et al.* noted that 'there is a difference between understanding each other's objectives and having aligned objectives — the objectives of each party might be evident to each other, but these might pull in different directions.' They went on to say that 'although the Andrews alliance had a partnering agreement signed by all members, the gain-sharing formula was the key method used to ensure that goals were aligned.' Although Barlow *et al.* did not believe that objectives have to be aligned for mutual trust to develop, they concluded that 'the introduction of an appropriate gain-sharing mechanism — as in the Andrews alliance case study — can act as a fast-track way of ensuring that organizational goals are pushing in the same direction and thereby help build mutual trust.'

Three of the seven pillars in the second Reading report[7] related to objectives: strategy, membership and equity. Strategy primarily relates to what the client wants to achieve and the broad framework for achieving it. This also relates to specific projects, as individual projects are a means of fulfilling the business objectives of the client. Value planning is a stage of value management and is an effective and auditable means of setting both business and project objectives (see Appendix 1). Although the second Reading report[7] did not mention the contractors' strategy, many contractors are now targeting partnering contracts because it provides better and more stable profit opportunities. Consequently, they are targeting specific types of clients. Equally, contractors are deliberately not associating with other types, for example, at the time of writing, the developers of Wembley Stadium!

In terms of membership, from a contractor's point of view, being in a club that provides greater tendering opportunities, reduced competition or even first refusal on a client's project is obviously a good stimulus to please a client. From a client's perspective, working with contractors on a repeat basis is far more likely to increase certainty of, and drive down, project costs and delivery time. This relates to the next aspect, equity, which is the different organizations' financial stake in a project and rewards flowing from it. The Reading report[7] stated that '**the goal should be to *align* everyone's interests with fully meeting the client's objectives. This means arranging the payments to each firm so that their profits increase directly with the success of the project.**' It also made the point that profits should not necessarily be shared out equally, but rather in a way that is relative to an organization's existing profit level and that within their industry. The example given was that of a property developer and architectural practice, in which the latter has not only a lower percentage profit on turnover but also less capital invested in the project (see the example developed in section 3.5).

If we look at more general literature on organizations working together, then Fasel's[11] first port of call is '*alignment* of purpose', with her three sub-bullet points being:

- develop a *common* vision regarding the desired outcome
- establish clear, measurable *objectives* and priorities
- manage the expectations of those involved.

It is for these reasons that the author prefers **aligned objectives** to mutual ones. The parties may not have mutual objectives, but if objectives can be aligned so that if one party gets what it wants then the other automatically gets what it wants then it is in both parties' interests to work together to achieve the same goals. **Aligned objectives should also take account of the importance of a goal, so that both parties put the same emphasis on achieving each goal relative to the others.**

More on the importance of aligning commercial objectives

Bennett and Jayes, in *The seven pillars of partnering*,[7] suggest that it is 'often best to begin the move to Partnering using a simple agreement to share any savings ... on some pre-determined basis'.

The European Construction Institute's report, *Partnering in the public sector*,[6] states that 'significant savings in cost that result from improvement in performance should also be shared in agreed proportions between the partnering organisations. The arrangement should be included in the contractual documents.'

The US Construction Industry Institute's Partnering II Research Team[12] found that in nearly all successful partnering relationships rewards were tied to team accomplishments and a 'belief in the potential for win/win outcomes ... and a willingness to pursue such joint gains'.

Kahn,[13] writing about the European Space Agency's experience in 1981, concluded that 'an elusive mixture of firm professional control combined with a spirit of co-operation and joint venture that best ensures the successful completion of a ... programme, and cost sharing formulae are one of the means for instilling and encouraging such an attitude.'

2.4.3 Changing culture and skills

Ultimately, it is people who design and build assets and, because to some extent each project is a one-off, how they work together and interact plays a key part in the successful outcome of a project. Changing people's values, beliefs and attitudes and, ultimately, behaviour can take time: people who have gained promotion, received praise and are perceived as being good at their job because they have acted in a highly contractual and perhaps aggressive manner for the past 20 years will find it hard to change overnight. Some will not be able to change, whereas for others it will take time. Having said this, well-designed workshops, both at the start and during a project, can stimulate significant shifts in attitude and behaviour, which then gain momentum and are reinforced by the practice of working together. Attitudes that are associated with partnering are trust, co-operation, teamwork, respect, communication, honesty, integrity and constructive feedback, to mention a few.

In the hard, commercial world of construction, culture is often not considered as something to be managed. Yet it can be. **And there is strong evidence to suggest that culture is one consideration, if not the key consideration, for success in business**.

Here is a rule of thumb for achieving cultural change from a former head of human resources in a large manufacturing company, who is now head of partnering for a construction company with an annual turnover of £400 million:

- It takes 3–6 months to copy a product.
- It takes 6 months to a year to copy the processes that led to the product.
- It takes up to 3 years to change the culture of a company.

This company had a highly successful track record of taking over and transforming failing companies or factories into top-performing companies. How long did it typically take them before the good results started to flow? About 3 years.

At the same time as changing individual attitudes and the project culture, **people need to be equipped with the skills to put this changed culture into action**. This might involve extensive retraining or just a change in focus in how skills are applied.

There are various ways of changing culture and skills at an organizational, project and individual level. Top-down commitment, publicizing early successes, training, facilitation and coaching are just a few ways in which culture and skills can be helped to change. But that is a topic for another book. For now, I will say that the **different contractual frameworks and conditions of contract can help build collaboration and change culture by:**

- aligning objectives and motivations so that by acting in its own best interests, a party is directly or indirectly acting in the other parties' best interests
- requiring transparency of costs and in programming

- being flexible enough to bring participants in at the point at which they can bring most benefit to the project
- avoiding subjectivity to reduce the temptation for participants to use that subjectivity to their advantage, for example by clearly defining risks, roles, responsibilities, etc.
- encouraging communication through the contract procedures.

The first three points are the subject of this book. The New Engineering Contract (NEC) family of contracts aims to improve on all of these aspects compared with traditional forms of contract. And based on my own previous research,[14,15] other research[16,17] and feedback from users (see, for instance, numerous articles in back copies of *NEC Users' Newsletter*, available on www.newengineeringcontract.com), it is a significant step forwards compared with traditional forms of contract (see also Appendix 3).

2.4.4 *Integrated processes and teams*

Two of the second Reading report's[7] seven pillars of partnering were integration (of teams) and (joined-up) project processes. Egan[8] talks about integrating processes, and Blockley and Godfrey's[18] book, *Doing it differently: systems for rethinking construction*, has a strong focus on systems thinking and adding value through integrating processes and teams.

> Mike Roberts, the former group technical director of BAA, said that 'if we are to move from the bad old days of confrontation-based contracting to the point where the construction industry [and here he quotes Egan] "works back from the customer's needs and focuses on the product and the value it delivers to the customer", then integration of the processes and the production teams to deliver value efficiently is absolutely key.'[19]

Barlow *et al.*,[9] in their study of partnering in practice, said that partnering in operation could be distilled down to a set of '*collaborative processes*'. I like this definition because, generally, partnering uses existing processes, for example value management (planning and engineering), risk management, total quality management, process mapping, etc., and applies them across contractual boundaries in a collaborative way. In this way, both effectiveness and efficiency are improved.

For instance, a reasonably forward-thinking client and contractor may separately process-map out all of their procedures for dealing with each other, but the number and timing of interfaces — points at which information is transferred — and the nature of information transferred will probably stay the same. Each party therefore does the same thing more *efficiently*. Alternatively, a client and contractor (who perhaps are going to be working together for a period of time) could decide to undertake a joint study of how they currently exchange information, decide which information is superfluous and when and to whom relevant information has to be transferred, and then map out new procedures. When their current software systems are due for replacement, they could decide to use compatible software to save time and money in transferring information. They are starting to integrate their business processes. They also schedule meetings to understand each other's concerns in order to make better decisions. This leads on to greater understanding, trust and collaboration and increased *effectiveness*.

2.4.5   *Closing the circle: continuous improvement*

Taking the situation above, as the success of the relationship starts to become evident — in terms of achievement of commercial objectives and relationships — each party's commitment to the relationship and trust in the other develop. The client and the contractor feel happy to renegotiate their contractual and commercial terms so that they are more aligned, both with each other commercially and with the reality of how they deliver projects. This further reinforces the change in culture and skills, leading to greater integration of processes and teams. Eventually, the project teams are sharing the same offices and functioning as one team without regard to which company they come from, forming a seamless team, so that a stranger coming into the office would be unable to tell for which company an individual works. At this point, they have formed a completely integrated team with integrated processes.

Do note that this will, at the very least, have an effect on the project organization. It may well also have an effect on how the companies are organized, which can lead into the whole area of organizational change.

One of my clients holds yearly workshops with strategic partners to improve relationships, integrate processes and sort out niggling issues. The results of this have been, for instance:

*   revised commercial terms and arrangements for pricing small schemes
*   organizing joint training days as both need training on the same topic
*   process-mapping out and revising existing procedures that are not working smoothly
*   reduced duplication in checking work.

Although the detail may be finalized outside the workshop, the principles, main action points and deadlines are agreed in the workshop.

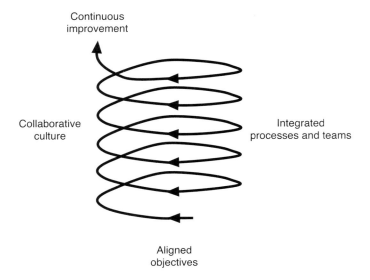

Fig. 2.5. The virtuous spiral of continuous partnering improvement

If this is the case, my model for partnering (Fig. 2.4) becomes a virtuous spiral of continuous improvement, as illustrated in Fig. 2.5. In my experience, it generally starts with aligned objectives, although in some cases it may start with a change in culture on a project procured under an established procurement route. However, I am unaware of any examples (in the literature or from my own research and consultancy experience) in which significant decreases in time and costs have been achieved without adopting different procurement approaches. The purpose of this book is to explore this area and give practical guidance to practitioners.

The concept of continuous improvement is also linked to that of total quality management and the techniques of benchmarks and benchmarking (see Appendix 6). Benchmarks are simply measures of how well you do what you do. This is the sixth pillar of Bennett and Jayes' *The seven pillars of partnering.*[7] Benchmarking means looking behind the figures to find out what other organizations within your benchmarking club are doing 'better' than you — or vice versa — in the different elements that make up a successful business. You then take the good ideas and modify them to your circumstances so that you improve what you do. The process of benchmarking also includes regular project reviews to learn from what worked and what did not. This provides feedback: the seventh pillar of *The seven pillars of partnering.*[7] The lessons learnt are then incorporated into the project processes and passed on to other project teams, thus providing continuous improvement.

Complex/high risk and/or high spend	Project-specific partnering	Strategic or term partnering
Simple/established technology and/or low spend	Competitive tender and negotiation on price, quality and service	Number of suppliers established by competition and negotiation. Efficiencies through refining processes
	One-off or occasional	Repeat order

Fig. 2.6. Matrix of when it is appropriate to partner (developed from Reference 10)

2.5   When is it appropriate to partner?

I have some bad news for partnering enthusiasts: it does not always make good business sense to partner!

Consider the matrix in Fig. 2.6. In the bottom-left corner is a client who is buying a relatively simple product on a one-off basis. A relatively simple product means that it is likely be fairly homogeneous across the marketplace, made en masse and with many sellers. This means that:

- There is minimal scope for an occasional client to affect the product by innovation as the technology is mature.
- There is much competition.

Consequently, the client will probably gain the best value by competition and hard negotiation on price, service and additional features. Even if the product is being made especially for the client's project, this still holds largely true (although if too hard a bargain is struck, quality and service may suffer).

For instance, if I want to buy a television, there are hundreds of models on the market and many suppliers. I define my requirements and narrow the potential models down to the ones that fulfil my criteria. I then approach a number of suppliers and negotiate with each, trying to optimize the balance of price, features and service, for example length of warranty etc. I buy when I have the deal that best satisfies my different criteria. There is little point in me approaching the manufacturer and suggesting how its mass-produced product could be improved, either to tailor it to my requirements or to take out costs that are passed on to me.

The concerns of a client in the bottom-right quadrant of Fig. 2.6 are similar. The product is likely to be of a similar type to that in the bottom-left quadrant: mature technology with a number of suppliers. Even a regular client will be unable to strongly influence what is produced. However, what is probably important is that the client is able to obtain a regular and smooth supply of the goods at a competitive price with minimum transactional costs. Therefore, the client will probably enter into non-exclusive agreements in order to obtain the discounts from bulk purchases and established service levels. If these service levels drop or the price becomes uncompetitive, the client will either order more from the other preferred suppliers or, ultimately, go elsewhere.

A chain of shops buying televisions might be in this position. It may have some influence in the long term on what is produced by feeding back what the end customer wants. However, it is not in a position to have 'specials' made and does not have the expertise to help reduce manufacturing costs, except through some economies of scale and an efficient delivery processes, for example multiple units ordered through an automated computer system and delivered at the same time, the purpose of which is to minimize human transactions. If that manufacturer's units become uncompetitive for any reason, the chain will order from another manufacturer.

The top-left quadrant of Fig. 2.6 is for complex, but occasional, purchases. The 'complex' implies that there is a development and implementation phase, that is a project. The process of supplying it may also be complex, with many constraints and risks. Therefore, interactions will take place over a long rather than a short period of time. This implies:

- more frequent interaction and, humans being humans, a relationship, meaning that there are benefits in collaborating, developing trust, etc.
- clients will want both to have input into defining the product and the supplier to have expertise in developing and delivering it to a budget.

If a client has pushed down the price to such an extent that the other party is likely to lose money, its internal emphasis will be on reducing costs, with the interactions focused on increasing the price to be paid by the client, both at the expense of quality.

Heavy investments in developing special components for a project and in integrating processes and teams have a limited scope for payback in hard financial returns because of the timescale of the project. However, it is still worthwhile aligning objectives over the duration of the project, investing in changing culture and skills and integrating processes and teams, but only to the extent that there will be a payback during the lifetime of the project.

An occasional construction client who buys a project from the construction industry once in every 5 years or less — and 80% of clients are in this category — fits this profile perfectly. Construction projects involve many interactions over a period of time and between a number of parties — client, consultants, contractor, subcontractors and suppliers — and the individuals employed by those parties. The extent to which investing in changing culture and skills and integrating processes and teams is worthwhile will depend on the complexity, magnitude and duration of the project.

The top-right quadrant of Fig. 2.6 is for complex projects (or products of a similar nature) that the client is purchasing on a regular basis. All the points that apply to the top-left quadrant, outlined above, apply even more so here because of the increased timescale of delivery, magnitude of spend and likely importance to the client company. This means that investments in changing culture and skills and integrating processes and teams, as well as in developing special components, have greater time and potential to make a payback.

The above situation is the case not only for repeat order clients, but also for contractors who supply a 'product' to clients on a regular basis, because they are repeat order clients to their subcontractors and suppliers. A classic example of this is Gazeley Properties, a developer that has positioned itself 'in the role of integrator, or the regular interface with, the supply market on behalf of clients with a fluctuating or "one-off" demand'[10] for the construction of food distribution or non-food retail facilities. As a developer, it supplies the whole package to clients. When approached by a client, having defined the needs and characteristics of the project, it will develop a contract strategy. For the standard components of a scheme, this may mean working with regular suppliers and subcontractors both to develop the scheme and to construct it. This has meant both integrating processes and developing special components, which would not be worthwhile and/or possible for a 'one-off' client to do. The result is that Gazeley Properties can supply a development tailored to the client's requirements quicker, cheaper and to a better quality than an occasional client would normally expect, while generating a 15% or greater profit on turnover for itself.

(Sources: references 7, 10, 19 and 20)

To quote the Construction Industry Board (Working Group 12):[5] 'Partnering … should not be confused with … long standing relationships, negotiated contracts, or preferred supplier relationships, all of which lack the structure and objective measures that must support a partnering relationship'; rather, in its view, partnering is 'a structured management approach to facilitate team working across contractual boundaries'. If the objectives are aligned, then the contract need not be a 'boundary'. Teamworking involves relationships and people. **From a business point of view, it is only worthwhile 'partnering' or investing in cultural change and integrating processes and teams if there is sufficient interaction over a period of time to generate returns that allow a payback on investment for all parties.**

2.6　Conclusion

There are many different definitions of partnering, and even more ways in which partnering has been put into practice. It is, above all, an evolving concept and practice, which in essence involves:

- aligning objectives, which is the role of procurement and the main theme of this book
- changing culture and skills
- integrating processes and teams
- continuous improvement.

However, 'partnering' is not a panacea and will not be appropriate in all circumstances. The decision as to whether two or more organizations should partner, and the extent to which they should, must be based on the type of business relationship the parties have and the extent to which investment in people, teams and processes is likely to pay back.

Review question 1 Reviewing the various models for partnering outlined in this chapter, which one makes the most sense to you? Why?

Review question 2 Be a critic! Using your experience and knowledge, what have I not covered that you think I should have? What do you disagree with? Why?

Review question 3 Ignoring procurement issues, what concepts could you take from this chapter and apply with benefit to all parties in the projects with which you are involved now? How specifically could you put these concepts into action? Are *you* going to act on this?

Review question 4 Revisit what you expected to gain from reading this chapter. If you have not gained anything, is it because the chapter did not cover what you expected or because you did not take it in fully at first reading and need to review? If you can identify your gain, summarize it briefly here.

Draw out a learning map to draw together and summarize what you have learnt from reading this chapter. This will also provide you with a very quick way of recapping your main learnings under this chapter.

References

1. Baden Hellard R. *Project partnering: principles & practice*. Thomas Telford, London, 1995.
2. Partnering Task Force. *In search of partnering excellence*. Construction Industry Institute (CII), Austin, Texas, 1991, CII Special Publication 17-1.
3. Latham M. *Constructing the team: final report of the government/ industry review of procurement and contractual arrangements in the UK construction industries*. HMSO, London, 1994.
4. Bennett J. and Jayes S. *Trusting the team: the best practice guide to partnering in construction*. Centre for Strategic Studies in Construction, Reading, 1995.
5. Construction Industry Board (Working Group 12). *Partnering in the team*. Thomas Telford, London, 1997.
6. European Construction Institute (ECI). *Partnering in the public sector: a toolkit for post award, project specific partnering on construction projects*. ECI, Loughborough, 1997.
7. Bennett J. and Jayes S. with the Reading Construction Forum. *The seven pillars of partnering — a guide to second generation partnering*. Thomas Telford, London, 1998.
8. Construction Task Force. *Rethinking construction*. Department of the Environment, Transport and the Regions (DETR), London, 1998.
9. Barlow J. *et al. Towards positive partnering: revealing the realities for the construction industry*. The Policy Press, Bristol, 1997.
10. Cox A. and Townsend M. *Contracting for business success*. Thomas Telford, London, 1998.
11. Fasel D. K. *Partnering in action — a guide for building successful collaboration across organizational boundaries*. Oxford, Pathways, 2000.
12. CII Partnering II Research Team. *Model for partnering excellence*. CII, Austin, Texas, 1996, CII Research Summary 102-1.
13. Kahn S. G. Partners in risk cost incentives in development contracts. *ESA Bull.*, 26 May 1981, 48–53.
14. Broome J. C. *The effect of the New Engineering Contract on the management of change*. University of Birmingham, Birmingham, PhD thesis, 1998.
15. Broome J. C. *The NEC Engineering and Construction Contract: a user's guide*. Thomas Telford, London, 1999.
16. Loosemore M. Dealing with unexpected problems — do contracts help? A comparison of the NEC and JCT 80 forms. *J. Engng, Constr. Archtct Mngmnt*, 1994, **1,** No. 2.
17. Bennett J. and Baird A. *Partnering and the NEC: the guide to building winning teams*. Thomas Telford, London, 2001.

18. Blockley D. and Godfrey P. *Doing it differently: systems for rethinking construction*. Thomas Telford, London, 2000.
19. Roberts M. Rethinking construction. *CIRIA News*, 2002, **1,** 1.
20. Smit J. Team players. *New Civ. Engr*, 28 September 1995.

3. The process and concepts of procurement strategy

3.1 Introduction

This chapter is predominantly about the concepts and process of procurement strategy. It first gives an introduction to the fundamentals of procurement strategy: what it is, what its purpose is and why it is important. It then gives an overview of the process for developing a procurement strategy. Subsequent sections then expand upon each stage of this process. Because the principles of risk allocation and sharing cut across many of these stages, these principles are simplified and illustrated. The aim of this chapter is for the reader to understand the process of and main principles required for developing a procurement strategy. Detailed knowledge of different procurement routes and the fine tuning of risk allocation, incentives, etc. is then provided in subsequent chapters.

The chapter also references various processes/methodologies that feed into the procurement process and aid good decision making and therefore better results:

(a) the concept of value in value management and the value planning process
(b) risk management
(c) the NEC family of contracts
(d) selecting contractors by value
(e) value engineering
(f) benchmarks and benchmarking.

These processes are considered 'off-line' in Appendices 1–6: Procurement tools. The original intention was to place these tools alongside the text of this chapter. However, because I wanted to give the reader enough detail about each tool for it to be applied, the amount of text expanded until the total almost exceeded the main text, so the material was moved to the appendices. As these tools are referred to elsewhere in this book, you are likely to want to read them at some point, so you might as well do so now!

Preview question   Look through this chapter and the procurement tools in the appendices. State below, as specifically as possible, what you want to gain from reading this chapter:

( )

( )

( )

( )

( )

( )

Now prioritize your aims, numbering each point.

3.2   The fundamentals of procurement strategy

3.2.1   *What is procurement strategy?*

When I started as an academic, we used to talk about contract strategy. Now we talk about procurement strategy because:

- the procurement profession now has much greater influence on how construction assets are bought and maintained, which means that
- projects are seen not necessarily as one-offs but as a series of purchases which can be put in the context of relationships and the business environment in which organizations operate and have potential for continuous improvement.

If we add these on to the traditional components of contract strategy,[1] then procurement strategy has the following components:

(a) It means understanding and defining the long-term business objectives and strategies of the potential parties. For instance, if one party is progressively moving out of construction, then it may not be wise enter into a long-term arrangement with it as the top-level commitment to the relationship will not be there.

(b) The organizational method or contract/package work breakdown structure is reflected in the procurement route that is selected, for example traditional route, design and build, target cost, project alliance.

(c) The payment mechanism specifies how the contractor is paid and rewarded and therefore affects motivations; this mechanism can include the use of incentives.

(d) The conditions of contract are traditionally selected on the basis of how closely they reflect the organizational method and payment mechanism chosen.

(e) The bidding procedure is reflected in how the parties to the project are chosen.

(f) There should be feedback and continuous improvement to meet the long-term business objectives — although there is no reason why this cannot also apply to one-off projects of any reasonable duration.

This book concentrates on the first three components of procurement strategy, although suitable conditions of contract are mentioned alongside procurement routes and payment mechanisms (see also Appendix 7).

> The CIRIA (Construction Industry Research and Information Association) report[2] on construction contract incentive schemes states, in relation to contract strategy, that 'there are fundamental issues relating to the allocation of risk, the combination of incentives, planning, cost management, auditing and monitoring of effective performance to be considered'.

3.2.2 What is the purpose of a procurement strategy?

In my view, the purpose of procurement strategy is to develop a commercial and contractual framework that aligns the objectives of the parties to the project, thus maximizing the likelihood of project objectives being achieved in the design and construction phases. The teams and people still have to implement the project for it to be a success, but the way in which they are selected, organized and paid, and the conditions of contract used, should not hinder the process. Indeed, I would argue that it should positively help by being the most appropriate framework to the circumstances.

3.2.3 Why is it important?

Research in the USA from as long ago as 1982[3] indicated that contract terms can affect project cost outcomes by plus or minus 5%. From my own observations in the UK, it is not uncommon for innovative procurement to stimulate cost savings of 10% on one-off projects and, in some cases, much more. In strategic alliances over a series of projects and a number of years, cost savings can be *at least 40%*, and a 50% saving in time from inception to operation can be achieved with increased quality, for example fewer defects, increased user satisfaction, lower running costs,[4] etc. This is far more than any client is ever going to achieve through competitive tendering alone.

The importance of procurement strategy

Yates[5] states that: 'Procurement advice can have an equally dramatic impact on a project's performance when measured in terms of cost and time as can design and engineering advice on project's performance when measured in terms of function and quality.'

The UK government's view is that: 'Contract strategy is the outcome of a series of decisions which are made during the early stages of the project. It is one of the most important decisions facing the project sponsor. ... Contract strategy has a major impact on the time scale and ultimate cost of the project.'[6]

3.3   Overview of a model for developing procurement strategy

I have not come across a published process model for developing a procurement strategy. Consequently, it is a black art to many and not really subject to much rigour, which is probably why, in the case of many failing projects, the principal reasons for failure can be traced back to the procurement phase. I offer the model illustrated in Fig. 3.1 as a starting point. A brief explanation of each stage is given below to afford the reader an overview of this process model. Each stage is explained in more detail later:

Stage 1: Information. This is the stage at which the different organizations and the project characteristics and context are identified and understood, before any decisions are made. In most decision-making models, information gathering is the first phase.

Stage 2: Select 'best-fit' procurement route. This is the overall organization of the contract packages that seems to be the most suitable for the circumstances of the project. This needs content knowledge, which is given in subsequent chapters, of both established (see Chapter 4) and newer procurement routes (see Chapters 7, 8 and 9).

Stage 3: Develop contract/work package breakdown structure. Within each procurement route there will be a number of participants. The aim is match up the capabilities or strengths of the potential parties to the project with the various elements and risks of the project. This includes to what extent design is allocated to a particular party.

Stage 4: Choose payment terms for each contract package. For instance, will it be a price- or cost-based contract? If it is the former, are incentives

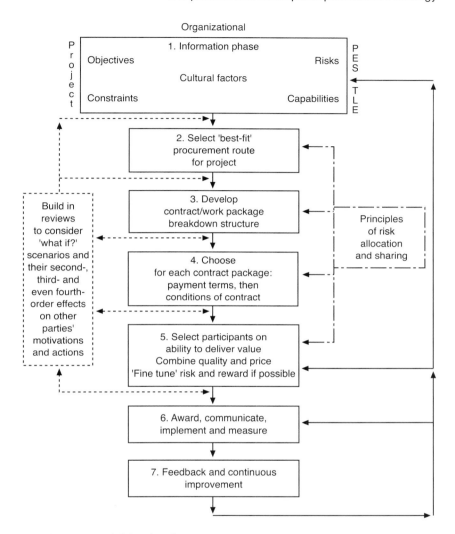

Fig. 3.1. A model for developing procurement strategy

applicable? If the latter, is it a target cost or alliance arrangement, and how will over- or under-runs in cost be shared? Having decided this, *select the 'best-fit' conditions of contract*, which may need some amending and fine tuning to the project's requirements.

Stage 5: Select participants on their ability to deliver best value. This does not mean simply selecting participants who provide the lowest cost tender, especially if, for instance, such participants have a history of making dubious claims and causing delays to other project participants. It means looking at the whole package of cost, technical and financial eligibility, and cultural suitability to obtain the best value package for the project. In particular, when entering into a partnering relationship, some discussion may be appropriate to ensure commercial and cultural alignment.

Stage 6: Award, communicate, implement and measure. This is the action phase, the idea being that if the whole project is set up for success from a procurement aspect then the implementation phase is much more efficient.

Stage 7: Feedback and continuous improvement. This is the closing of the loop, not just returning to the *information* phase.

The principles of *risk allocation* and *sharing* apply in all these phases to varying degrees. For this reason, they are considered in detail immediately after the initial information phase.

Build in *reviews* and consider *'what if?' scenarios* and their second-, third- and even fourth-order effects on other parties' motivations and actions. This involves generating different scenarios, such as 'what if this risk actually happens?', and then putting yourself into others' shoes and asking yourself what you would do if that risk was allocated to you. Their response (or your response in their shoes), both at tender and during the contract if the risk occurs, can actually undermine your reason for allocating the risk to them in the first place. It can also often undermine the achievement of other objectives. When conducting training on procurement strategy with clients, this is often the biggest eye-opener for participants!

A consequence of this is that **each successive phase of the procurement process may well have some impact that feeds back into the process and affects a previous phase, so the process of developing a procurement strategy is very much an iterative one**. This is why there are two-way arrows in Fig. 3.1.

> **Review question 1(a)** If you already have a good knowledge of procurement in construction, assess this model. For instance, what is good about it? What oversimplifications does it make? How would you adapt it?

> **Review question 1(b)** If you are a relative newcomer to construction procurement, imagine that you want to be able to analyse it as in 1(a). What further information and/or experience do you need to be able to assess it? How could you gain this?

3.4 Information phase

This section briefly discusses the meaning behind the words in the information phase of Fig. 3.1. On a day's consultancy I might spend almost the whole morning exploring and understanding the project and its complexities with the potential participants, before starting to develop the procurement strategy with them. However, once the information has been gained, the subsequent stages are relatively easy.

3.4.1 Organizational and project

I distinguish between these two levels because of their interdependency. For instance:

- A project's purpose is to further organizational objectives, so organizational objectives should be defined before the project objectives. Project objectives should be derived from organizational objectives.
- Organizational constraints and risks may act on a project, whereas some project-level constraints and risks might not and vice versa. If they do, then, although a risk might be held at project level, it has organizational consequences that need to be considered.

The reason why 'organizational' is used instead of 'client' is because all parties' issues — client, contractor, consultant — need to be borne in mind at a strategic level.

PESTLE is an acronym for:

- Political
- Economic
- Social
- Technical
- Legal
- Environmental

These are broad considerations from which different stakeholder objectives, risks, constraints, etc. may originate and have an impact on a project to varying degrees. For instance, political risks, such as the effect of a change in government, are far more likely to affect a government agency than a private company, which is far more likely to be affected by economic risks, such as a downturn in the economy.

3.4.2 Objectives

- *Organizational*. If a project or series of projects do not contribute to a business's long-term objectives, why is the business or organization doing it? Especially before entering into a strategic arrangement, all parties should be clear about their long-term business objectives and aware of the organizational and cultural changes necessary to achieve them. Understanding the business context is helpful not only in developing the procurement strategy, but also when working together.

- *Project.* Projects can have many varied and different objectives, each with a different emphasis or level of importance attached to them. Increasingly, clients are using the value planning phase of value management to define and weight their objectives and then select the 'best value' outline scheme. This method, along with the concept of 'value', is explained in Procurement tool 1 (see Appendix 1). I have used this method in training, straight consultancy and as a facilitator to help clients do this and can testify, from their reactions, to the clarity that the process brings to decision making.

One thing that surprises many participants in partnering workshops is just how similar and mutual many general project objectives are for the parties to a project (Table 3.1). However, from a procurement viewpoint, do remember that each party does not necessarily attach the same importance to one objective as the other party! Regular, repeat order, profitable work is in bold type because, from talking with contractors, this seems to be the biggest incentive. Although many of these are mutual, others need to be more thoroughly thought through. For instance, what is the balance between the desire for minimum cost and certainty of cost?

3.4.3   *Constraints*

Constraints are things that put limits on what you can and cannot do. Constraints can include such things as budget, cash flow, planning consents, procurement legislation, impact on the environment, etc., for example the topics in PESTLE. It is worthwhile identifying and understanding these before developing both the procurement strategy and the technical brief. It is also worthwhile challenging them by asking the following:

- 'What is stopping you from …?' or 'What is making you …?', which identifies the source of the constraint.
- 'What would happen if you did/did not …?', which identifies the consequences.

3.4.4   *Risks*

Risks are events or incidents that might stop or hinder you from achieving the defined objectives. At the information stage, we are interested in the principal project PESTLE risks. Section 3.5, which follows this section, describes the principles of risk allocation and sharing.

Table 3.1. *The typical project objectives of the parties to a project*

Client	Contractor/consultant/supplier
No health and safety accidents and minimal incidents	No health and safety accidents and minimal incidents
Minimum environmental impact and incidents	Minimum environmental impact and incidents
No negative publicity from above and, if possible, positive publicity leading to enhanced public and corporate image	No negative publicity from above and, if possible, positive publicity leading to enhanced public and corporate image
Minimum 'hassle' in terms of unplanned effort and cost to achieve other objectives	Minimum 'hassle' in terms of unplanned effort and cost to achieve other objectives
Predictable cash flow	Positive and predictable cash flow
A balance between potential for minimum cost and certainty of time and cost	A balance between potential for maximum profit and certainty of profit
Quality in terms of:	A happy client leading to improved
• functionality/fitness for purpose • conformance to standards, e.g. minimum defects	• reputation leading to **regular repeat order** • *profitable* **work**
Contractors, consultants and suppliers who want to work for client	Good publicity leading to an increased client base
Others?	Others?

3.4.5 *Capabilities*

These are the strengths and weaknesses of the likely parties to the project. At the information phase it is likely to be the current capabilities of the industry. The reason for identifying these is that, in developing the procurement strategy, you want to match the parties' strengths in managing risks with their responsibilities for meeting important objectives. For example, if good public relations have been identified as critical to the achievement of the project objectives, there is little point in selecting a contractor that has little or no experience of managing public relations and then making it the contractor's responsibility. Either select one that has the necessary experience or arrange the procurement strategy so that another party manages the public relations interface.

Other strengths and weaknesses could include the experience of the client in construction, whether there is potential for repeat order business, the relative financial strengths of the parties, their experience of design and build, size and type of job and how it relates to the parties' experience, etc.

3.4.6   Cultural factors

Different companies have different cultures. It could be argued that behaviours are driven by what is held to be important in that company. For instance:

- Over what timescale does the company think, for example is the managers' performance judged on short- or long-term profit on turnover? Or is it on return on capital invested?
- Are you judged to be a good employee if you follow the rules or if you challenge them?
- Does the company reward a high-visibility, reactive, all-action 'fire-fighting' approach or a more thoughtful proactive approach?
- Does it trust others until proven otherwise or start out on the basis of little or no trust?
- Does the company have a risk-averse or risk-taking culture?

All these factors, and others, affect how decisions are made, both before and during the implementation phase. Often they lie beneath the conscious awareness of organizations, yet drive the individual and therefore the organization's behaviour. Sensitivity to awareness of and, in some cases, challenge of these cultural values affects what procurement strategy a client will feel comfortable with and who it will be comfortable doing business with.

Review question 2 Reviewing this section, in your opinion, what general category of information that is relevant to developing a procurement strategy could I have missed?

3.5   Principles of risk allocation and sharing

There is much detailed literature on risk allocation[7-9] (see also the references in Appendix 2). I would argue that not only are these principles ripe for refining, they also need to take account of risk sharing. **Risk sharing is happening more because of the greater use of target cost contracts and project alliances, but it also happens in traditional procurement routes under price-based payment mechanisms.** For instance, in traditional contracts:

- If time damages are stated, unless the whole of the cost to the client of late completion is put on the contractor, then the financial risk of a time over-run caused by the contractor is shared.

- If a clause transferring the risk of, for example, exceptionally adverse weather to the client is included, then the contractor has to take the risk up to a stated threshold. If that threshold is exceeded, then theoretically the contractor takes the consequences of that risk up to that point, while the client takes the consequences beyond that point. The greater the overall consequences, the greater the client's share of the overall risk.

For these reasons, the principles of risk allocation and sharing are central to procurement strategy.

Risk allocation

Abrahamson, as long ago as 1979,[10] stated that 'the draconian view which seeks to place all risk on the Contractor and the belief that a Contractor should be safeguarded against all risk and in effect guaranteed his costs plus a profit are both an over-simplification. Each risk has to be examined separately and it may be that different solutions are appropriate.'

Trench's view[11] is that: 'the more risk the employer transfers to other parties, the more he must expect to pay for the privilege. Thus the employer should ensure that risk is wisely transferred as it is in his own financial interests.'

The US Construction Industry Institute[12] states that: 'project cost benefits can be realised when risk allocation is tailored to the circumstances of the individual project. Owners who routinely force maximum assumption of risk on the contractor are likely to incur higher project costs. Contract preparation that allocates risk with a balanced input from all parties will be most effective.'

As a consequence, the principles of risk allocation and sharing will be referred to throughout this book and are considered in detail below. However, **before risk can be allocated or shared, it is has to be identified and assessed in terms of likelihood of occurrence and potential impact, and some initial thoughts need to be developed on how it can be managed and who is most able to take the necessary actions.** Once allocated, the actions need to be developed and implemented. **Risk management is a process for doing this, and an overview is given in Appendix 2.**

My definition of **risk is a source of uncertainty in achieving defined objectives, with the level of uncertainty associated with an individual risk being a combination of the likelihood and the impact of its occurrence on those objectives.** Note that, by this definition, **risk can also be a positive opportunity** in which objectives are exceeded. My principles of risk allocation and sharing are, in order:

Principle 1. The extent to which the consequences of a risk are allocated to a party should take into account the overall effect on that party's business, both positive and negative.

Principle 2. Risk, both positive and negative, should be allocated to a party in proportion to the extent to which it can influence the likelihood of that risk occurring.

Principle 3. Negative risk should be allocated to a party in proportion to the extent to which it can minimize the consequences if that risk occurs, with all things being equal, the second principle taking priority.

Principle 4. For minor risks, clarity of allocation should take priority over the other principles, with a tendency towards allocating these risks to the contracting party, especially when those risks are likely to occur frequently.

Consider **principle 1**: the extent to which the consequences of a risk are allocated to a party should take into account the overall effect on that party's business, both positive and negative. The extreme of this principle is the 'rule' not to allocate a risk to a party that would become unable to deal with it if it occurred, for example through bankruptcy or lack of resources, as it will simply revert backwards up the contractual chain.

Stukhart[13] states that when allocating risk 'the relative ability of the parties to protect themselves against the risk must be considered'.

Ashley *et al.*[14] observe that 'the degree of risk aversion exhibited by a decision maker increases as his ability to absorb losses decreases. With contractors and designers undercapitalized relative to the size of the risks they face, the costs ... of accepting such risks would be higher than to the owner, who is typically less risk averse.'

Barnes, in a paper given to a conference in 1991,[15] proposes that: 'Contractors are typically risk averse and clients are typically risk neutral', before going on to say, 'if this is true, the client achieves a marginal economy if, other things being equal, a risk is allocated to him. This is one reason why the basic rule of risk allocation leaves risk over which neither party has influence to the client.'

The overall effect on a party's business is related to its turnover, profit on turnover and return on capital invested.

In the civil engineering and building industries, profit on turnover is typically 2–3%, with return on capital invested typically in a ratio of 1:6–1:7. Therefore, a 1% change in project construction costs has a 6–7% effect on a contractor's return on capital invested. For a client, a 1% change in construction costs equals a 1% change in capital costs, which may be insignificant over the operating lifetime of a project. Now assume that the contractor and the client have the same turnover. So, for an uncontrollable risk over which neither party has any influence, although the consequences of the risk are the same in absolute terms, for whom are the consequences greater in relative terms?

The contractor. Thus, who will charge a higher premium for taking that risk? Again, the contractor. Obviously, this ratio of return on capital invested varies between sectors and within sectors; for instance, some construction companies own almost no plant whereas others almost consider construction a down-line activity of their plant or aggregates business, which is where they make their real money. The latter invest far more in capital than the former.

Now let us put value for money and risk aversion into the equation. Imagine that you are a small client company with a turnover of £10 million and a profit of £0.5 million per annum. You want a new factory built and are given out-turn costs ranging from £4.8 million, if no risks occur, to £6 million, if all the identified risks occur. A risk analysis indicates that the most likely outcome is £5.1 million. A contractor says that it will build the factory either for £5.25 million, taking all the risks, or for £4.8 million, but with the client paying for identified risks as and when they occur. Which, as the client, would you accept?

Most participants on my courses go for the £5.25 million 'all in' offer because of the effect that all the risks occurring would have on the business. They go for certainty.

Now imagine that you are the same client, but with a turnover of £100 million and a profit of £5 million per annum. How does this affect your decision? In this case, most participants on my courses reconsider their positions and go for the £4.8 million offer but with risks excluded.

Go back to the scenario in which the client has a turnover of £5 million and decides to go for a lump sum contract with all risks taken by the contractor. There are two contractors; both know that the most likely out-turn cost is £5.1 million and they are equal in every respect. However, one has a turnover of £200 million and a profit of £5 million, while the other has a turnover of £20 million and a profit of £0.5 million. Who is likely to charge the larger 'premium' for taking on the risks?

And, therefore, who is likely to offer the client a more competitive tender price and better value for money?

Here is an example of allocating uncontrollable risk to the financially weaker party. One public sector client with a large annual spend across the UK had a policy of allocating the costs of adverse weather — an uncontrollable risk — to contractors but allowing extensions of time for it. Large time-related damages were then placed on the contractor for over-running the contractual date for completion. Because the client wanted to encourage contractors to minimize the impact of adverse weather when it occurred, they decided to take away the extension of time clause. Depending on the area of the country, tender prices rose overnight by 20–50%. Unsurprisingly, the client rapidly changed back to the old policy as it was not getting value for money.

To recap, **principle 1** is: the extent to which the consequences of a risk are allocated to a party should take into account the overall effect on that party's business, both positive and negative. I hope that the above questions and example have illustrated the importance of the first principle and why, **whether a risk is controllable or not, the first principle should be the starting point when considering how to allocate and share risk**.

Now let us consider **principle 2**: risk, both positive and negative, should be allocated to a party in proportion to the extent to which it can influence the likelihood of that risk occurring. This is often stated in the construction press as 'risk should be allocated to the party who can best manage it', but does this mean prevent it or minimize the consequences if it does occur?

> Trench[11] (ignoring my other principles) states that 'each risk has a cost which must ultimately be borne by the employers of an industry if it is to remain profitable and thus survive. The party best able to control the circumstances that could lead to loss will price the risk of that loss the lowest. Therefore to reduce the cost to the employer that party should be allocated the risk.'

For downside or negative risk, **principle 2** means that the party that can best prevent it occurring is given a sufficient stake in its consequences to motivate it to do that. For positive or upside risk, this means that the rewards for managing it well are commensurate with the expertise and effort put into obtaining a positive result. However, we also need to consider the first principle of risk allocation.

Consider an architectural practice with a base fee totalling 2% of the projected project costs on which it makes a 25% profit, so that the total fee paid to the architect is 2.5% of the forecast project cost. The client decides to motivate the practice to produce savings by giving it a 50% share of any savings made through good design, compared with the industry standard. This seems fair, doesn't it?

Consequently, the architectural practice invests twice as much time and money in the design and, through innovative design and value engineering, saves 10% on project costs, of which the practice receives half, that is 5%. This would mean that, although the practice's design costs double to 4% of the original project costs, its income goes up to 7.5%, so its profit increases sevenfold, from 0.5% of the original project estimate to 3.5%. Does this now seem fair from a client's perspective?

And do you think that the architectural practice may be overmotivated to reduce costs at the expense of quality? While this might be a little contrived, what share of any savings on project costs do you think would motivate the practice to spend time on saving costs yet not overmotivate it to reduce quality? (See Chapter 5 for more on this.)

Now take the same cost base of 2% of project costs for doing design, but with the architectural practice taking half of any cost over-run compared with projected out-turn costs. What risk premium would you, as the head of the practice, add on to the base costs to protect yourself?

Principle 3 is that downside or **negative risk should be allocated to a party in proportion to the extent to which it can minimize the consequences if that risk occurs, with all things being equal, the second principle taking priority**. Why should the second principle take priority? It should do so because it encourages a proactive response to risk minimization rather than a reactive 'fire-fighting' approach. Ground conditions are a classic example of this: although the contractor controls the resources to minimize the consequences or impact of unexpected ground conditions occurring, the client typically has far more influence over site location and layout of the asset and is able to reduce the likelihood by good site investigation. Consequently, ground conditions risk, above a certain threshold, is typically allocated to the client in civil engineering contracts. If it is not, then a client may pay a high risk premium.

Transferring risk and control to the contractor

The Scottish Office (now the Scottish Executive) has often allocated ground conditions risk for road projects to the contractor, with savings being generated. Suddenly, unusable earth becomes usable! However, the contractor has also had far greater early input into the project, being able to do additional site investigations, which are ultimately reimbursed, before signing the contract. Additionally, within the constraints laid down, the contractor is given greater control of design, allowing far more innovative design of structures and use of earth control techniques. Lastly, the contractor is asked for alternative tenders, with, for instance, ground conditions risk being included and excluded. Consequently, the Scottish Office has sometimes taken back the risk if it thought the premium being paid did not give value for money.

(Source: reference 16)

This principle does say 'all things being equal'. So, if, by spending a relatively small amount, the contractor can avoid or dramatically reduce the likelihood of a high-impact risk, which a client would normally take, then it may be worthwhile to allocate that risk to the contractor. For instance, on one project within an existing tunnel, there was a high likelihood of the tunnel flooding if the drains were not regularly cleaned. The costs of doing this were included in the contractor's negotiated target and the contractor took the risk of flooding for normal weather conditions.

An example of poor risk allocation?

The Heathrow Express tunnel collapse was perhaps the biggest civil engineering disaster in the UK in the 1990s. Let us consider the risks:

- The works were tunnelling, traditionally a risky type of job in which risks are often shared because of the effect on progress of variable ground conditions.
- They involved the use of innovative tunnelling technology for the first time in the UK: the new Austrian tunnelling method (NATM). By this method, although the line, level and internal dimensions of the tunnel are given to the contractor, the thickness of the tunnel lining and structure is effectively designed as the tunnel progresses, depending on the earth encountered and measured displacement around the tunnel.
- The works were under an area particularly sensitive to displacement: Heathrow is one of the world's busiest international airports. The impact of a tunnelling risk occurring would be large.

Additionally, it was decided to let the contract under what was, at the time, a relatively innovative form of contract — the *New Engineering Contract*, 1st edn — and innovation is always a risk in itself. However, one of the benefits of that family of contracts is the better transparency and control of financial and time management that it gives both parties. This is an advantage to the client in that it is much harder for the contractor to make up for a low tender or blame time delays on the client.

The contract was let with tendered price being the predominant attribute, and the contractor chosen apparently tendered approximately £5 million less than the other contractor on a contract worth more than £60 million. The option chosen was option A: Priced contract with activity schedules. Effectively, this was a lump sum contract, with the contractor being paid only when predefined activities were completed (see section 4.4.7 for a fuller description of activity schedules). The contractor was made responsible — and therefore carried the risk — for design and quality assurance as the tunnel progressed. Short of deleting the physical conditions clause for extra payment, the client could hardly have put more risk on to the contractor.

What do you think happened when the contractor started to slip behind on progress and not meet the forecast budgets, and then found that the loss could not be made up through the contract? Could quality and health and safety have suffered and have been two of the contributory reasons for the collapse? This was one of the conclusions of the Health and Safety Executive report. Legally, the contractor was responsible, but who chose the risk allocation and conditions of contract, possibly creating the commercial drivers for poor quality and poor health and safety?

Principle 4 is for minor risks: clarity of allocation should take priority over the other principles, with a tendency towards allocating these risks to the contracting party, especially when frequently occurring. If they are minor risks, then the parties are relatively indifferent about who takes them, so what is not wanted is arguments of ownership. Thus, clarity takes precedence over the other principles. Why should frequently occurring risks be allocated to the contractor? There are two reasons:

- If they are allocated to the client, there will be frequent discussions in agreeing their impact and the adjustments to the time the contractor is allowed and the additional price paid by the client. These transactional costs might be out of all proportion to the impact of the risks.
- If they are frequently occurring minor risks, then the contractor can allow for them in the tender. Having allowed for them, the contractor is then motivated to minimize both the likelihood and the impact of their occurrence.

3.5.1 Summary

The appropriate allocation of risk spreads through all phases of the procurement process and has effects that carry into the implementation phase. It therefore needs to be managed throughout these phases by identifying it, assessing it and then developing responses and implementing those responses — in other words **risk must be managed.** This is why I have included Appendix 2. Part of the response phase is to allocate or share risk appropriately. I hope that the arguments and examples given in this section make people question the popular mantra of 'allocate it to the party best able to manage it'. This is too simplistic. Equally, I hope that I have both expressed more succinctly other authors' principles of risk allocation and extended them to include the concept of risk sharing. In shorthand, my four principles for risk allocation and sharing are:

(a) Who can best bear it?
(b) Who can best prevent it?
(c) Who can best minimize the consequences of it?
(d) Clarity takes precedence over the above for minor risks.

Review question 3 Look at the shorthand principles for risk allocation and sharing expressed in the summary. Without looking back through the rest of the section, express them in full in your own words. How do they differ from my full principles? What are the differences? Do you think your principles are better expressed and, if so, why?

(1)

(2)

(3)

(4)

(5?)

3.6 Choose the 'best-fit' procurement route

The procurement route is the broad strategy by which the parties will achieve the project objectives, taking account of the constraints and risks that act on the project, the strengths and weakness of the parties to it, and their cultures, that is the information gleaned from the information phases. **Once this is clear, selecting the 'best-fit' procurement route is relatively easy if you have the content knowledge of different procurement routes**. This is given in Chapter 4 for price-based payment mechanisms and conventional procurement routes and in Chapters 7–9 for more innovative routes. **In effect, you are deciding the 'best-fit' organizational structure for the project.** Once this is done, we can then start the process of fine tuning each contract package to the project circumstances. Some authors[17] would refer to this as having 'fit for purpose' contractual relationships.

3.7 Develop contract/work package breakdown structure

The aim of this phase is to match up the capabilities or strengths of the potential parties to the project with the various elements and risks of the project. At this stage of the procurement process, it is a broad-brush approach, more to do with evaluating the strengths and weaknesses of the industry as a whole than those of individual contractors and consultants. This usually means breaking the project down into technical elements and allocating each element to a party that has the capability to deliver it. It also means avoiding allocating an obligation or risk to a party that is weak in that area.

> Take a process plant. There may be a particular item that is absolutely critical to the technical success of the project and all other processes etc. feed into it. Obviously, one contract package has to include the supply of that particular item. However, are manufacturers also best placed to design it as well? And what about installing it?
>
> If this item is both the critical item technically and the biggest in terms of expenditure, should whichever supplier is selected also manage and co-ordinate the other packages in the project? Or should the client, a consultant or main contractor manage the other packages?
>
> The only realistic answer is that it all depends on the suppliers' and others' capabilities, which are related to their experience of doing design and installing and/or managing other packages.

Balanced against this, **a good principle is to aim to keep the contractual interfaces to a minimum.** Clients should note, however, that just moving the interfaces down the contractual chain does not necessarily give the best practicable answer!

3.8 Choose payment terms and select 'best-fit' conditions of contract for the individual contracts

The **payment terms** in each contract govern how the contractor is rewarded. For instance:

- Is the contractor or consultant paid on the basis of cost or inputs, for example person-hours, or on the basis of the firm price(s) tendered to do the work? The funding risk that the contractor or consultant takes on is a factor here.
- Which risks are allocated within the contract to the contractor and which are taken by the client?
- If client risks occur, how should the contractor be paid? At cost? With profit? At bill rates?

- Is it appropriate to use incentives, negative and/or positive? On what measures of performance should these be placed, and how much should the bonus/damage be?

The choices made at this stage affect individual contractors' motivations to partner or become confrontational and decisions as to whether to put more emphasis on pursuing certain objectives compared with others. As with choosing the 'best-fit' procurement route, content knowledge is needed and given in subsequent chapters.

Different conditions of contract have different payment mechanisms and allocate risk in different ways using different language. They also allow for different extents of contractor design and are applicable in different industry sectors. They allow for different and varying degrees of client control and influence both project management and quality assurance.

The impact of contractual language

Ashley and Workman[18] express the view that: 'The owner sets the stage for the attitude of the contractual relationship through the tone of the language used and incentives included in the contract documents. Clearly, this attitude can impact project performance and the resulting project cost.'

Dorter,[19] writing in the *Journal of the Institute of Arbitrators*, states that 'fundamental and finally fatal' to partnering 'is the failure to relate the "philosophy", "mindset" and "process" of partnering to the benefits, rights and liabilities of the parties under the contract'.

I would argue that the words in the contract should reflect the business objectives and context and risks associated with the project. Consequently, the 'best-fit' conditions of contract should be chosen after the previous stages have been done. Only then, and if necessary, should they sparingly be fine tuned to precisely reflect the project circumstances.

Yet how often do lawyers, either internal or external, take time to understand the business objectives and context of the client, and the risks associated with a project, before recommending the conditions of contract and writing additional, often unnecessary and defensive, clauses? In my experience of reviewing what lawyers have written, very few do. In consultancy terms, the 'diagnosis' phase is left out.

I am aware of one client who made a decision to enter into strategic relationships with a limited number of contractors and consultants with the intention that each project was let on a target cost basis under the NEC Engineering and Construction Contract. This client asked its law department to comment on the contract, and it then passed the document on to an external law firm. When the response came back, ten pages of additional clauses had been written without any consultation or understanding of why the client was thinking of using the conditions therein. Consequently, much of the ethos of the contract was undermined. After 3 months of negotiations with the internal lawyer, the additional clauses were reduced to about one-and-a-half pages.

At a more micro-level, how often do lawyers consult with the people who will actually be running the contract to check that users can, first, understand what is written and, second, apply it? There is little point in having a legally foolproof contract that is incomprehensible to project participants and/or impracticable, for example if the parties do what the work actually requires they will be in breach of contract.

My personal view is that the NEC family of contracts is the most flexible and integrated family of contracts available. Its other principal objectives of clarity and stimulus to good project management are also compatible with partnering. For this reason, I have included Appendix 3. Having said this, I would not necessarily always recommend it. For instance, if a client has no desire to partner or is poor at project management it is not the contract to use.

3.9   Select project participants on their ability to deliver value

Clients are becoming increasingly aware that competitive tendering with the contract being awarded at the lowest tendered price does not necessarily mean that they get the best value. Why is this? Because any business's first priority is cash flow, so a contractor or consultant has to win work to support its fixed costs, for example head office costs. This may mean bidding low to win the contract. Once a contract is won, the priority becomes profit, and this may mean skimping on quality, health and safety, etc., and playing contractual games to increase the contract price. This means that the client not only may not get the asset wanted and may pay out more than originally thought, but also has to spend money defending its contractual and commercial position. If this contract has knock-on effects on other contract packages in the project, then the resulting time and cost effects can far outweigh any initial benefit from selecting the lowest priced tender.

In design and build projects, the lowest cost approach takes no account of the additional benefits of different contractors' designs over and above the minimum requirements stated in the client's project brief, including whole-life costs, which for a building can be three to four times the capital cost.

> The view of the European Institute of Advanced Project and Contract Management[20] is that 'the traditional approach with the lowest bidder winning the contractor order is likely to produce variation orders and claims for late deliveries and delays resulting in cost over-runs. There is no alignment of cost drivers and business objectives, and an adversarial relationship is frequently developed. Bluntly speaking, the suppliers are considered as "spot sellers", rather than potential partners. In this way both parties deploy a significant effort in "fighting" each other. … In some cases the parties come to a cease fire, but frequently they carry on fighting until the disputed issue is resolved finally through litigation.'

For these reasons, **more enlightened clients have modified their approach, to one resembling that outlined in Appendix 4.** In the third phase of developing the contract/work package breakdown structure, we are trying to match each contract package to the capabilities of the industry as a whole. In this phase, we are trying to find the individual contractor or consultant that best fits the contract package. This will be a combination of price, scheme proposals, if there is a significant element of design, and the overall quality of the contractor or consultant. The last can be broken down into eligibility factors such as technical competence, experience and financial strength and suitability factors such as culture and commitment to continuous improvement.

Having selected one contractor or consultant for each package, or at the very least narrowed it down to two or three, a client may wish to start discussions — subject to any constraints from EU procurement legislation. If there is one contractor, they would have preferred contractor status (see section 4.3.3). These discussions could be over clarifications to the technical specification of what the contractor is to provide, perhaps leading to some design development or changes in scope or quality and thus leading on to negotiations over the contract sum. They could also be to finalize details of an incentive scheme to ensure that the contractor pursues the client's objectives in a balanced way (see section 5.3).

Review question 4 Bearing in mind Procurement tool 4: Selecting contractors by value (Appendix 4), in what ways could the way in which you select suppliers — be they consultants, contractors or subcontractors — be improved?

3.10 Build in reviews to consider 'what if?' scenarios and their second-, third- and even fourth-order effects on other parties' motivations and actions

These reviews could be part of periodic 'gateway' meetings in which the next phase of the project is sanctioned. It is strongly suggested that, at these reviews, those who sanction the next phase of the project are not the developers of the procurement strategy or the implementers of the project, as they will be 'trapped' in their mindset of thinking. Instead, they will have to justify their decisions so far to people remote from the day-to-day development of the project.

A recent CIRIA research report[2] stated that 'there should be clear separation between the roles and responsibilities of the proposer of the scheme and the approving body, such that there is transparency in how the scheme is to be applied and managed.'

As the arrows in Fig. 3.1 suggest, the results from any review could mean revisiting earlier phases in the development of the procurement strategy, either to tweak or, in extreme cases, start again. As previously stated, this involves putting yourself into others' shoes and asking yourself what you would do if that risk was allocated to you. Alternatively, you can ask the parties involved! Their imagined response, both at tender and during the contract, if the risk occurs can actually undermine your reason for allocating the risk to them in the first place. It can also often undermine the achievement of other objectives.

For instance, allocating a risk that is predominantly in the control of the client's team to the contractor will mean that the client's team is less motivated to manage it. Ignoring the financial strength of the parties, the increased likelihood of it occurring means that the 'premium' charged by the contractor in its tender would be greater than the 'contingency' allowed by the client in its budget. The contractor, as well as allowing a premium in its tender, may also push the risk down the contractual supply chain on to a subcontractor, who also charges a premium. Would you, as a client, wish to pay for premiums on premiums?

Probably not. Are these premiums included at tender likely to cover the contractor's and subcontractor's costs if the risk does occur? Again, probably not. So what will they try to do?

Try to push the reason for the risk occurring back up the contractual chain by saying that the client and/or contractor is somehow in breach of contract and that this has caused the risk to occur. What is the natural reaction of the client's team and/or the contractor? Each defends its position. What happens next?

This negative attitude and focus not only applies to the specific risk, but often spreads to other areas of the contract, undermining all the potential benefits of co-operation. How often do clients and their advisors consider the full consequences of risk allocation?

Two real-life examples illustrate what can happen if issues are not thought through:

Paying for defects on the Channel Tunnel rail link

Most of the first stage of the Channel Tunnel rail link has been let under the NEC Engineering and Construction Contract, option C: Target contract with activity schedules. The client wanted to motivate the contractor to notify and then correct defects, without having to use excessive supervisory staff itself to check on the contractor. Therefore, an additional disallowed cost was added to the conditions, which disallowed the contractor from being reimbursed the cost of correcting a defect if it was notified as a defect or discovered by the client's supervisor more than 48 hours after the work was done. This result was that the contractor tended to notify the supervisor of possible defects in any work that had been done, leaving it to the supervisor to find and confirm or disregard them. The consequence was that the supervisor's team had just as much work as if this clause had not been inserted, perhaps even more work. It is questionable whether such a 'get-out' clause improves the contractor's motivation to produce defect-free work.

The effects of allocating ground risk to the contractor in Hong Kong

The Hong Kong Housing Authority (HKHA) had progressively shortened the duration of contracts and imposed higher and higher damages on its contractors for the delivery of high-rise housing blocks. This was because of advances in construction technology and higher returns once the flats were let. Indeed, the damages were set at a level that reflected the HKHA's loss of income. Additionally, no clauses for unforeseen ground conditions were included in the contract, so arguably the biggest risk in a construction project in Hong Kong lay with the contractor. Contractors consequently passed the risk down the contractual chain to their piling subcontractors. The level of competition meant that very little risk premium was included in these tenders, with the level of the damages apparently meaning that the average piling subcontractor would go out of business after 5–6 weeks of damages being applied. So, what did subcontractors do when they found that they could not complete the work within the subcontract timescale?

Rather than continue down until the piles hit the rock, some bribed the supervisory staff to sign off the piling. When this was discovered, several tower blocks had to be pulled down because they were unsafe. The HKHA's initial response was encouraging: it added 5–6 weeks on to the contract duration and halved the level of damages, not just on new contracts but also on current ones.

Both of these examples illustrate how risk allocation affects the motivations and actions of the parties to the contract. I am aware of numerous other less dramatic examples. **If you are involved in setting procurement strategy and you seem to have recurring problems in your contracts, could it be that the way in which risk is allocated is partly to blame?** If so, it may be time to review your procurement strategies taking account of second-, third- and possibly fourth-order effects on other participants' motivations and actions.

Review question 5 Are there recurring problems on the projects with which you have been involved? If so, analyse the situation, asking yourself to what extent the procurement processes and risk allocation are to blame.

What could be done differently in future?

3.11 Award, communicate, implement and measure

Normally, the contract is awarded after the commercial and contractual terms have been agreed and tied down in the contract. When this is not the case, particularly in one-off projects, disagreements and disputes often occur at a later stage. However, any contract can be modified by agreement between the parties to it at any time. As the contract progresses, the business context, as well as project circumstances, may change and it may be in both parties' interests to modify the contract accordingly.

Previous research, both my own[21] and others',[22] has found that **unless the shift in the contractual framework and conditions of contract is**

communicated to contract participants, then, unsurprisingly, they carry on acting in the traditional manner.

In partnering workshops after the contract has been awarded, I also encourage understanding of the commercial terms. This has two benefits:

- It means that project participants understand how their commercial objectives are more aligned and that it is in their interests to co-operate.
- In some cases, it results in the commercial terms being adjusted by an agreement to modify the contract, for instance introducing value engineering clauses and shared saving clauses among the principal subcontractors to promote co-operation between them and the main contractor.

By 'implementation phase', I am referring to both the design and the construction phases. In these phases, apart from the normal financial and programming monitoring and planning processes, two other processes or tools are increasingly being used. Risk management is being used, to varying degrees, to increase certainty over project delivery time, cost, quality and safety. It can be used in each previous phase of the procurement process, if each party to the project is separately using risk management on its contract, then not only is this wasteful of resources, it is also likely to be far less effective. The risk management process is outlined in Appendix 2.

In addition, the value engineering phase of value management is increasingly being used as a process to reduce whole-life costs while maintaining the functions of the asset as defined in the first phase of value planning (VP1) from which the best option is chosen to fulfil these requirements in the second phase of value planning (VP2; see Appendix 1). **The value engineering process is described in Appendix 5**.

As with risk management, separating design from construction, in terms of both people and information, seems inefficient and less effective, and more enlightened clients, consultants and contractors are at the very least sharing this information, if not working together on both processes. Further, it could be argued that value engineering identifies and exploits opportunities for decreasing whole-life cost, whereas risk management identifies and minimizes opportunities for whole-life cost increases. Because the processes are similar, as many other authors have stated, there is scope for integrating the two processes. An outline method of doing this is also presented in Appendix 5.

Measuring performance can be viewed as monitoring, except that the breadth of measurement tends to be wider than simply comparing actual time and cost performance against planned. At its most basic, measuring has two purposes:

- It confirms to the project participants and stakeholders that they are on course to achieve the project aims or that corrective action is needed.
- It can be used to evaluate project teams and/or the individual organizations participating in the project, which can then be used to judge whether further work — or what percentage of further work in a strategic relationship — is given to them.

Currently, nobody who is anybody in the construction industry measures performance, they 'benchmark'! **An additional use of benchmarks is as the measure of performance upon which the contractor or consultant is rewarded when an incentive scheme is being used to stimulate improved performance. An overview of the principles and practice of using benchmarks is given in Appendix 6.**

3.12 Feedback and continuous improvement

Note that this is also the last stage of my model for partnering presented in the previous chapter (Fig. 2.4).

The benefits of measuring performance are limited if they do not result in any improvement. Although comparing benchmarks against each other may establish who is 'best' at the time, apart from acting as a spur for improvement, it does not necessarily help other organizations become 'better' as there is no detail behind the numbers. Benchmarking, as opposed to just the use of benchmarks, looks behind the numbers to find out why there is a difference in performance in order to learn lessons which can be applied on other projects. These lessons can be then be applied for continuous improvement. Again, I refer to the procurement tools, in this case benchmarks and benchmarking, in Appendix 6.

Continuous improvement in procurement arrangements can also take place in order to align motivations more fully, for instance by reallocating risk to the party best able to manage it, changing payment terms or fine tuning an incentive scheme. This could happen:

- in the pre-contract negotiation stages prior to award
- at, or as a result of, a partnering workshop when some commercial misalignment is realized or to enhance an existing alignment
- during a project, either if misalignment becomes apparent or if project circumstances change, so that the original premises upon which the procurement strategy were based are no longer valid
- in a strategic relationship, in which the nature of the relationship has changed.

An example of continuous improvement in procurement relationships: the BAA/Amec pavement team

Amec was employed as the contractor in a 5-year framework agreement to build runway and taxiways (pavements) at BAA's airports in southern England, with each project being let under the NEC Engineering and Construction Contract, option C: Target contract with activity schedules. The target for each contract was originally assembled from a schedule of input rates given by the contractor along with productivities etc. for a typical project. These outputs were benchmarked on each project, and each time a benchmark was improved that became the new standard to be used for building up the target on the next contract. However, this approach had a number of problems:

- Civil engineering works are notoriously method related, and airports have many constraints that affect methodology. Thus, methods and productivities alter from one project to another.
- These methods and resulting productivities change during the project as a result of changes in scope and additional constraints imposed at the last moment by the operational side of the airport.
- Under a target cost contract, the target still needs to be adjusted when compensation events occur; this was causing some friction.
- There was an additional source of friction: it was not in Amec's short-term commercial interests to contribute to the scheme until the target was agreed because that way it gained a pre-agreed proportion of any suggested savings compared with the target. However, this would not have pleased BAA because it would have developed the scheme in consultation with Amec, only for Amec to suggest ideas for time and cost savings once the contract was signed! It was not in either party's long-term commercial interests to fall out.

As a consequence, after 18 months of the relationship in which a lot of trust had been built up, the decision was made to switch to a pure cost-reimbursable contract with the benchmarks still in place to ensure continuous improvement. Amec received an increased fee percentage on actual costs incurred to compensate partly for changing market conditions, but mainly for its loss of profit from its share of savings on the target on the individual contracts.

(Source: interviews and various presentations)

3.13 Summary

It is my opinion that the purpose of procurement strategy is to develop the commercial and contractual framework so that the objectives of the parties to the project are aligned, thus maximizing the likelihood of project objectives being achieved in the design and construction phases. Research has shown that procurement arrangements can have as large an effect on project outcomes, in terms of time and cost, as can technical decisions, in terms of quality and fitness for purpose.

This chapter has built up a model for developing procurement strategy, which is illustrated in Fig. 3.2. This is essentially the same diagram as in Fig. 3.1 but with the procurement tools that feed into the process added. These tools are explained in Appendices 1–6. To my knowledge, such a model has not been presented elsewhere in the literature, although many procurement professionals will follow a similar process in their heads when developing a procurement strategy. This model can be used not only to develop a procurement strategy for the types of contract outlined in this book, but also for public finance initiative and term maintenance contracts.

Three issues that I particularly wish to highlight are:

- It is necessary to have content knowledge of different procurement routes, before refining a procurement route, its contract packages and finally each contract. This content knowledge is given in other chapters of this book.
- It is important to understand and apply the principles of risk allocation and sharing at virtually all stages of the procurement process. This is why I spent some time in section 3.5 of this chapter refining, explaining, illustrating and quoting other authors on the principles of risk allocation and sharing. These are, in shorthand, allocate or share risk in accordance with:
  - who can best bear it
  - who can best prevent it
  - who can best minimize the consequences of it
  - clarity over the above for minor risks.
- The importance of risk allocation and sharing is reflected in the number of stages at which risk management techniques can be applied.
- It is important to have regular reviews as the process is followed and the detail is crystallized. In these reviews, the 'what if?' scenarios need to be considered for the second-, third- and even fourth-order effects on motivations and behaviours. Failure to do this is probably the biggest cause of a breakdown in contractual relationships. It is also the biggest revelation to participants in my training sessions.

The last comment that I would like to offer is this: as with any model, it is only a model of reality and not reality itself. Use it while it is useful, modify it or abandon it when it ceases to be!

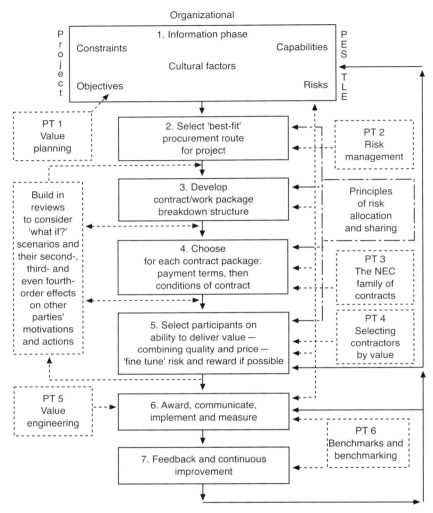

Note: PT = procurement tool.
These tools, perhaps with the exception of value engineering,
feed into the procurement process

*Fig. 3.2. A model for developing procurement strategy with procurement
tools added*

Review question 6 Look through Appendices 1–6: Procurement tools. Which one of these tools would, if applied, have the biggest impact on the projects with which your organization is involved?

Which one procurement tool would be the easiest for you, as an individual, to learn and start using on a regular informal basis? When would the first opportunity for you to use it arise?

Review question 7 Look back at review questions 1(a) and (b). Having now read this chapter to varying levels of detail, how has your answer now changed? What does this imply?

Either draw a learning map or prepare your own process model for developing a procurement strategy to encapsulate your learnings from this chapter.

References

1. Potts K. *Major construction works: contractual and financial management*. Longman Scientific & Technical, Harlow, 1995.
2. Richmond-Coggan D. *Construction contract incentive scheme — lessons from experience*. CIRIA (Construction Industry Research and Information Association), London, November 1999, Funder's report CP/76.
3. The Business Roundtable. *Contractual arrangements — a construction industry cost effectiveness project report*. The Business Roundtable, New York, 1982, Report A-7.
4. Bennett J. and Jayes S. with the Reading Construction Forum. *The seven pillars of partnering — a guide to second generation partnering*. Thomas Telford, London, 1998.
5. Yates A. Procurement and construction management. In *Investment, procurement and performance in construction*, eds P. Venmore-Rowland, P. Brandon and T. Mole. E. & F. N. Spon, London, 1991.
6. Central Unit on Purchasing. *CUP guidance No. 36: contract strategy selection for major projects*. HM Treasury, London, June 1992.
7. Abrahamson M. W. Risk management. *Intl Constr. Law Rep.*, 1983, **1**, No. 3, 241–63.
8. Barnes M. How to allocate risks in construction contracts. *Intl Constr. Law Rep.*, 1983, **4**, No. 3, 24–8.
9. Hayes R. W. and Perry J. G. Risk and its management in construction projects. *Proc. Instn Civ. Engrs*, 1985, **1**, No. 77, 477–521.
10. Abrahamson M. W. *Engineering law and the ICE contracts*, 4th edn. Applied Science Publishing, London, 1979.
11. Trench D. *On target: A design and manage target cost procurement system*. Thomas Telford, London, 1991.
12. Construction Industry Institute (CII) Contracts Task Force. *Impact of various contract types and clause on project performance*, CII, Austin, Texas, July 1986, Publication 5-1.
13. Stukhart G. Contractual incentives. *J. Const. Engng Mngmnt*, March 1984, **110**, No. 1, 34–42.
14. Ashley D. B. *et al.* Allocating risk and incentive in construction. *Journal of the Construction Division of the ASCE* (American Society of Civil Engineers), September 1990, **106**, 297–305.
15. Barnes M. *Risk sharing in contracts*. Paper presented at Civil Engineering Conference, 24–25 January 1991.
16. Innes J. Taking initiative and responsibility. *The Latham action plan: reducing construction costs by 30%*. The Chartered Institute of Purchasing and Supply, London, 13–14 September 1994.
17. Cox A. and Townsend M. *Strategic procurement in construction: towards better practice in the management of construction supply chains*. Thomas Telford, London, 1998.

18. Ashley D. B. and Workman B. W. *Incentives in construction contracts.* CII, Austin, Texas, April 1986, CII Source Document 8.
19. Dorter J. B. Partnering — think it through in arbitration. *J. Inst. Arbitrs,* Aug. 1997, **63**, No. 3.
20. European Institute of Advanced Project and Contract Management (EPCI). *Complex capital projects and life cycle perspectives.* EPCI, June 1995, Working Paper.
21. Broome J. C. *The effect of the New Engineering Contract on the management of change.* University of Birmingham, Birmingham, PhD thesis, January 1998.
22. Perry J. G. *et al. Target and cost reimbursable contracts: Part A: A study of their use and implications; Part B: Management and financial implications.* CIRIA, London, 1982, CIRIA Report 85.

4. Conventional procurement routes and price-based payment mechanisms

4.1 Introduction

The purpose of this chapter is to give the reader a greater insight and understanding into conventional procurement routes and price-based methods of payments. By 'conventional' procurement routes, I mean those that are established and commonly used, which is not yet the case, in my opinion, for target and cost-reimbursable contracts and alliances. Conventional procurement routes and payment mechanisms are discussed for two reasons:

(a) Innovative procurement routes, such as target cost contracts and alliances, are not always appropriate. Equally, conventional procurement routes, which normally use price-based contracts, are not appropriate in certain circumstances but are in others, providing they are matched to the project circumstances.

(b) When using incentives, which are discussed in the next chapters, it is at least as important to select the 'best-fit' procurement route before fine tuning the motivations through incentives, whether the route is conventional or more innovative.

The next section of this chapter briefly highlights the fundamental difference between price- and cost-based contracts. The chapter then has two main sections:

- The first discusses, with their variances, conventional procurement routes, namely the traditional design followed by construction route and the contractor-designed and management contract routes.
- The second discusses price-based payment mechanisms, highlighting their suitability for partnering.

In the case of both procurement routes and price-based payment mechanisms, a description of what they are is followed by a discussion of their advantages and disadvantages, so that the reader can understand the reasoning behind my conclusions on when to use them.

The order of this follows the process for developing a procurement strategy whereby the 'best-fit' procurement route is selected, followed by contract or work breakdown structure, before the payment terms for each contract package are chosen (see Chapter 3 and in particular section 3.3). The next stage in this process is to match payment terms to the conditions of contract. To go into the details of each standard conditions of contract is beyond the scope of this book, although a table of suitable conditions of contract for particular procurement routes and payment methods is given in Appendix 7.

Before we proceed, a note of caution: with all the definitions, not just in this chapter but throughout this book, the reader should not presume that the definitions are absolutes. They more describe the general meaning of the terms used. This is partly because construction procurement is currently undergoing a rapid evolution, so, particularly with more innovative routes, precise definitions do not exist. The descriptions offered here are my own definitions. Another construction procurement professional's descriptions may vary, but hopefully not by too much!

> **Preview question:** Having read the introduction, now scan through the chapter and read the conclusion. How is this chapter relevant to what you do now? Bearing this in mind now, what specifically do you want to gain from reading this chapter?

4.2 Price- (output) vs. cost- (input) based contracts

A **fundamental distinction** is drawn between price- and cost-based contracts.

- A **price-** or **output-based contract** is one in which the basis for paying the contractor is that an output is achieved or completed, typically a milestone of some sort or a unit of quantity (the advantages and disadvantages of each are discussed in section 4.4). In this type of contract, the client is not directly concerned with what it costs the contractor to achieve that milestone or produce that quantity as the contractor will only be paid what it offered and was accepted by the client on enacting the contract.
- A **cost-** or **input-based contract** is one in which the basis for paying the contractor is that costs are reimbursed, plus some profit, or payment is made per unit of input at a pre-agreed rate, for example per hour of a labourer in contracts in which the hourly rate has been tendered. What the contractor is finally paid may vary according to an incentive mechanism.

These different means of paying the contractor have repercussions; the second is used in the more innovative procurement routes.

4.3   Conventional procurement routes

This section discusses and explains what conventional procurement routes there are, the advantages and disadvantages of each and when it is appropriate to use them. As stated before, by conventional I mean established and commonly used. There are three basic routes, each of which has variances. These are the traditional design followed by construction route, the contractor-designed routes and the management contract-based routes. As with all definitions, these are generalizations, and how they are implemented varies in practice, depending on the precise circumstances, conditions of contract used, how the parties to the project are selected, etc.

4.3.1   The traditional route: design followed by construction

What is it?

When people talk about the traditional approach to construction, they typically mean the following:

- The client, either internally or through a consultant, develops a detailed and complete scheme design without consulting any contractor. The design will describe, through detailed drawings and specifications, what the final project will look like and may also contain extensive constraints and descriptions of how the contractor is expected to provide it — for instance, at a micro-level, a mix design for concrete, rather than a performance specification, in terms of $N\,m^{-2}$.
- While the above is taking place, expressions of interest are sought from contractors, which are then pre-qualified by a combination of basic questions on availability, financial standing, previous experience, etc. The list of contractors expressing interest is then reduced to normally not more than six that are asked to tender.
- The client then puts the completed design out to the selected tenderers to price up, telling them the dates by which the tenders are to be returned and, if the contract is awarded, when they are expected to start and complete the works.
- The tendering contractors then price up the scheme and return their tenders within 4–6 weeks of being issued the tender documents. The contract is normally price based.
- Providing a contractor's tender satisfies certain minimum criteria, the contract is usually awarded to the lowest priced tender within another few weeks.
- The organization that developed the design is normally involved in the administration of the contract to provide continuity.

The outline contractual and communication links for a consultant-designed and -administered route are illustrated in Fig. 4.1.

Advantages and disadvantages

The **advantages** of this approach should be that:

(a) The selection process uses competition to achieve the minimum price for the work.
(b) Once certain minimum criteria are met, price becomes the only basis for selection and the winner is very easy to determine; it is therefore very auditable as the final selection process involves little subjectivity.
(c) The client, having had full responsibility for the design, gets exactly what is wanted.
(d) Provided that the client has specified exactly what is required, there is certainty of financial outcome.

However, this approach has some **disadvantages,** the first three of which result from the assumption that the client has specified exactly what is wanted, down to almost the last detail, before the scheme is awarded:

(a) If this assumption is not true — and almost certainly it will not be to some extent — then a change results that may lead to an increase in the price paid to the contractor and/or an extension of time.
(b) As there is no contractor involvement in the design stage, the design may lack 'buildability' and be overly expensive or, in extreme cases, impossible to construct. Consequently, the client is forced to make changes that increase the price paid to the contractor.

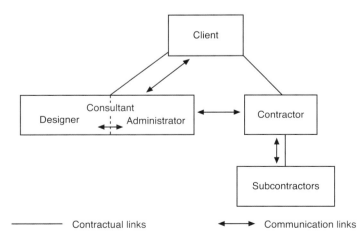

Fig. 4.1.   The contractual and communications links for the traditional design followed by construction route

(c) The contractor, particularly in times of depression, may have tendered its price at or below the estimated costs and then have used changes resulting from poor design and/or administration by the client and its consultants, combined with the subjectivity of traditional conditions of contracts, to push up the price and recover costs.

> I am aware that, in the past, some contractors have had two teams working on the tender for a contract: one to work out how much it will cost to build and the other to work out the potential for claims. They have then subtracted the latter from the former to give their tender price and, having won the contract, mercilessly engineered scenarios to increase the price paid to them.
>
> Alternatively, circumstances may not arise that allow the contractor to claim and/or the contract is too tight for the contractor to make up for its low bid, so quality and health and safety are compromised. This has been hinted at as one of the main reasons behind what was described as the biggest UK civil engineering disaster of the last decade: the collapse of the Heathrow Express tunnel in 1995 (see case study box entitled 'An example of poor risk allocation?' in section 3.5).

This last and the previous two points may mean that the client's certainty of cost and time is undermined. Providing that the contractor has passed certain criteria at the pre-qualification stage and that its tender bid satisfies certain minimum criteria, the cheapest tender wins. Thus, there are more disadvantages of this route as follows:

(d) As one senior estimator for a contractor said to me: 'As an estimator, you have probably got your estimate about right when you come in second or third. When it is the lowest you have probably missed something out or made a mistake somewhere.' The result is that, having won the contract, the site team is almost pushed into displaying the type of behaviour described in the point *(c)* above.

(e) The quality of the contractor is not taken into account in the final selection process.

(f) As there is no design and construction overlap, this form of procurement is unlikely to be suitable for clients with fast-track or time-dominated projects (as opposed to minimum time for construction).

(g) What are the implications for procurement routes for partnering? First, there is no partnering before the construction contract is awarded as the contractor has had no involvement in the design prior to this point. Second, because the contract has been won under tight price competition, which takes little or no account of the contractor's partnering experience

and ethos, there is little incentive to partner. Indeed, in order to maximize income to make up for a low tender, the contractor's motivation might be quite the opposite.

However, a number of **refinements to the traditional route** are possible, which partly overcome some of the disadvantages:

- A contractor or ex-contractor is employed as an adviser during the design phases both to check the completeness of design and to ensure that 'buildability' is designed in (partly overcoming disadvantage *b* and, to a lesser extent, *a*). However, particularly in the public sector, this would tend to exclude the advising contractor from tendering for the construction contract as it would confer an unfair advantage.
- Contractors are allowed to submit alternative bids in addition to the bid for doing the work as per the tender documents. In effect, they offer a price reduction to the client for achieving the same result in a different way, for example by using a different bridge design but one that is still able to carry two-way traffic (overcoming disadvantage *b* for major items).
- Detailed design is left to the contractor (overcoming disadvantage *b* at a more detailed level). However, design interfaces then have to be stated clearly and the standard methods of measurement under a bill of quantities approach do not allow for this (see section 4.4.1). Additionally, with the exception of the NEC Engineering and Construction Contract, most conditions tend towards either full contractor design or full client/ consultant design, with little in between.
- Clients can ask for programmes, resources and assumptions to assess the realism of contractors' tenders. Tenders that are believed to be unrealistic are discarded (attempting to overcome disadvantage *c*) although, in practice, the temptation to accept a low tender seems to be rarely resisted.
- Modern forms of contract, such as the NEC Engineering and Construction Contract, have much tighter definitions of risk, and of roles and responsibilities, and more rigorous methods of assessing entitlements to additional time and cost. This means that there is less scope for contractual 'gamesmanship', reducing the extent of deliberate underpricing (as in disadvantage *d*), but potentially increasing the likelihood of poor quality and health and safety standards if this has been the contractor's tendering policy.
- In order to overcome disadvantage *(e)*, contractors are selected partly on quality or on the added value that they can bring to the project (see Appendix 4).
- In order to promote partnering once the contract is let, a partnering workshop is held at the start of the construction contract to promote

consensus over the project objectives, processes to achieve them and teamwork (attempting to overcome disadvantage *g*). A capital expenditure or value engineering clause can also be added to the contract to promote a joint search for cost savings (see sections 6.2 and 6.3).

The last two bullet points, that is holding a partnering workshop combined with the 'selecting contractors by value' approach (see Appendix 4), could be labelled first-generation partnering. However, although this approach to partnering may reduce the likelihood of adversarial behaviour breaking out, the reality is that most of the commercial pressures that push the parties into acting in certain ways are not addressed.

When to use the traditional route

The traditional route lends itself to projects that satisfy the following criteria:

- The project, from inception to the end of construction/start of operation, is not time driven. This is both because design and construction do not overlap and because the consultant needs time to develop and complete the design before putting it out to tender. However, a project may be time driven once the construction operations start. For instance, the exact time of year that a motorway resurfacing job starts is often not critical, but, once let, it becomes very time driven in order to minimize disruption to the travelling public.
- The client knows exactly what it wants and/or is very particular, for example in the case of the construction of a particularly prestigious building.
- Either the client or its consultants have greater expertise in design, for its particular requirements, compared with the contracting side of the industry.
- The project is a one-off using mature technology and/or the client/ consultants cannot (perhaps because of a short contract timescale) or do not want to have substantial input into the construction phase, for instance an occasional client wanting a factory extension for which cost certainty is a priority. Consequently, 'best value' is obtained through competitive tender, not through working with the contractor to achieve cost or time reductions.
- The works are *not* likely to be subject to a high degree of change, for example due to risks occurring, the client changing its mind, consultants not having time to complete the design, innovative technology or extensive interface problems of a technical or planning nature outside the contract. This is because of the relative lack of cost transparency under price-based contracts and the consequent difficulty of evaluating change.

4.3.2 Contractor-designed procurement routes

What is it?

Contractor-designed procurement routes using price-based contracts are called a number of things depending on the industry sector:

- in the power, process and heavy engineering industries, turnkey contracting
- in the civil engineering sector, design and construct
- in the building sector, design and build.

Another variant is the package deal. The nuances of these definitions are discussed below.

Turnkey contracting tends to use **performance specifications**, in which the level of performance can be quantified, for example the power station will produce X MW at Y% efficiency using this type of fuel, satisfy all existing regulatory requirements and be built in this place. The 'turnkey' refers to the client 'turning a key' to switch the plant on at the end of construction. These procurement routes usually involve testing and commissioning phases once everything is in place

Design and build/construct contracts tend to use more **functional specifications** in which the client develops an outline design to varying degrees of detail and states the functional requirements that the assets have to meet, although often mechanical and electrical requirements in buildings are stated as performance specifications.

Package deals are also used to describe contracts in which the contractor is responsible for the majority of the design. The nuance is that the contractor's duties can extend to finding the most suitable site, obtaining planning permissions and even financing the project until handover, that is the contractor's duties cover the whole 'package'. The name tends to apply more to contracts in the power, process and heavy engineering industries. When the contractor has more extensive duties, as in the building and civil engineering industries, these contracts are sometimes called **develop and build/construct**.

The approach taken under the contractor-designed route is similar to the traditional route, except for the following points:

- The client or its consultants do not develop a full design. The extent to which the design is developed varies. For instance, one major client's design and construct conditions are often colloquially referred to as to as 'refine and construct' because the look of the finished asset is virtually defined by the time the contractor starts work on the detailed design.
- Fewer contractors are typically asked to tender because the costs of tender are proportionally higher than for a fully designed contract. This is because contractors have to carry out some outline design to price the project accurately.

- As a result of the above, the time allowed for contractors to return their tenders is longer than with traditional contracts, normally 6–8 weeks.
- The payment mechanism is milestone, lump sum or activity based, unlike the traditional route, which tends to be bill of quantities based.

Sometimes, the client's design team is seconded to the contractor. This reduces the learning curve and can provide continuity of the design ethos. From a contractor's perspective, one of the risks of this (which will be priced) is that the design team still thinks that it is reporting to the client!

The organization is illustrated in Fig. 4.2. In the past, the design- and quality-checking functions were in contract with and communicated directly with the client. Increasingly, contractors are asked to self-certify both for design and for quality of the physical work, with the certificates being passed on to the client. The client's or consultant's role is reduced to auditing the checkers. The arrows indicate the general flow of information.

Advantages and disadvantages

The **advantages** of contractor design are:

(a) Project timescales are reduced because, although there is a longer period for tender, detailed design can overlap with construction. In commercial terms, this means that the client can be gaining a return on its investment earlier.

(b) The Design and Build Foundation claims that, on like-for-like buildings, design and build is cheaper. This is probably for two reasons: the

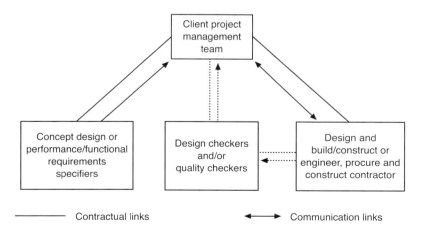

Fig. 4.2. Typical contractual and communication links for the contractor-designed procurement route. Dotted lines indicate optional communication links depending on the specific arrangement

contractor will have a much stronger input into the design, improving 'buildability', and there is less interaction between the two parties, thus saving on administration costs.

(c) The contractor is supplying goods that have to be fit for purpose. Services carry a lesser level of liability, that of reasonable skill and care, so, under the traditional route, the materials and workmanship of the contractor have to be fit for purpose, while the design services of the consultant are to a level of 'reasonable skill and care'. Consequently, under the traditional route, providing the design consultant exercised reasonable skill and care, the client is left with the liability for an underperforming asset resulting from poor design. Under the contractor-designed route, if the works are not fit for purpose for any reason, then:

   (i) There is a much reduced likelihood of argument over who is responsible for the lack of performance.

   (ii) The level of liability for the whole works is fitness for purpose and it falls on the contractor … providing the client has specified the purpose or it can be reasonably inferred.

(d) Risk generally, and in particular the programming design/construction interface risk, is transferred to the contractor, so if design is late, then it is a contractor risk. Again, this gives the client greater price certainty.

However there are certain **disadvantages**:

(a) The client has to be able to give the contractor a clear statement of the function and/or performance required of the asset. The client cannot watch the contractor develop the design and then say 'No, that is not what I really want'.

(b) If the client does initiate, or is contractually responsible for, changes after the contract is let, it will cost dearly. This is because:

   (i) It is hard to evaluate the change in costs from possibly a performance specification with no design to a revised detailed design for construction.

   (ii) Construction follows design very quickly. Consequently, if the client wants to change the contractor's detailed design, it will have to act quickly to avoid a knock-on effect on the construction programme.

   (iii) Lump sums and milestone payments give little transparency of cost.

Birkby,[1] a specialist lawyer in construction procurement, writes 'The cost of a variation under this form of contracting is likely to be more expensive than under other forms, as the client has very little knowledge or control over the contractor's methods of operation.'

For these reasons, the contractor not only has legitimate reasons to ask for comparatively large uplifts to the price, but is also able to use subjectivity to increase it beyond the real cost. All the literature that I have consulted says **do not use contractor-designed *price-based* contracts if the client is unsure of what it wants and is likely to change its mind!**

(c) Consequently, the client is advised to have minimal involvement once the contract is signed, with either its own or its consultant's role being limited to that of quality assurance.

(d) The quid pro quo for the contractor having fit-for-purpose liability for the design (see advantages) is that the client needs to ensure that the contractor is proficient in managing the design/build interface and the professional designers. A client wants a fit-for-purpose asset, not to be fighting a legal battle because it is not! Because contractors find it difficult, if not impossible, to obtain 'fit-for-purpose' insurance for design, contractors bear the liability directly and will therefore fight not to pay it.

Some best practice tips

A common complaint of design and build/construct from designers is that the contractor does not understand the iterative process of design and consequently asks for design modifications too late. Meanwhile, contractors complain that the consultant does not appreciate the lead-in time necessary for ordering and the resulting delay and disruption costs arising from late or changed design. There is some truth on both sides.

Equally, there is a cultural element: some contractors may not be able to change their approach to managing design sub-consultants as professionals, while some designers do not like being beneath contractors contractually and having to take orders from them.

What this implies is that, when evaluating the quality bids from contractors, it is desirable to take into account the contractors' experience of managing the design/build interface as well as their design consultants' experience of working under this procurement route.

When to use contractor-designed price-based contracts

The main reasons for using contractor-designed price-based contracts are:

- The project timescale is tight.
- The client wants a high price certainty.
- The contractor is better placed to do and/or manage the design.

However, before using this procurement strategy, it is advised that:

- The client knows what it wants and will not initiate changes once the contract is let.
- The client can express what it wants as an outline design and/or performance or functional specification.
- The contract is not likely to be affected by significant changes outside the contractor's control. If it is, the client should consider either transferring these to the contractor, for which it will pay a premium, or adopting a different route.

From a partnering viewpoint, the client, contractor and subcontractors, and design consultants can work together to develop the design and ensure that the client has the end asset that is wanted in the pre-detailed design and construction contract stages. However, from a contractual aspect the client and its consultants are best advised to adopt a more 'hands-off' approach once the contract is signed.

4.3.3   The preferred contractor approach to design and build/construct

What is it?

A comparatively recent development, although a not uncommon practice now, is that tendering contractors offer their outline design and prices in the normal way, except that the client's brief and the contractor's outline design are both less defined than in a straight design and build contract. The preferred contractor is selected on a combination of price and quality, with quality including that of the proposed outline design. Prior to the full design and build/construct contract being signed, the contractor and principal subcontractors develop the design with the client and its consultants' input. This can either be on a consultancy basis or for the prize of winning the construction contract. Changes in requirements that result in cost variances from the original prices are agreed as the design is developed. When the design is sufficiently advanced for the client to know what the end asset will look like and how it will function, the final contract price is agreed.

Advantages and disadvantages

The **additional advantages** of this approach, **compared with the normal design and build/construct approach, are:**

(a) There is less consultant input at the start.
(b) Tendering contractors have less work to develop the design prior to becoming the preferred contractor. Industry overheads are therefore decreased.
(c) Clients have more input into and better knowledge of what their end asset will look like, how it will function, the materials that will be used and

the whole-life costs as the design is more tied down at the signing of the contract.

(d) Consequently, there is a reduced likelihood of changes.
(e) If there are changes, the client has more insight, resulting from the pre-contract negotiations, into the contractor's cost base, which reduces problems in quantifying the effects of any changes.

The **potential disadvantages** are:

(a) The client has to have the expertise to input into the design.
(b) To gain the benefits, the design has to be more advanced before signing the contract. This reduces its applicability in time-driven projects.
(c) As time progresses the client becomes more locked into using the preferred contractor, which gives the contractor a negotiating advantage. It is advisable, therefore, from a client's viewpoint, to intend to sign the contract some time before construction is programmed to start in order to reduce this leverage. If the contractor then starts to play games escalating the price, a replacement can be brought in. Again, this does not suit time-driven projects.

When to use the preferred contractor approach

Use it in the same circumstances as the contractor-designed route, but in cases in which:

- The client wants to and is able to develop the design with the contractor to ensure that the end asset is more precisely what is wanted. This could be because the client wants to continue a successful relationship from a previous project.
- Greater price certainty once the contract is signed is desired, as changes during the contract are less likely.
- The project is not as time driven.

4.3.4 Management contract routes

What are they?

Management contracts are those in which the client employs a contractor as a management professional, on a fee basis, to manage on its behalf the different work packages that make up a project. They have the following features:

- The contractor does very little, if any, of the physical works.
- The physical work packages are normally let under price-based lump sum or bills of quantities-based contracts, although I am aware of them being let under target and occasionally, more recently, cost-reimbursable contracts.

- The designers are either subcontracted to the contractor or, although under contract to the client, report to the contractor.

When to use management contracts

Management contracts are normally used when a combination of the following factors are present:

- When the project is complex, involving numerous different specialist contractors and therefore numerous programming and technical interfaces. This can include external interfaces that have not been tied down at the start of the contract but will be by the time the affected work package is let. The approach allows flexibility in implementation to allow for changing circumstances.
- The client does not have sufficient resources and/or sufficient expertise to manage the project itself.
- The client does not have a steady workload. The management contractor's staff are employed during peak times.
- The **project is time driven with the client unable to express its requirements clearly at the start. This is a prime reason for using this approach rather than a contractor-designed price-based contract.** This enables the outline design to be developed and then detailed design on, say, the excavations to be started. Once this is complete, the excavation package can be let; the foundation design is started as the outline design for the excavations is completed and then let. Each successive phase overlaps the previous phase for both design and construction (Fig. 4.3).

Advantages and disadvantages

The main **advantages** are that this route can be used in the circumstances described above, when other previously described procurement routes are unsuitable. Other advantages are:

(a) There is early contractor design and programming input, which leads to a more collaborative 'partnering' approach.
(b) Compared with the contractor-designed price-based contracts, the risk when each construction package is let is less as these are much more defined, in terms of both scope and the external interfaces. Overall, less risk is therefore passed to the contracting industry, so the client should pay a smaller risk premium for the project overall.
(c) Each works contract can be let using a procurement route and payment mechanism best suited to its circumstances, rather than under an umbrella main contract, which assumes the same characteristics for all types of work involved in that project. Again this is likely to reduce the risk premium paid by the client.

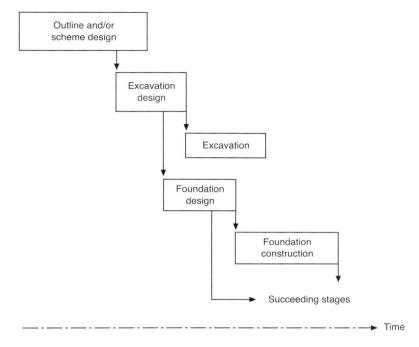

Fig. 4.3.   An illustration of how design and works packages are let under a management contract arrangement

The main **disadvantages** arise mainly from the circumstances of the project and not from the type of contract. These include:

(a) There is likely to be some overdesign in the early work packages, because the final detailed design for later packages has not yet been finalized. For example, the exact weight that the foundations of a building have to support cannot be determined until the structure has been designed in detail. In the traditional approach, the design can be fine tuned.

(b) There may be reworking or changes required on early work, again because the requirements for later packages are not finalized. For example, the voids in the structure for mechanical and electrical services might not be sufficient because the requirements had not been fully defined when the structural package was let.

(c) There is no price certainty for the client when construction commences as only the first work package will have been finalized. Consequently, the client is at risk of ending up with a more expensive project than originally envisaged. However, the client may also save money compared with the cost expected!

(d) The literature consistently highlights duplication of roles, and therefore bureaucracy, as a problem, because the client's project managers check on the managing contractor, which in turns checks the work of the works contractors. This can be reduced by the following:
(i) Select a contractor that is trustworthy and professional.
(ii) Clarify roles and responsibilities.
(iii) Decide on the appropriate level and degree of checks.

(e) The benefits from early completion and the size of the project have to be sufficiently large to justify the increased management overheads. Consequently, management contracts are rarely used for small to medium-sized projects (say less than £5 million).

Management contracts take two forms:

- The **management contracting approach.** The managing contractor sits contractually in between the client and specialist contractors. The contractor is reimbursed the costs of the specialist work packages and some of its stated costs, plus a fee. This fee can be a percentage of costs or a fixed sum (see below for a brief discussion and section 7.4.3 for a more detailed discussion on fees).
- The **construction management approach**. The managing contractor is employed as a consultant to manage the specialist contractors on the client's behalf. The specialist contractors, which would normally be subcontractors, are contracted direct to the client.

These two approaches are illustrated in Fig. 4.4.

Under the management contracting approach, the dotted line indicates that the contractual link is sometimes between the designer and client and sometimes between the designer and contractor. Contractors prefer the latter because otherwise designers tend to communicate through the client. This diffuses and confuses responsibility, inhibiting effective management of the project. A variant on this theme is that the contractor designs the work internally, in which case it is often referred to as **design and manage**.

The brief of construction management or the scope of services that the construction manager is to provide can vary enormously depending on the experience of the client and the balance of the client's/contractor's team. For instance, it could be that the client's project manager literally just signs what the construction manager produces or, at the other extreme, the client's project manager may lead an integrated team consisting of his or her own staff and the construction manager's team.

In the management contracting approach, the contractor's own costs are sometimes paid for as a percentage of the works subcontract packages, sometimes as a lump sum, sometimes on an agreed hourly rate basis plus other defined costs, and sometimes as a combination of these. For instance, the costs may comprise a lump sum for elements of physical work, hourly rates

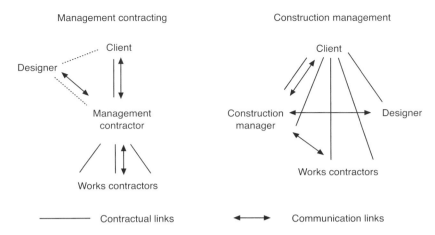

Conventional procurement routes and price-based payment mechanisms

Management contracting

Construction management

Client

Designer

Management
contractor

Works contractors

Client

Construction
manager

Designer

Works contractors

——————— Contractual links

◄——► Communication links

*Fig. 4.4. The contractual and communication links for management
contracting and construction management*

for people costs, plus rent and rates of the hired facility and a percentage for
contribution to head office overheads and profit.

In the construction management route, the contractor is sometimes
reimbursed on the basis of an hourly rate plus other defined costs, sometimes
on a lump sum basis and sometimes by a combination of these. Whichever
option is chosen, how the contractor is paid in order to recover costs depends
on the project circumstances and obviously affects motivations. For instance,
on a lump sum fee any savings in management costs mean more profit for the
contractor but less effort put into the project. However, on an hourly fee basis,
the contractor may want to put in hours that are not strictly needed.

4.3.5   Management contracting vs. construction management

Management contracting became very popular in the mid-1980s but started
to decline in popularity in the early 1990s. The main reasons for its reduced
popularity were:

• The management contractor has a contractual position to defend if the
  works subcontractor does not perform because the contractor is liable both
  for the performance of the asset — by supplying goods, the contractor has
  a 'fitness-for-purpose' liability — and for the delivery time. Consequently,
  management contractors tend to pass these risks down the supply chain
  and on to the works subcontractors, which include a risk premium in their
  tenders. This is not helped by some clients putting high damages on to the
  management contractor.

> I heard of one project in which the management contractor's delay damages were £20000 per week. The roofing was on the critical path and the small specialist subcontractor had a 3-week contract worth £60000 with the same time damages on it. If this subcontractor had not completed the work on time, it would very rapidly have ceased trading.

Additionally, works subcontractors are usually liable for potentially large contra-charges if a delay caused by them has knock-on effects on other works subcontractors. Again, works subcontractors allow a premium for this, which is ultimately passed on to the client. Note that clauses of this nature can also be written into the contracts for the works contractors under the construction management approach with the same results.

- The contractual position of the management contractor means that when the client changes something or does not do something that should have been done under the contract, for example provide access, the contractor's main concern can be to extend the timescale allowed under its contract in order to escape damages and/or increase the project budget, rather than solving the problem with minimum impact. This also happens when a works subcontractor does not perform. There is a clear lesson here: contractual considerations and risk allocation do influence behaviour and therefore results.
- Regardless of the previous points, some contractors' staff have been unable to make the attitudinal and cultural change, from working 'against' the client to acting 'for' it and in its best interests.

As a result of the above, the other approach, construction management, grew in popularity from the early 1980s to the mid-1990s for the following reasons:

- The lack of ambiguity between the professional role and contractual and commercial position of the construction manager means that he or she acts in a more professional manner in representing the client, so that fewer checks on performance are necessary. It is also much easier for the client to terminate the contract of the construction management contractor at any time if performance is poor, because the works contracts are agreed directly with the client and not through the management contractor!
- The client has more involvement and say in how the contract is run and the works packages are let.
- Direct contractual links between the client and the works contractors mean that payment is generally quicker and more secure. This will be reflected in the works contractors' prices.
- More direct lines of communication with the client can help specialist contractors input into the project.

To take advantage of the last two points though, clients have to be willing, and have the expertise, to be actively involved in the project, that is they need to be intelligent and experienced. From talking to contractors, the dangers of this are that:

- Communication routes are not properly established or complied with. Consequently, the works contractors and client cut the construction manager out of the communication loop, which, just as with designers contracting directly with the client under the management contracting approach, diffuses and confuses responsibility.
- The client is willing but not intelligent and makes ill-advised decisions!

Both problems undermine effective management, and consequently construction management now tends to be used by more experienced clients, who have a working knowledge of the industry and technology.

An innovative use of construction management

The Highways Agency traditionally procured its bridge refurbishment projects by asking its term consultants for a particular area to do the scheme design and let it by the traditional route to a main contractor under a bill of quantities contract. Once let, the contract was managed by the term consultants. The problems with this approach are:

- There is no involvement at an early stage in the project cycle of either the main contractor or the specialist contractors which carry out the physical work.
- Five contractors and an unknown number of subcontractors incur tender costs for the same contract. This results in excessive cost to the industry, which the repeat order client ultimately pays for.
- During the contract, when things change, as they inevitably do on a refurbishment project, the main contractor is between the people doing the work — the works subcontractors — and the client's consultants, which authorize extra work and agree payment. This means:
  - The works subcontractors will defend their contractual position against the main contractor, which in turn will defend its against the client. This inhibits communication and often means that decisions are made based on second-hand information.
  - When delays occur, the client is paying for both the main contractor's and the works contractors' delays and disruption.

The Highways Agency, with the full support and involvement of its consultants, W S Atkins Transportation Engineering Ltd of Tamworth, decided to do something different in order to overcome these disadvantages:

- It brought in an experienced construction manager from elsewhere in the W S Atkins Group.
- It appointed on a 1-year term basis eight works contractors from the main trades that make up a typical bridge refurbishment project, namely:

traffic management	bridge deck waterproofing
general civil engineering works	temporary support works
carriageway surfacing	concrete repairs and protection
safety fencing	cathodic protection

  Some of these works contractors covered two or more trades.
- On appointment each work contractor was paid a £1000 retainer so that a contract was formed, that is consideration was exchanged.
- These works contractors were involved at an early stage in the design of the each project so that buildability was improved, cost driven down and programming requirements could be fleshed out. Depending on the extent of their involvement, this could be reimbursed on a hourly rate basis.
- Only one works contractor from each trade was asked to price up its part of the scheme. This reduced the overheads. This price was submitted together with the calculations, assumptions, etc. to the consultant, which went through it in detail. Justification was asked for any unexplained costs or poor efficiencies. In reality, because all parties had built up an understanding of the work involved and an element of trust, there was generally not too much discussion.
- Once the details were finalized, the contract for each trade was let on an activity schedule basis as a compensation event under an amended NEC Engineering and Construction Contract.
- If changes occurred, the consequences were discussed and agreed directly between the consultant and the works contractor without the defensive posturing associated with normal price-based contracts. This is partly because it was restricted by the form of contract, but mainly because the consultant had a thorough understanding of how the works contractors' costs were built up and what they included.
- The works contractors knew that, to some extent, the amount of work put their way depended upon how well they were judged to have contributed to the preparation phase and performed in the implementation phase. There was therefore a motivation to contribute and perform.

The trial was sufficiently successful for it to be extended to other areas of the network on a 3-year term. Additionally, the whole scheme has been benchmarked to ensure that value for money is being achieved.

However, management contracting does have some advantages over construction management in that it enables a harder-edged contract arising from the contractor's 'fitness-for-purpose' liability rather than 'reasonable skill and care' under construction management. Therefore, if the asset does not perform, the management contractor can be held liable. The quid pro quo is:

- The client has to be able to specify what the performance or functional requirements are at the time of signing the contract for this liability to be effective.
- The client has to have a more 'hands-off' approach and not substantially change these requirements during the contract because otherwise the contractor may put its efforts into defending its contractual position rather than solving problems.

Thus, if the performance or functional requirements are not well defined, a client would be well advised to adopt the construction management approach, certainly until the requirements are sufficiently well defined. At this point, the client may choose to switch either to the management contracting approach or, if it is willing to pay the risk premium and lose much of its ability to intervene, to a contractor-designed route.

The use of management contracting in the telecommunications industry

Until its recent recession, the telecommunications industry was driven by speed to market because of the pace of change, with the global clients, often developers, sometimes commissioning large one-off projects in different countries. These clients therefore had little construction expertise, particularly in a single country, and, being developers, had little desire to become involved in the day-to-day management of construction activities.

'Switches' are essentially large electronic information exchanges where information comes in and is distributed back out through the Worldwide Web. An Internet hotel/data centre is similar, except that organizations rent an area in which computerized data are held and stored. These areas, and the data held in them, are connected with the renting organizations, again by the Worldwide Web. Both types of building are technologically complex, involving many disciplines and therefore interfaces, but have similarities in layout, structural requirements and non-IT mechanical and electrical requirements, that is extensive cooling and back-up power supplies. They can also be described in terms of performance requirements.

One such £100 million plus project started as a switch and had all of the above characteristics. It therefore lent itself to a management contracting approach: a large, complex project described through a performance specification; a demanding client that did not have the capability or desire to manage the project on a day-to-day basis yet wanted 'fit-for-purpose' liability; and a high likelihood of change with minimum time as a primary objective. As an example of the last point, piling began on-site prior to the roof, on which the heavy coolers sit, being designed.

The client still wanted a close relationship with the management contractor and selected, in agreement with the contractor, the NEC Engineering and Construction Contract, option F: Management contract to help facilitate this. Partly because of the high likelihood of change, the contract was amended so that the management contractor's people costs were reimbursed on an input basis, rather than being included in the fee.

The management contractor naturally wanted to be as 'back to back' contractually as possible and to have similar close relationships with the works subcontractors. It therefore decided to let its subcontracts under the NEC Engineering and Construction Subcontract, predominantly under option A: Priced contract with activity schedule, rather than bill of quantities. This was to save on measurement costs and allow for elements of subcontract design. These subcontract work packages were let increasingly often with extensive subcontractor involvement in design and risk management prior to the contract being signed. In addition, damages were specified in the conditions in proportion to the size of the contract, with no contra-charging allowable. In this sense, much of the reduced risk was taken out of each contract, with the client, through the management contractor, taking a large share of the risk profile. The aim was to free up minds and attitudes to working with others because rapid progress was essential to the success of the project. The project management procedures within the NEC also helped in this respect.

As a result of the changing business context, namely the global and, in particular, telecommunications slowdown, the switch changed into an Internet hotel/data centre during the project. Despite this, the project, at the time of writing, is almost complete, on time and on budget. It is expected that the final accounts of the works subcontractors and of the

> management contractor will be virtually complete on the contractual completion of the project.

Summary of management contracts

Management contracts are suitable for use in the following situations:

- The project is complex, involving numerous different specialist contractors and therefore numerous programming and technical interfaces.
- The client does not have sufficient resources and/or sufficient expertise to manage the project itself.
- The project is time driven with the client being unable to express its requirements clearly at the start.

There are two variants: the management contracting approach — in which the works contracts are let through the management contractor — and the construction management approach — in which the construction manager has a more professional role and the works contracts are let directly with the client. The clear advantage of the former is that there is a greater contractual onus on the management contractor to perform in terms of time and fitness for purpose. This means that the project requirements have to be more closely defined. The disadvantage is less flexibility for the client once the implementation phase starts and the management contractor possibly adopting a more 'defensive' contractual position rather than a 'can-do' attitude when circumstances change. This has obvious implications for partnering, although, overall, both routes encourage a partnering approach compared with the traditional and contractor-designed routes.

4.3.6 Engineer, procure and construct (EPC)

Engineer, procure and construct contracts are similar to the management contracting approach outlined in the previous section. The differences are:

(a) The terminology tends to refer to heavy engineering projects. The 'procure' part of the EPC title is because much of the value of the work is carried out in factories and then brought in on a 'supply only' or 'supply and install' basis to the construction area.
(b) They have tended to be used for high-value projects, for example North Sea oilfields.
(c) Because of the size and complexity of these projects, the 'management of management' becomes an issue.
(d) As a result, the management contractor tends to be integrated into the client's project management team in the way the construction management

contractor can be. However, the same contractual and commercial pressures as with management contracting still apply, encouraging the contractor to focus on defending its contractual position when a risk occurs, rather than minimizing the impact. This is perhaps why the 'alliancing' concept came in from the North Sea oil industry.

4.3.7 *Summary*

The established procurement routes of the traditional approach (design followed by construction); contractor-designed (turnkey, design and build, design and construct and package deal); and management (management contracting, construction management and engineer, procure and construct) have been discussed. In each case, what they are, their advantages and disadvantages and when to use them were described, together with some brief comments on their suitability for partnering.

Chapter 3 gave a framework for the process of developing a procurement route. The first stage is to understand the project characteristics (objectives, risks, constraints, etc.). Having done this, the next stage is to choose the 'best-fit' or most appropriate procurement route. This section has given readers the content knowledge of conventional procurement routes to enable them to do this.

Review question 1 Select a contract you are, or have recently been, involved with that used one of the procurement routes outlined in this section. Determine the main project characteristics in accordance with the guidelines in the previous chapter. Reviewing the content of this section:

- Do you think the procurement route chosen was the most appropriate one?

- If not, why not? If yes, why? Now select another project until you find one in which you do not think the most appropriate route was selected.

- Which route would have been more appropriate?

- If you had to justify your choice to someone who had not read this chapter, how would you do it?

The more you do this, the better at procurement strategy you will become and the more you will take on the contents of this chapter. So select another project with different characteristics!

4.4 Price-based payment mechanisms

Having decided upon the 'best-fit' procurement route and the contract/work breakdown structure, the next stage in the process is to choose the most appropriate payment terms for the individual contract. This could be at main contract or subcontract level. This would normally be under price- or output-based contracts.

This section clarifies what is meant by various commonly used terms for price- or output-based contracts, before discussing their advantages and disadvantages, and when to use them. It should be noted that the exact way in which each payment mechanism is used depends on the conditions of contract under which the contract is let. It follows that this section has necessarily to deal in generalizations.

4.4.1 Bills of quantities

What are they?

A bill of quantities (BoQ) is a payment mechanism in which the client or its consultant has taken off quantities from the drawings and specifications and structured the overall format and description of each item in a way that normally matches an industry standard. In civil engineering this is normally the Civil Engineering Standard Method of Measurement 3 (or CESMM3 for short) and, in building, the Standard Method of Measurement 7 (or SMM7 for short). This bill is distributed with the contract documents to the tendering contractors, which put a price against each unit item. Each unit price is then multiplied out by the expected quantities and the sums of these multiplications are added together to give the tender price, which is used to compare the tenders of different contractors. At each assessment during the contract, the contractor is paid for the quantity of work completed since the last assessment.

Two distinct advantages of bills of quantities are the simplicity of the concept (price = quantity × rate) and their familiarity. The remainder of this subsection draws heavily on a paper written by Hoare and myself and published in the *Journal of Construction Procurement*,[2] to which readers are referred for a full reference list. However, the text immediately following draws heavily on the work of Potts.[3] It highlights some commonly held beliefs about bills of quantities, which, although they all contain some truth, are equally certainly not true in all situations:

(a) BoQs presume that design is complete at tender and therefore prompt the design team to finalize the design before the bill can be prepared. True, but if, as often happens, it turns out not to be true, it can cost the client dear. This is not only because the quantities may change, but also because most contracts allow the rates to be adjusted if there is a change in the character of the work

or the conditions in which it is carried out. If design cannot be complete at tender, a more appropriate contract strategy should be used. Further, it can be argued that with the increasing specialization and subcontracting within the construction and heavy engineering industries, the best people to do detailed design are those specialist subcontractors. Best practice therefore suggests that design should be incomplete at tender! However, BoQs, written in accordance with their standard method of measurement, do not allow for this.

(b) A BoQ avoids the need for all contractors to measure the works themselves before bidding and avoids duplication of effort with the resultant increase in contractors' overheads, which are eventually passed on to clients. While fundamentally true, the widely accepted Pareto principle indicates that 80% of the cost is accounted for by 20% of the items. Most contractors will, at the very least, recalculate the quantities for the major items in order to check their accuracy, and hence suitability, for the 'games' outlined in the next myth. There is evidence that the US system, in which contractors prepare their own quick quantities, is in fact more efficient and cheaper overall than the traditional full BoQ system used in the UK.

(c) A BoQ provides a commonality in tenders, thus providing the opportunity for realistic tender evaluation. It is true that the items and quantities on which contractors base their tenders are the same. However, the legitimate 'games' that contractors can play, intended to improve their ultimate return and cash flow, complicates tender evaluation on a pure comparison of rates basis. These games include non-uniform allocation of overheads across bill items, 'rate spotting' of items that are likely to increase or decrease in quantity, 'front-end loading' of rates and spotting the ambiguity or inconsistency between and within the various contract documents. Because the BoQ is an additional document to the drawings and specifications, there is an increased likelihood of ambiguities and inconsistencies. Because the client or its consultant prepares the BoQ, legally the risk of ambiguities or inconsistencies is more likely to fall on the client (the legal *contra preferentum* rule).

It is more true to say that a BoQ provides a convenient way of evaluating tenders.

(d) The unique coding system identified in many methods of measurement against each item in a BoQ enables contractors to utilize computers efficiently for estimating. Again, while essentially true, the cost factors contributing to apparently similar work in different locations may make the use of standardized codes of dubious value. This is even more true in civil engineering, in which costs are much more method, as opposed to quantity, related. For instance, one foundation excavation may be in firm ground, enabling steep-sided excavation, whereas another is in softer ground, requiring sheet pile support, and yet

another requires pumps to remove water. Despite widely varying costs per unit quantity, the item coverage of a rate may well cover all three operations.

(e) The BoQ can be used as a basis for monthly interim valuations. This is true, and the monthly valuation's main purpose is to maintain a regular and steady cash flow to the contractor. However, it is arguable whether the time and effort spent in determining how much of every item has been performed each month is worthwhile, because it does not actually add any value to the construction process.

> I worked as an engineer for a contractor on a confrontational site in the early 1990s. At the end of each month, the engineers on both sides of the contractual fence were distracted from their engineering duties for a week by the need to measure things, which included quite detailed surveys of earth moved etc. Each side's engineers, having done a survey, would submit the figures to its quantity surveyors, who would then collate them in their own intermediate BoQs, before disagreeing. Consequently, the engineers would quite often go out and do a joint survey. The process would then be repeated the following month. How were we 'adding value' to the construction process?

(f) BoQs can assist the parties in the control and financial management of the works. The extent to which this is true depends on several factors. These include how closely the BoQ is based upon the costs of undertaking the item of work. As outlined below, often the contractor will have evaluated its true cost of undertaking the work, and will then have back-calculated the unit rate to insert in the BoQ. Another factor is the accuracy of the quantities stated in the BoQ. Additionally, if the cost and resulting impact on the price paid by the client for variations and change are not evaluated until after the changed work has been completed or until the entire contract work has been completed, then the value for financial management is negligible. There are better systems.

(g) Rates contained in BoQs can be used as a basis for the valuation of variations. This may appear to be true, but often the rates are inapplicable because:

- Circumstances change: the work is of a different nature and/or character.
- The rate does not represent the contractor's cost base because of the 'contractual games' referred to in *(c)*.
- The item coverage of the rate applies across a number of construction activities, which have different productivities and costs bases, as in the example given in *(f)*.

- The rate does not or only partially covers the contractor's indirect costs and assumes efficient planned working (see Fig. 4.5). As illustrated in Fig. 4.5, in straight BoQs, in which the price paid is directly proportional to the quantity:
  - Fixed costs and time-related costs are ignored. Indeed, it could be argued that Fig. 4.5 should have a z-axis for the time-related costs. In a claim, these time-related costs come under the heading of delay and disruption.
  - The contractor has a comparatively small area in which to make any profit, which is largely affected by time-related costs. With profit margins typically only 2–3% in the building and civil engineering industries, it is critical for the contractor that planned efficiencies are achieved.

The real cost of changes

A survey in Canada[4] looked at over C$1 billion of construction at tender and found that the typical cost escalation on these projects averaged 33.5%. Of this:

- 11.4% was in the direct costs of doing the work, which would have been incurred if included in the contract at tender
- 8.9% was due to the extended duration of the contract
- 1.7% was due to the need to accelerate the work
- 11.5% was due to loss of productivity/disruption.

What is inferred from this? That when a change is instigated after a contract is let, it costs the contractor, and therefore the client, approximately *three times* as much as if the work had been in the original contract documents! This delay and disruption cost is not covered by assessing the change using BoQ rates, hence much of the argument at the end of contracts.

What is inferred from all of the above points about bill rates? Although providing some cash flow relief to a contractor for variations, they are unlikely to accurately reflect how the costs are incurred and therefore bill rates will only accurately reimburse the contractor's costs on the smallest of variations. The typical result is tension during the contract as the contractor focuses attention on building up a claim and the client on defending it. This is not conducive to partnering!

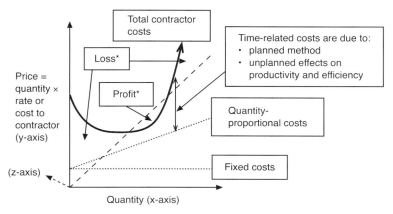

Fig. 4.5. An illustration of the mismatch between how the contractor is paid under bills of quantities and how the contractor actually incurs cost (*The vertical difference between the thick black line and the dashed line (– – –) is the contractor's profit or loss)

When to use bills of quantities

As a result of the flaws with straight BoQs, I would suggest that they are used on only the simplest of contracts and/or when the contracting party is not sophisticated enough to understand its cost base, for example to build a simple brick wall when the subcontractor is a specialist in building walls. The subcontractor knows that by charging a certain rate per m² it will win work and make a profit on it. The subcontractor is not interested in how that profit is made up.

4.4.2   Bills of approximate quantities

A bill of approximate quantities is one in which the contractor is supplied with approximate quantities because the detailed design information is not available. Such bills might also be used on the preferred contractor approach to design and build contracts as the starting point for negotiation, prior to signing the contract but after further design development. This enables a contractor to be appointed early, and gives the client some knowledge of the likely out-turn price. However, this has all the disadvantages of bills of quantities, and in particular the exclusion of method-related costs, with the added complication that programming, and therefore pricing, is difficult for contractors. Consequently, there are likely to be discussions on the suitability of rates from the outset of the contract. This again is not conducive to partnering. In summary, bills of approximate quantities bring few advantages and additional problems!

4.4.3 Method-related bills of quantities

What are they?

In a method-related bill, contractors are allowed to tender lump sums for one-off activities, for example setting up a site office, and time-related activities, for example the weekly on-site costs of maintaining that site establishment. The idea is that the bill more closely resembles how the contractors' costs are built up and there is more transparency of these cost, so that when changes in quantity occur or there is a claim there is less dispute over what is a fair amount.

Advantages and disadvantages

Method-related BoQs try to overcome some of the deficiencies of straight bills (highlighted in section 4.4.1, point *g*) by allowing the contractor to price separately for fixed and time-related costs, for example setting up the site and a weekly on-site cost. The idea is that, with greater transparency of the contractor's costs in the pricing document, the agreement of additional costs is easier. This is also relevant to point *(d)* in section 4.4.1. Additionally, if the contractor is to complete the design of something, then both the design activity and construction activity can become a lump sum, thus overcoming the disadvantage highlighted previously in section 4.4.1, point *(a)*. However, note that:

(a) The use of method-related bills does not address at all some of the other inherent problems of bills of quantities outlined in *(b)*, *(e)* and *(f)* of section 4.4.1.

(b) Without detailed planning information, there will still be little insight into the effects on productivity and efficiency of unplanned events, which are one component of a claim. It could also be argued that traditional conditions of contracts do not facilitate this. They therefore do not fully address the problem highlighted in *(g)* of section 4.4.1.

(c) Because it is the contractor which specifies what the lump sum method-related charges are, it further undermines the advantage stated in 4.4.1, point *(c)*, for providing commonality in assessing tenders, and allows greater opportunity for loading rates and method-related charges.

(d) Method-related BoQs therefore rely upon the contractor being open and matching the estimated costs it will incur if it wins the contract to how the method-related bill is priced. If the contractor has priced the contract below its costs, this cannot be to its advantage.

Thus, **method-related bills only partly overcome the disadvantages of straight bills of quantities**.

When to use method-related bills of quantities

Use them whenever possible instead of straight bills of quantities, provided the sophistication of the contractor allows for it, that is it understands its cost base and can price the method-related bill meaningfully. Generally, I much prefer the activity schedule approach (see section 4.4.7). However, I would move towards recommending method-related bills for:

- building work in which costs can be much more proportional to quantity
- refurbishment and renovation work, in which it is much easier to remeasure the quantity of work done compared with calculating the costs of the additional work
- work in which the client or industry is changing over to a new form of contract, and using the normal payment method on the first contracts reduces the level of innovation and therefore risk.

> I acted as trainer and consultant for the Northern Ireland Road Service, when introducing the NEC family of contracts in the province. On the initial lower value contracts, it was accepted that the contractor's — and client's — staff would have enough on their plates gaining familiarity with the NEC Engineering and Construction Contract and its operation. To minimize the risk, option B: Priced contract with bills of quantities was chosen for the first contracts. An additional factor was that some schemes had already had a BoQ prepared for them.

However, in all three cases, it has to be accepted that, even **under method-related BoQs, if the degree of change is high, at some point remeasuring will still break down as an accurate means of reimbursing the contractor its costs**. This is because it does not take account of the loss of productivity/ efficiency aspects due to disruption. **Consequently, they are only suitable if the likely changes in quantity mean that the changes in the contractor's costs will be approximately equal to the change in quantity multiplied by rate.** They are not suitable for projects in which the type of work is not defined.

4.4.4 Schedules of rates

What are they?

A schedule of rates is similar in concept to a bill of quantities in that tendering contractors put a rate against each item. However, there are two main differences:

- Although the work type may be defined for each item, the estimated quantity is not specified. They therefore tend to be used for term maintenance contracts, in which items are called off as needed, or for refurbishment and scheduled maintenance projects, in which the quantity of work needed is uncertain until the existing facility is uncovered. Examples of the latter can range from renovating historic houses to shutting down boilers in power stations.
- A schedule of rates often includes input prices as well. These can be hourly rates for labourers, designers and/or construction plant. They therefore tend to be used for service-related contracts and/or those in which both the type and quantity of work is unknown. For instance, one government agency has a term services contract for preparation and supervision of major construction schemes, in which hourly rates for different categories of designers and supervisory staff have been tendered.

Sometimes contracts include a section for hourly rates of labour, which is known as dayworks.

Advantages and disadvantages

Many if not all of the criticisms applied to straight bills of quantities also apply to the use of schedules of rates. Indeed, because the contractor may not even be given indicative quantities of work that it is to carry out, they could apply even more so. A method-related schedule of rates, in which set-up and time-related costs are paid separately, will transfer much of the risk, both positive and negative, from the contractor to the client for variations in the expected quantities of work ordered.

However, much of a contractor's costs will be related to having a smooth workload in order to keep resources fully employed (and no more and no less) and, under an output-based schedule, to the efficiency with which the operations can be done. It should be noted that, **under a schedule of rates, there is no direct motivation for the client to help the contractor balance its resources**: the client just pays the tendered rate. To counter the efficiency point, the rate that the contractor is paid is often banded depending on the quantity called off at the same time and/or location. The greater the quantity called off, the greater the efficiency so the less the rate (this is sometimes referred to as a **schedule of prices**). However, by calling off a large quantity at any one time, the rate for a particular item may enter a different band, which is cheaper for the client, but more expensive for the contractor, which has to bring in more expensive and/or less efficient workers and construction plant.

When to use schedules of rates

As previously stated, price-based schedules of rates tend to be used for standard maintenance work, in which items are called off when needed, or for refurbishment and scheduled maintenance projects, in which the quantity of work needed is uncertain until the existing facility is uncovered. Input-based schedules of rates are used where the quantity and type of work is uncertain.

In terms of partnering, the flaw is that, for items covered by the schedule of *output* rates, for example cleaning out a drainage gully, the client is not interested in the contractor's cost as it pays the tendered rate regardless. However, if the work is not covered by an output rate, the contractor will be paid by *input* rate, for example price per unit person-hour. The contractor therefore has little interest in decreasing the number of hours worked per resource. If the input rates are good for the contractor and the output rates are poor, the contractor will be constantly claiming that the work is not covered by an output rate. I have observed this in practice on a number of occasions. This argument is not conducive to partnering.

4.4.5   Lump sum contracts

What are they?

Lump sum contracts are those in which the contractor tenders a lump sum for the whole of the works or, much more commonly, breaks the contract down into a series of operations for which a series of lump sums are given. These lump sums are derived from a BoQ-type document called the 'pricing document', which is usually given to the client for use in evaluating variations and claims. The pricing document is sometimes prepared by the client and, in its preamble, states that quantities are indicative only and that the contractor must satisfy itself of their accuracy and that no claim will be entertained for any inaccuracy. Despite these disclaimers, there is still a danger of misrepresentation, so the onus for preparing the pricing document is put on the contractor. The contractor is not, however, paid for a completed operation that ties in with the lump sum tendered, but is paid at each assessment date according to the percentage of work completed on the corresponding operation.

Advantages and disadvantages

Lump sum contracts have **advantages** over quantity-related payment mechanisms, in that:

(a) They can accommodate method-related charges for both fixed and time-related costs, as well as non-measurable activities and finished construction operations. They are therefore more suitable for contracts in which there is a large element of contractor design.
(b) If it is the contractor that prepares the BoQs and takes off the quantities, then the contractor is legally responsible for any errors in them, so price certainty for the client is greater.

(c) If the contractor has priced up a BoQ, then the evaluation of simple variations and claims is, on the face of it, much easier than with milestone payments or activity schedules (see below), as they can be valued using the BoQ.

In terms of **disadvantages**:

(a) Although agreement over payment is easier compared with BoQs, arguments still happen over what percentage is complete, for instance whether the contractor should be paid for work with defects in it.
(b) Athough there may be a BoQ in place to evaluate the direct costs of changes and variations, the advantage of this method breaks down for all but the simplest changes as it fails to take account of the method- and/or time-related costs of a variation or claim, that is delay and disruption (see section 4.4.1 for further discussion on this point).
(c) Evaluation of claims and variations for delay and disruption is hard for two reasons:
    (i) Because the contractor is paid according to the percentage of the operation completed, the 'lump sum' operation tends to be fairly broadly described, so when trying to agree the cost of the change there is little detailed pricing information to go on.
    (ii) Traditional conditions of contract use lump sums, which do not require detailed programmes.
There is therefore comparatively little transparency of costs when delay and disruption occurs.

When to use lump sum contracts

The principal advantage of lump sums is that it is the contractor which draws up the series of operations, which are then priced as lump sums. This means that, providing the contract allows for it, the specification can also be expressed as:

- a performance specification in the heavy engineering and process industries
- a functional specification in the building and civil engineering industries
- detailed and complete designs of what the contractor is to build;
- or as a combination of all three.*

They lend themselves to technically quite complex projects, but only those in which the interfaces of responsibilities and expertise require little transaction, that is where clients can clearly define what they want and there is little need to work together. This suggests that, for partnering purposes, client involvement is limited to being helpful to the contractor rather than changing

---

*However, the only form of contract that allows this full flexibility, to my knowledge, is the NEC Engineering and Construction Contract.

the requirements or developing how they are put into effect during the contract. As with all price-based contracts, the client does not see any direct monetary benefit from savings made by the contractor, unless there are clauses sharing savings written into the contract (see sections 6.2 and 6.3).

4.4.6   Milestone payments

What are they?

Milestones are specified stages that the works have to achieve along the road to completion of the project so that the contractor can be paid for a proportion of the work. It is normally the client which specifies the milestones that the contractor has to achieve. In extreme circumstances, the milestone is completion.

Advantages and disadvantages

Three **advantages** spring from the use of milestones compared with lump sums:

(a) Because the client specifies them, there are usually relatively few, so the financial administration of the contract is fairly simple.
(b) Once a programme is in place, the cash flow requirements become visible.
(c) Once into the contract, the contractor is motivated to work to achieve the milestones to gain payment.

However, there are **disadvantages**, most of which spring from the client specifying them, because **the value of each milestone tends to be a high proportion of the total contract size and payment milestones may have very little to do with the construction activities**. The **consequences** of this are:

(a) There is even less cost transparency than with the lump sum approach, which means that, when a variation or claim event occurs, it is becomes very hard to evaluate the effects. They are therefore unsuitable when a high, or even reasonable, degree of change is expected, for example if the client wants to add work.
(b) The payment milestones may describe a temporary state of completion that does not match what the contractor would, or sometimes can, achieve on the way to completion of the whole of the works. Consequently, the contractor modifies the construction method to gain cash flow at the expense of the least cost.

(c) The contractor is having to finance the works much more. Typically, contractors are less financially strong than clients, so the cost of a loan or overdraft is higher to the contractor. This cost is passed on to the client.

(d) If there is an ambiguity in the description of the milestone, on the balance of probability, it will be interpreted in the light most favourable to the contractor because the client proposed it (the *contra preferentum* rule).

Because of these disadvantages, milestone payments tend to lend themselves to a 'hands-off' approach by the client. There is therefore an inconsistency between the commercial motivations and a partnering approach.

When to use milestone payments

Milestones lend themselves to projects that are well defined by the client. Note that this does not necessarily mean fully designed but, rather, that the client has defined the scope of the contract so that the completed asset will perform the function required, perhaps leaving the design to the contractor. Because the client is defining the milestones, it suggests that the project will be either:

- simple in nature, so that there can only be one construction sequence for the client-defined milestone payments to relate to
- one in which the client anticipates little, if any, change to its requirements once the contract is let as these become extremely hard to evaluate.

This, of course, presumes that the client is prepared to live with the disadvantages and does not want to adopt a partnering approach once the contract is let.

4.4.7 Activity schedules

What are they?

The term 'activity schedule' was introduced by the Institution of Civil Engineers in its NEC family of contracts (see Appendix 3). Activity schedules are similar in concept to a series of lump sums in that the contractor breaks down the construction operations into activities for payment purposes. The differences are these:

- The contractor is not expected to produce a bill of quantities that will then be given to the client to evaluate variations and claims. In reality, though, the contractor will take off the principal quantities and divide the quantities up into construction operations, which are perhaps merged with other items to form an activity for payment purposes. These activities are then shown in an activity schedule, a simplified one of which is shown in Table 4.1. Some clients specify that an extra column is added on the right, which states the expected monthly outgoings. In this sense, **the activity schedule is as much a cash-flow document as a pricing document.**

Table 4.1.   A simplified example of an activity schedule

Activity no.	Activity description	Price
001	Set up site offices	£2000.00
002	Dig out foundation	£2500.00
003	Pour foundation	£3500.00
...	...	...
...	...	...
00n	Demobilize and remove everything from site	£1000.00
	The total of the prices =	£25 000.00

- These activities have to be completed without defects, which cause delay, or are covered by following work for the contractor, in order to be paid for.
- In the NEC Engineering and Construction Contract, these activities have to be shown in the programme, which also has to show methods and resources for each operation.
- Claims and variations — or compensation events in NEC terminology — are assessed by costing up the changed methods and resources due to the compensation event, plus a fee percentage, which is applied to the change in costs. This fee percentage is for off-site overheads and profit.

Advantages and disadvantages

Because the activities and other information is shown in the programme, with method statements and resources attached, there is much greater transparency of how the contractor's costs are built up. Because of this, and of the way in which additional costs are calculated, the calculation of the change in the prices is more rigorous, less subjective and takes account of time-related costs. **Other advantages** are:

(a) Any significant level of contractor design is easily accommodated, because design does not have to be complete for the contractor to price an activity: the detail can be left to the contractor or subcontractors. Any substantial design becomes an activity in itself. Like lump sum contracts, they therefore accommodate performance and functional specifications.

(b) Because the contractor takes off quantities, the client is not leaving itself open to ambiguities and inconsistencies either within the bill of quantities or with other documents.

(c) Because, unlike lump sums, contractors are not paid for an incomplete activity, they tend to plan the job more thoroughly before they prepare the activity schedule, which links into their cash flow. They therefore tend to have greater confidence in their tendered total of the prices.

(d) Cash flow requirements for both parties are more visible.

(e) In order to receive payment as planned, the contractor has to complete an activity by the assessment date, which is normally every 4 weeks or monthly. Consequently, there is good motivation not only to programme realistically but also to keep to that programme during construction.

(f) The assessment of the amount due to the contractor and monitoring become one and the same action. Payment and programming become more integrated generally.

(g) The risk of quantity change is transferred to the contractor, unless an instruction changing the original specification is issued. However, certainly in projects in which the quantity of work is uncertain, clients will pay a premium for this privilege.

(h) Assessment of the amounts due to the contractor is easier and involves many fewer person-hours with an activity schedule than with a bill of quantities: typically a half- to quarter-hour walk round the site once a month. This saves labour costs, because there is no need to remeasure repeatedly.

(i) Because the contractor has to complete the activity to be paid, an operation is broken down into smaller activities. This, together with the NEC Engineering and Construction Contracts programming clauses, gives much greater information and less subjectivity when evaluating claims and variations (or compensation events in NEC terminology).

Activity schedules therefore overcome many of the disadvantages that milestone payments and lump sums have.

However, there are some **disadvantages** compared with both straight and method-related bills of quantities:

(a) Taking off a bill of quantities can be a very good check on the quality of the specifications and drawings and, having identified the deficiencies, allows you to do something about them. Not doing so exposes a client to the possibility of claims/compensation events for small 'niggly' things.

(b) Not supplying any quantities does give tendering contractors more work compared with clients supplying quantities and increases the person-hours needed to prepare a tender. Consequently, clients may wish to put potential work out to fewer tenderers, in order not to push up the overheads of the industry, which they ultimately pay for.

(c) Bill rates do not exist and therefore cannot be used for simple changes where there are no time-related costs. Although I question how often this is the case, it can mean that the time needed to evaluate minor claims/compensation events is out of all proportion to their value. If there are a large number of small changes, then this disadvantage can outweigh the advantage of not having to constantly remeasure the quantity of work done, resulting in increased person-hours for contract administration.

(d) Some contractors have tended to break down the activity schedule into too many activities, in the client's opinion, in order to ensure cash flow throughout the contract. This not only means very long, complicated and unwieldy programmes, it also means that considerable time has to be spent agreeing which activities are complete for payment purposes, which tends to lead to reverting to the bill of quantities approach of measuring everything. Consequently, some clients have started limiting the number of activities in the activity schedule or specifying a minimum duration or price per activity to avoid long and complex programmes.

When to use activity schedules

As a result of the flexibility of activity schedules — and of the NEC Engineering and Construction Contract with which they are used — they can be used from simple projects to complex projects and with full client design or contractor design or anywhere in between.

As with milestone and lump sum contracts, providing the client does not issue a variation (or change the works information in NEC terminology), the risk of changed quantities lies with the contractor. Consequently, the client will pay a premium for this transfer of risk if quantities are uncertain, and so may be better advised to use method-related bills of quantities or a schedule of rates for this type of project.

An amalgamated approach for highways maintenance

I was asked in 1998, along with a team from W S Atkins Transportation Engineering Ltd, to write a contract based on the NEC Engineering and Construction Contract (ECC) for term maintenance of the motorways and trunk roads around Bristol for the Highways Agency. In its unamended form, the contract is mainly used for new-build and/or refurbishment contracts. Option A: Priced contract with activity schedules was used as the base option. Activity schedules were used to cover two types of work:

- method-related activities, in which the contractor had to carry out certain operations at certain times of the year according to a prescribed method, for example cleaning out gullies using the Highways Agency standard method at the start of winter
- performance-based activities, in which the contractor had to maintain a level of measurable performance throughout the year, for example visibility of signs from a certain distance, length of grass within a certain distance of the motorway, etc.

For each of these activities, the site was divided into 16 sub-areas for payment purposes. The idea was to transfer to the contractor responsibility for things that had to be done, so that the amount of work was known and the contractor could therefore estimate the cost. By being in control of these things, it could plan the use of resources more efficiently. For the method-related activities, the contractor was not to be paid until an inspection confirmed that the work had been done satisfactorily. In the case of the performance-based activities, if the level of performance was not maintained within the sub-area for that month, the contractor was not paid for the maintenance operations within that priced activity.

Furthermore, an additional compensation event was inserted whereby the client, through its consultant, W S Atkins, could call off items from a tendered schedule of rates. This could be used for minor improvement and refurbishment works, as well as emergency works ranging from traffic management, if an accident occurred on the network, to recleaning a gully which had become blocked before its scheduled clean. Finally, operations not covered by the activities or schedule of rates were assessed using the normal procedure for assessing compensation events under the ECC.

The contract also had more extensive programming requirements written in and I have since adapted it for other term maintenance and service contracts, for example maintaining reception and security services.

4.4.8 Conclusion

This section has discussed different price-based payment mechanisms: what they are, their advantages and disadvantages and when to use them. If using a price-based contract, in which there is a *tolerable* level of uncertainty over quantities, I would tend towards a method-related bill of quantities or method-related schedule of rates, depending on the circumstances. By tolerable, I mean that the payment mechanism does not break down as a means of accurately reimbursing the contractor's costs. For other contracts, I would tend towards activity schedules. The note of caution stated in the introduction is worth repeating: what has been discussed are general definitions, which will vary depending on the precise wording of the contract.

However, **with all price-based contracts, there are two principal disadvantages from a partnering viewpoint**:

• To varying degrees, the client is always second guessing how the contractor's prices are built up as it does not have direct access to the cost build-up. Consequently, when variations, claims or compensation events occur, disagreement over the additional costs is likely to occur to varying degrees. This is the biggest cause of dispute in the building industry, so if this can be 'cracked' a major pressure against partnering is nullified, and price-based contracts do not help in this respect.

• From the client's point of view, once the contract is signed there are only indirect incentives to minimize construction costs, or the unit costs under the schedule of rates. Motivations are therefore not directly aligned.

The focus from the client's viewpoint under price-based contracts tends therefore to be on restricting increases in *prices*, rather than helping to reduce the contractor's *costs*. The contractor's focus tends to be on increasing the prices to cover its *costs* plus making a contribution to head office overheads and profit. Thus, a generalized conclusion is that **the fundamental flaw of price-based payment mechanisms with respect to partnering is that they do not create alignment of financial objectives.**

Review question 2 List the typical problems of a commercial or contractual nature that you have encountered on the price-based contracts you have been involved in. Working backwards, to what extent do you think these problems can wholly or partly be attributed to the payment mechanisms described so far?

Based on your current knowledge, what would you do differently?

4.5   Conclusion

Although cost-based payment mechanisms and procurement routes (with the exception of management contracts) have not been discussed, the general spectrum in which the different payment mechanisms and procurement routes sit is illustrated in Fig. 4.6. This is, however, only a generalized summary!

Review question 3 Look at Fig. 4.6. It is a generalized diagram with each procurement route placed in a position relative to six parameters — three on each axis — plus arguably another on the diagonal. Do you think that each procurement route is placed in the right place for each parameter relative to the other routes? If not, where should it be for that parameter?

Procurement routes for partnering

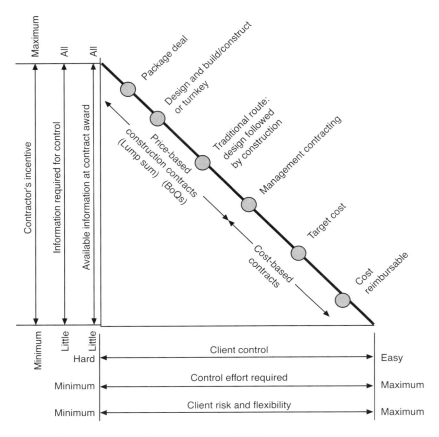

Fig. 4.6.   The general characteristics of different procurement routes (developed from reference 5)

Review question 4   If you had to write a conclusion to this chapter, what would it be?

How does this relate to what you wanted to gain from reading this chapter at the start of it?

Draw out a learning map to draw together and summarize what you have learnt from reading this chapter. This will also provide you with a very quick way of recapping your main learnings from this chapter.

References

1. Birkby G. Making the most of contract relationships. *Project — the Magazine for the Association for Project Management*, 2001, **14**, No. 5, 12–13.
2. Hoare D. J. and Broome J. C. Bills of quantities vs. activity schedules for civil engineering projects. *J. Constr. Procur.*, 2001, **7**, No. 1, 11–26.
3. Potts K. F. *Major construction works: contractual and financial management*. Longman Scientific and Technical, Harlow, 1995.
4. Revay S. G. Can construction claims be avoided? In *Construction conflict management and resolution*, eds P. Fenn and R. Gameson. E. & F. N. Spon, London, 1992.
5. Barnes N. M. L. Advanced construction management techniques. *Continuing Engineering Studies Seminar*, Civil Engineering Department, The University of Texas, Austin, Texas, 2–3 November 1983.

Bibliography

The following books have also been drawn upon for this chapter. Credit is thereby given:

Ashworth A. *Contractual procedures in the construction industry*, 2nd edn. Longman Scientific and Technical, Harlow, 1991.

Franks J. *Building procurement systems: a client's guide*, 3rd edn. Addison Wesley Longman with Englemere, Harlow, 1998.

Headley J. and Griffith A. *The procurement and management of small works and minor maintenance: the principal considerations for client organisations*. Addison Wesley Longman with Englemere, Harlow, UK, 1997.

Potts K. F. *Major construction works: contractual and financial management*. Longman Scientific and Technical, Harlow, 1995.

Smith N. J. (ed.) *Engineering project management*. Blackwell Science, Oxford, 1995.

Turner A. *Building procurement*, 2nd edn. Macmillan Press, Basingstoke, UK, 1997.

5. Concepts and process for the intelligent use of incentives

5.1 Introduction and overview

This chapter discusses concepts and mechanisms for the intelligent use of incentives by clients. But **what is the purpose of an incentive?** The author suggests that it is **to align more closely the motivations of the contractor, consultant or supplier to those of the client, so that any of the participants, by working for the success of their organization, is indirectly working for the success of the project.** This does not necessarily mean that they have to work together as some procurement methods do not lend themselves to this approach, for example a design and build lump sum contract, but **an incentive will put more emphasis on achieving a client objective than a contractual obligation alone**.

> Calardine,[1] at a Construction Productivity Network event in 1996, defined an incentive-based contract as 'a form of contract which provides additional motivation in order to achieve certain targets which are of benefit to both parties compared with the basic requirements of the contract.'
>
> The chairperson at the above event, Professor Nigel Smith, stated that 'the prime aim of incentive based contracts is to provide a vehicle for collaborative working to achieve defined goals with incentives to ensure that gains and risks are appropriately shared by the various parties to the contracts and that all receive benefits from the process.'

A basic premise of all that is discussed in this chapter and book, and a basic premise for the use of any incentive, is that, however performance is defined, the contractor makes:

- average profit for average performance
- improved profitability for better than expected performance
- reduced profit for poor performance.

> As Blyth[2] states: 'the general principle (of designing incentive contracts) is straightforward. It is simply to take advantage of a contractor's general objective to maximise his profits by giving him the opportunity to earn — and I emphasise earn — a greater profit if he performs the contract efficiently.'

The intelligent use of incentives relates to designing a multi-incentive plan so that the contractor, in pursuing its business objectives, is indirectly placing the same emphasis or weighting on each of the client's project objectives as the client does. While this is the ideal of a balanced incentive plan, it is rarely completely achieved. However, by more closely aligning objectives, you are more likely to create a focused project team, whose changed culture will accommodate any minor commercial misalignment.

> Sir Michael Latham,[3] in his review of the construction industry in the UK, *Constructing the team*, stated that modern contracts need to 'provide for incentives for exceptional performance'.*
>
> HM Treasury[4] draft procurement guidance in 1999 suggested that 'an incentive mechanism is a process whereby the parties to a contract are rewarded for performance significantly over and above that contracted for, which is of material benefit to the client and can be measured. Incentives may be financial or non-financial or a combination of the two.'*
>
> Fincham[5] is less extreme than the previous two authors, stating that the purpose of incentives is to 'motivate the contractor to produce a system that will meet or surpass performance goals, on or before a target date or within or at a target cost'.

While the incentive will predominantly be in monetary form, it could take other forms: more positive cash flow, reduced risk, improved tendering opportunities leading to greater likelihood of repeat business, and positive publicity, including awards, leading to an increased likelihood of new business, to name a few (see Table 3.1).

This chapter gives a headline model for developing a balanced incentive plan, identifying and discussing the concepts and considerations that need to be taken into account. Without awareness of these concepts and considerations, the

---

*Although I agree with the overall sentiment of these quotes, I do not agree that it has to be for 'exceptional performance' or 'significantly over and above that contracted for'. Just above that contracted for can be worthwhile having!

danger is that the mechanism chosen and how it is put into effect will not align motivations. Consequently, contractor, consultants and suppliers will either not pursue client objectives or, in the extreme, actively pursue objectives that are counter to the client's! The next chapter details incentive mechanisms in which emphasis is put on the achievement of only one project objective. Mechanisms for developing a balanced multi-incentive plan, which could include adding incentives to a target cost or alliance arrangement, are discussed in Chapter 9; the majority of considerations outlined in this chapter still apply.

Before proceeding, and especially by the end of the chapter, the reader might ask 'is it worth the effort to design an incentive mechanism?'. The following evidence is presented:

A US Construction Industry Institute (CII)[6] survey of 472 projects in May 1995 reported that clients 'have realized benefits averaging 4.5% of the project total installed cost for their projects through the use of incentives and innovative contract clauses'. Of these, 104 achieved savings of 10%.

Three of the most recent of the CII publications[6–8] contain plenty of case studies of projects in which the use of incentives has certainly contributed to the achievement of project objectives. The more striking examples are given below:

- a $14.5 million saving on a $115 million project budget in which the contractor's personnel were given part of the savings
- a $3.3 million saving on a budget of $120 million with a schedule saving of 6 months on a 36-month contract, in which incentive proposals were solicited from contractors during bidding and the 'fee-at-risk' principle was used
- a 27% cost under-run relative to budget and a reduction in the contract period from 8 to 6.5 months, in which incentives were developed jointly during project kick-off and team-building meetings
- a 64% increase in craft worker productivity on an electricity utility maintenance contract
- a combined productivity and safety bonus to workers led to a 20% reduction in total person-hours compared with that expected at start of the project; this was a significant factor in the construction period being reduced from 24 to 18 months
- a 4% improvement in plant production availability compared with the previous plants, partly as a result of performance-in-use incentives on plant

> • a reduction in an alliance contractor's overheads by 22%, partly as a result of periodic bidding of work to contractors outside the alliance.

Much of this chapter, especially from section 5.5 onwards, draws on two publications co-authored by Ibbs.[9,10] Consequently, unless a direct quotation is used, this work is not credited in the text. Acknowledgement is given here.

Preview question   Scan through this chapter. Note what you do know. Note what you do not know. Note what you want to know.

5.2   Uniqueness

As stated in the introduction to this chapter, the purpose of using an incentive is to align more closely the motivations of the contractor with those of the client, so that the contractor, in pursuing its business objectives, is indirectly pursuing the client's project objectives. **As every project is unique to some extent, it suggests that each incentive plan will be unique to some extent.** For example, although the basic structure of the incentive plan may stay the same for projects of a similar type, the exact monetary incentives may vary depending on the weighting of each client objective, size of the project, risks, etc.

> **To reinforce the point**
>
> Blyth[2] makes the point that 'the problem in devising a multiple incentive contract is … one of allocating fees to each of the areas of contractor effort … so that in looking after his own interests — earning maximum profit — the contractor will always take the decision that is in the best interests of the customer. The approach and resulting arrangement will obviously depend on the circumstances of each individual procurement.'
>
> Ibbs[9] states quite categorically that 'to be effective each plan must be tailored to fit the specific application'.
>
> A CII study[11] found that 'the development of Contractor compensation plans that lead to owner success is highly individualized to the specific project and personalities and philosophies of the project leaders that craft the contract.'

> Howard and Bell[8] cite one client having a standardized incentive plan, which project teams, with the help of guidelines, tailor to the unique circumstances of their individual contract in consultation with the chosen alliance contractor.

5.3   Overview of the process

Although every project, and therefore incentive plan, is unique to some extent, it does not necessarily mean that the process of developing an incentive plan need be unique. An outline process is illustrated in bold in Fig. 5.1, which is additional to the process for developing procurement strategy given in Chapter 3 (Fig. 3.1). Before going through the additional elements, note that **fine tuning an incentive plan is unlikely to yield significant benefits if the procurement route, contract breakdown structure and basic payment terms are fundamentally wrong for the project or individual contract:**

(a) Weight project objectives. Having identified objectives in the early stages of the procurement process, the specific project objectives need to be

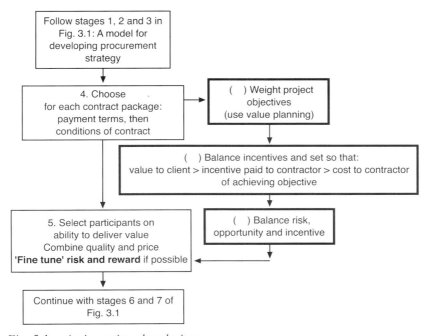

Fig. 5.1.   An incentive plan design

weighted. This is effectively stage 2 of the value planning phase (see Appendix 1). This weighting should be reflected in the incentive plan.[12] Consequently, **only when the specific project objectives are clearly defined and weighted should the client start developing an incentive plan.** However, a benefit of developing a balanced incentive plan is that it forces the client to think more clearly about the translation of business objectives to project level.

(b) *Balance incentives and set so that value to the client is greater than the incentive paid to the contractor, which, in turn, is greater than the cost to contractor of achieving the objective.* This statement is important and considered fully in section 5.4.

(c) *Balance risk, opportunity and incentive.* This statement relates to risk allocation and sharing. It is considered in detail in section 5.5.

When joining back into the model process for developing the procurement strategy, I would stress the importance of two points:

- There is a need to ensure by, at a minimum, some discussion with the contractor that points *(b)* and *(c)* above are taken into account and objectives have been truly aligned (see sections 3.9 and 5.6). This is why the arrow from box *(c)* of Fig. 5.1 feeds back into 'fine tune risk and reward having selected the contractor'.

- There is also a need to communicate both objectives and how the incentive plan works and how it is now in project participants' commercial objectives to work together (see section 3.11). **Communication is helped if**, despite the fairly extensive considerations outlined in the rest of this chapter, **the final incentive plan is as simple as necessary to do the job and expressed in clear and easy to understand language.** I am aware of a number of examples, both from my own research and in the literature,[9,13] of changed contractual stimuli that were not communicated to project participants. Consequently, they carried on acting as they had always done.

Stukhart[14] states that 'incentives, along with commensurate penalties, are the means to an end and, unless the objectives are clearly understood by both parties to the contract and correlated with their expectations, they are not usually effective'. Consequently, he 'encourages owners to communicate [objectives] more effectively, both within its organisation and to contractors'.

Abu-Hiljeh and Ibbs[15] found that 'incentive plans ... require owners to define their objectives more clearly. They also encourage owners to communicate their objectives more effectively, both within their own organisation and to their contractors.'

The summary of the Construction Productivity Network workshop event[1] on incentive-based contracts states that 'success is dependent upon a high level of trust and openness and everyone having a clear understanding of the project objectives. Agreements underpinning these have to be simple, clear and owned by all parties before the project begins.'

Mechanisms for communicating objectives and the incentive plan include:

- identification and possible development of an incentive scheme at the partnering project start-up meeting
- partnering charters, which reinforce the mutual and now aligned objectives of the parties
- posters to remind people, and even videos on large projects to induct people, which include mention of the financial benefits of working together
- regular joint reviews of how all parties are doing in terms of achieving their objectives
- regularly updated charts to show project participants how the parties are doing.

5.4 Balancing value, incentive and cost

In full, the above title reads: balance incentives and set so that value to the client is greater than the incentive paid to the contractor, which, in turn, is greater than the cost to the contractor of achieving the objective. **This statement has to be true for all parties for it to be worthwhile having an incentive.** Therefore, **it is a basic consideration when setting incentives** and is illustrated in Fig. 5.2.

Behind the fairly obvious statement, illustrated in Fig. 5.2, lies this consideration:

- The client knows (A) and (B) and is interested in the difference between them, that is (A) minus (B), which is the added value that using an incentive may produce.
- The contractor knows (B) and (C) and is motivated by the difference between them, that is (B) minus (C), which is the additional profit from successfully achieving the client's objective.

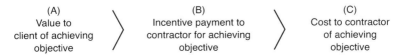

Fig. 5.2. The basic considerations when setting incentives

Consequently, particularly when designing a multi-incentive plan, what is important is that the relative profit for the contractor on each incentive (B minus C) reflects the weighting of the client's objectives (A minus B), and *not* that an individual incentive reflects the value to the client if that objective is achieved.

Smith *et al.*,[16] in effect, state this, albeit less explicitly: 'if a contract is so structured that the contractor makes a higher profit by achieving those objectives on which the owner places the greatest importance, then the owner has wisely harnessed the profit motivation to work for his own ends.'

Stukhart[14] states 'that owners must be careful how they combine cost, schedule, or technical incentives in any one contract, so that incentives do not result in imbalances' and that 'such imbalances might motivate the wrong behaviour or over emphasise some objectives at the expense of others'.

The recent CIRIA report,[17] entitled *Construction contract incentive schemes,* states that when multiple incentives are used 'these require care in determining priorities, designing the incentive controls and understanding the interaction between them'.

An example in which incentives were not balanced!

A Canadian city was due to host a world fair and wanted to have a new light railway transport system in place. The project had a fairly tight and fixed deadline. A contractor was employed on a package deal, target cost basis, with the contractor being reimbursed its management and administration fees and construction costs and rewarded both for bringing the project in ahead of schedule and by sharing any savings. However, any over-run was to be taken completely by the client.

Early on in the project cycle, it emerged that costs would not come in under the target so the contractor's only opportunity of earning additional profit was to bring the project in ahead of schedule. This aim it aggressively pursued, spending the money for which it was fully reimbursed, with no concern for the client's budget. It was only by threatening termination that the client persuaded the contractor to renegotiate the contract.

(Source: reference 18)

This highlights the importance of asking the 'what if?' questions outlined in section 3.10.

5.5   Balancing risk, opportunity and incentive

The discussion and conclusions in section 5.4 ignore one significant factor: **if there is no uncertainty in achieving the objective, why put an incentive on it? Just specify it as a contractual obligation** that the contractor can price up in the usual manner! At the other extreme, **if the achievement of the objective is impossible or subject to risks completely outside of the contractor's control, what is the point in putting an incentive on it?** Thus, risk, both negative and positive, has an impact on developing a balanced incentive plan and therefore **the discussions on risk allocation and sharing** (in section 3.5) **are just as pertinent when applied to positive incentives or bonuses.**

Ashley et al.[19] state my second and third principles of risk allocation and sharing for incentives as 'there is no benefit to either party to base incentive payments on a pure gamble from the outcome of uncontrollable risks'.

As Howard and Bell[8] state, a logical consequence of this is that it 'implies that owners can bolster the power of incentives by structuring projects to put contractors more in control of their performance', that is altering the procurement route, contract breakdown structure, etc.

One client[8] took this to the extreme on a $115 million design and build project for a new corporate headquarters by having only two of its employees supervising the construction and then fit-out contract. The idea was to completely shield the contractor from influences external to the project team, that is other client employees. Their views were taken on board prior to the main construction contract being let, and then prior to the fit-out contract being let, but they were not allowed to intervene once each contract had been let.

If only risks that the contractor can manage are allocated to it, then its performance and the performance of the contract, in terms of achieving objectives, is governed by its ability to manage these risks. If, as stated in the introduction to this chapter, a basic principle of incentives is that the contractor makes average profit for average performance, sees improved profitability for better than expected performance and reduced profit for poor performance, then this implies that the **starting point of any incentive plan has to be realistic targets of performance**. This is emphasized throughout literature on the use of incentives.

Stukhart[14] concludes that 'to ensure that incentive contracts achieve the efficiencies that owners want, it is essential that targets be realistic … This implies that owners must emphasise … reliable targets rather than elaborate sharing schemes and complex incentives.'

Ward *et al.*[20] state that 'objectives may be set that are conditional on the non-occurrence of specified risks or that include contingency allowances … Whatever objectives are set, there is a need for realistic levels, otherwise contractual parties will not be fully motivated to achieve them.'

The discussion on risk allocation and sharing in section 3.5 also implies **that any significant risks that are not predominantly within the contractor's influence and could hinder it from achieving the incentive-based performance target should be allocated to the client. The performance target would therefore be adjusted if they occurred and there needs to be a mechanism to do this within the contract.** There are two reasons for this:

* Where damages are being applied, if the client has an obligation under the contract to do something that affects the achievement of the performance target, and it is not done, then, unless the performance target is adjusted, the contractor could potentially sue the client for breach of contract. For instance, if standard conditions of contract did not include clauses for extensions of time for a breach occurring, contractors could complete the works within a 'reasonable time', avoiding any damages, except in exceptional circumstances.[16] This is referred to as 'time at large'.
* Once the contractor perceives that the rewards from obtaining the target outweigh the costs to it, then it will lose motivation. Either the target or the incentive needs to be adjusted to maintain the motivation.

Calardine[1] states that 'the arrangements need to be able to deal with variations in the project scope in a manner that ensures that the rewards still reflect the original intention and that one party is not disadvantaged by change. In addition, contracts need to be managed so that when changes do occur they are taken into account as soon as they happen. If this is not the case, then there is a strong possibility that difficulties and arguments will arise later, as with more traditional contracts.'

Abu-Hiljeh and Ibbs[15] recommend that project participants 'handle changes promptly and efficiently, taking into account any effects that they might have on incentive plan targets'.

5.6   Who designs the incentive plan and when

5.6.1   Overview

There are four ways to balance the incentive plan: through the client imposing the incentive plan (pre-planned[†]); by the contractor proposing an incentive plan (responsive[†]); by negotiation; or by introducing/modifying an incentive plan after the contract is let (reactive[†]). These are considered in order below.

5.6.2   Client-imposed plans

The potential **advantages** of a client-imposed plan are that:

(a) Selecting competing contractors is both easier and more auditable, as there is no proposed incentive plan to evaluate and compare and then justify the decision to auditors.

(b) They can be implemented earlier, which may be necessary if early involvement of the contractor is desirable (otherwise the contractor may hold back on its contribution until the time that it derives benefit from contributing) or on a time-driven project.

(c) They require less time and effort to develop.

(d) Incentives are less likely to be perceived as excessive by senior client management.

The potential **disadvantages** of a client-imposed plan are:

(a) The client does not appreciate the cost or risk to the contractor of achieving the objective and therefore either puts too great an incentive on the measure, so that it is overemphasized, or puts too little incentive on it, so that it does not sufficiently motivate the contractor to pursue it at all.

(b) In an extreme situation, the contractor may accept the incentive plan just to win the contract.

(c) The client needs to have the expertise and information to set credible targets.

For these reasons, **I am generally not in favour of client-imposed plans, except in the case in which one project objective dominates, almost to the exclusion of others.** Consequently, only one objective should have an incentive placed against it. Lane rental contracts on motorways, which are extremely time dominated, are an example (see section 6.4.3).

[†]'Pre-planned', 'responsive' and 'reactive' incentive schemes are the categories used in the CIRIA report, *Construction contract incentive schemes*; see reference 17.

5.6.3   Contractor-proposed incentive plans

The client, when asking for a contractor-proposed incentive plan, needs to communicate its objectives to potential contractors before asking for these proposals. Otherwise, how can the contractor design a plan that reflects the client's unknown and/or unweighted objectives? Alternatively, the contractor may propose them without the client asking. The advantage over client-imposed incentives is that the contractor will propose incentives that it considers are achievable and worthwhile pursuing, rather than accepting the client's plan in order to win the contract. It also provides an indication of:

*   how clearly the client has communicated its objectives and/or how well the contractor has understood them
*   the contractor's view of the likelihood of these being achieved — the more its payment is dependent on achieving the objectives, it could be argued, the greater the contractor's confidence in its ability to achieve them
*   whether the contractor's thinking is compatible with the client's.

The main disadvantage is that the process of evaluating and comparing what may be structurally different incentive plans can be quite subjective, which makes this approach less appealing to the public sector, in which the basis for evaluation has to be more clearly established for public accountability purposes.

5.6.4   Negotiated incentive plans

The advantage of a negotiated plan is that there is more ownership of the plan by the contractor because it is more likely that:

(a) The contractor would not accept the incentive plan if the targets set are unrealistic.
(b) The incentives for each client objective are set at a level that make them worthwhile for the contractor to pursue.
(c) All three areas illustrated in Fig. 5.2 have been identified. The weighting of the rewards for the contractor in pursuing the different client objectives should more closely match the client weighting of those objectives.
(d) The process of creating the plan is likely to lead to greater understanding of each other's positions and encourage ownership of the incentive plan, which leads on to greater teamwork once into the implementation phase.

The CII study in 1996[11] concluded that 'a high level of trust and communication between the Owner and Contractor is needed to develop effective compensation plans, recommending 'joint development by owner and contractor personnel of the specifics of incentive plans. This creates a sense of ownership and commitment. When owner personnel genuinely want the Contractor to achieve the maximum incentive because it corresponds to maximum owner success, team work and co-operation can produce exceptional results.'

Howard and Bell[8] comment that 'a sense of ownership of the incentive plan appears from several of our case studies to be key to effective team motivation.'

Abu-Hiljeh and Ibbs[15] agree, whilst noting the principal drawback: 'Negotiated targets result in greater ownership and commitment by the contractor, but take longer to establish and might delay project start somewhat.'

The two main disadvantages of negotiated incentive plans are:

(a) the same as with contractor-proposed plans: establishing clear criteria for their evaluation
(b) the time and resources needed to negotiate and finalize the plan.

For these reasons, it is unlikely that the negotiated approach is appropriate for either:

- a time-driven project for which the work needs to start quickly or
- a project for which more than three tenderers are still competing for the work (if a preferred contractor has been selected, negotiation could take place to fine tune either a client- or contractor-proposed incentive plan).

5.6.5 *Reactive incentive plans*

Reactive plans are incentive plans introduced reactively in response to some changed circumstances. If the project objectives are properly defined and the incentive plan properly structured to reflect both client and contractor motivations, then it could be argued that there should be no need to introduce incentives over time. However, situations in which it may be beneficial to reactively introduce or modify the incentive plan for a project that is already being implemented could include:

- Project objectives change due to external circumstances. For instance, in order to be first in the market, it might become a commercial necessity to have a factory in operation earlier than originally planned, thus an additional time incentive could be introduced. This would be a client-proposed bonus.
- The original incentive plan is found not to be producing the desired balance of motivations, so the contractor is putting more emphasis on

achieving one of the client's objectives at the expense of others. Either party could propose a modification to more closely align motivations.

- An event that happens early in the project means that the original bonus is no longer sufficient to motivate the contractor to meet the original performance target. This could be due to a risk occurring for which there is no means of adjusting the now unachievable performance target.

> The CII study,[11] reported in 1996, recommended 'monitor the impact of the compensation plan during the project and adjust if required. If factors outside the Contractor's control prevent achievement of targets, and there is still potential for improvement, consider adjusting targets.'

- The end of project objectives are seen as too remote or ill-defined, so an incentive for an intermediate target is introduced to provide more immediate motivation.

5.6.6 Summary

It is obviously not desirable to start a project with the intention of introducing or modifying an incentive plan once the project is under way as this implies that the project is currently unlikely to achieve its objectives. There may, however, be circumstances in which to do so reactively will increase the likelihood of a failing project meeting its objectives.

Client-imposed, contractor-proposed or negotiated incentive plans take a more proactive approach. Having communicated objectives, **I have no preference for whether an outline incentive scheme is proposed by the client or by the contractor**, although public sector clients will probably prefer the former. **However, before signing the contract, genuine and open consultation should** *at a minimum* **take place with the other party to ensure that commercial objectives are aligned. If they are not, the incentive plan should be fine tuned or renegotiated to ensure a balanced plan.**

5.7 Use of positive and/or negative incentives

5.7.1 Use of negative incentives

Research in the USA found that practitioners think that 'positive incentives have "some" to "much" impact, whereas negative incentives have "none" to "some" impact'.[12] Or, put another way, the perception in the USA is that bonuses are more effective than damages. Why is this so?

From an applied psychology viewpoint, people focus either on 'pursuing pleasure' (a positive 'moving towards' motivation) or on 'avoiding pain' (a negative 'moving away from' motivation).[21,22] From a commercial viewpoint, the benchmark level for the setting of negative incentives is that of industry standards or competence with sufficient tolerance for human error.[23] So the level of performance initially aimed for is mediocrity or just above the point at which pain is encountered or, for example, damages are levelled. When things change, rather than focusing on how to meet the client's objectives, participants on all sides are in the mindset of 'avoiding pain', which often takes the form of transferring blame to the other parties.

Ibbs,[9] when talking about negative incentives, states: 'the focus is shifted towards avoiding penalties, which is accompanied by a pre-occupation with potential claims and adversarial relationships', advising clients, in another co-authored paper[21] to 'not employ incentive schemes that make use of penalties exclusively'.

Ashley and Workman,[12] in their research, found that 'negative' incentives appear to hamper project performance. They, in fact, appear to lower performance outcomes below the level obtained with 'no incentives at all'.

Ibbs and Ashley[13] in their later joint paper go further, stating that: 'No evidence exists that negative incentives, used by themselves, enhance project objectives; in fact, except for perhaps public sector contracting, negative incentives may have no role in modern contracts.'

Head,[24] a practising lawyer, reviewed in his MSc dissertation the damages clauses of various conditions of contract in use in the UK today. He concluded that the 'contractual remedies are considered either ineffective, too drastic or, if improperly applied, a source of financial danger to the owner's position'.

The last quote above connects with a further issue arising from the rise of partnering, in that decisions are often made jointly, and the documentation to support decisions is often lacking.[25] Consequently, responsibility for implementation becomes blurred, so proving or disproving liability becomes harder.

In summary, damages/negative incentives alone tend to lead to negative performance! Why? Because they tend to be hard to enforce and focus participants' minds on avoiding negative performance, rather than inspiring participants to strive for above average to exceptional performance. Therefore, my conclusion is: **do not use damages/negative incentives on their own!**

5.7.2   Use of positive incentives

Positive incentives, on the other hand, set the target at an above average, or even an exceptional, level of achievement. Thus, participants focus on more positive inspiring goals, so when issues arise that may affect their achievement they will continue to focus on these objectives rather than on transferring liability to 'avoid pain'.

Uff and Capper,[26] two distinguished UK lawyers, claim that 'bonuses are far more effective psychologically than liquidated damages in obtaining performance and timely completion.'

Newman[27] of Bechtel illustrates this by stating that 'our experience is that positive incentives, for some reason, have a much lower risk of causing aberrant behaviour, even when the monetary effect is the same. Applying a 20% fee penalty, as with a negative incentive for a cost over-run, is somehow more painful to a contractor than getting an 80% score on an award fee basis.'

Ibbs,[9] in his research, found that 'positive incentives encourage positive actions, behaviours and relationships. Contractor's energies are directed toward developing more effective ways to achieve project objectives.'

In a partnering environment in which the incentives are genuinely aligned, one party's 'win' should automatically mean that other parties 'win' too.

All this suggests that **the use of positive incentives is far more likely to stimulate above average to exceptional performance than negative incentives/damages, which will only stimulate, at best, 'above mediocre' performance.**

5.7.3   Combining positive and negative incentives

So should *only* positive incentives be used? No, I would argue, for three reasons:

- **If damages are not stated in the contract**, then they are not capped, so, if things do turn out badly, the client will be able to sue the contractor for damages that can be *reasonably* attributed to the contractor's lack of performance. First, the 'reasonably' almost inevitably means that there will be dispute over the amount. Second, this means that **the contractor's liability is not capped and some contractors, particularly in the process sector, may refuse to contract**. Others may add a premium to the contract price.
- Some people are predominantly motivated, in the psychological sense, to 'avoid pain', in which case positive incentives alone will have little effect. They need negative incentives to be motivated!

- As well as going for 'win–win', it could be argued that **'lose–lose' should also be built into the incentive plan, with the plan structured so that it is still worthwhile for the partners to co-operate so that joint losses are minimized. They are therefore true partners through good times and bad!**

Consequently, I conclude that a combination of negative and positive incentives will be most effective in stimulating improved performance from the contractor and, if objectives are truly aligned, the whole team. Research from the USA indicates that this approach is marginally more effective than positive incentives alone, which, in turn, are significantly more effective than negative incentives alone.[12] Having some damages also protects the parties if things do not turn out well.

> Bechtel's experience in the USA would confirm this, with Newman[27] stating that their 'experience is that a good mix of positive and negative incentives, generally reflecting the same risk/reward issues that the project owner is facing, provides the best alignment of contractor and customer'.

5.7.4 *Extent of positive and negative incentives*

If a combination of positive and negative incentives — or bonuses and damages — is likely to produce the best performance from the contractor, then the next question is at what level each should be set. **A good starting point is to say that, however performance is defined, the contractor should make:**

- **average profit for average performance**
- **improved profit for better than expected performance**
- **reduced profit for poor performance.**

Consequently, some damages are appropriate. However, if set high — and, in particular, higher than the bonuses — then the contractor is likely to focus more on avoiding negative performance. The effects of this have been discussed in section 5.7.1.

> Ibbs and Abu-Hiljeh[28] advise owners to 'consider the use of bonus-only incentive plans as a means of motivating contractors, but if provision for penalties is made, to design the plan so that bonus awards are as great and at least as likely as penalties.'

Particularly if there is a financially strong client able to offer the stimulus of repeat order business, then I would suggest that **damages are set at as low a level as possible, which the client will find tolerable and be able to bear if the desired performance is not achieved.** This is because clients are generally better able to take the consequences of risks occurring. **If there is not the repeat order stimulus, then the same applies, but with damages at a level sufficient for the contractor to care and not walk away from the project, that is 'lose–lose' would result.**

At the other extreme, there is a legal reason why damages cannot be excessive. In the UK, Europe and much of the rest of the world (excluding the USA), damages, to be effective, cannot be more than 'a genuine covenanted pre-estimate of likely damage'.[29] In terms of a project, this means that they have to be calculated as a genuine pre-estimate of the likely loss that the client will encounter as being due to the poor performance of the contractor in terms of time or end product performance. If they are not, then the courts will interpret them as a penalty,‡ which is not enforceable by law in the UK and most of the world outside the USA. **Clients therefore should not set damages at a level above that which cannot be justified on conservative assumptions.** Having done this, they should keep the calculations in order to be able to justify the damages should a dispute arise.

For bonuses, the reader is asked to briefly revisit sections 5.4 and 3.5. The argument in the latter is that clients are typically better able to absorb the consequences of negative risk, compared with contractors, as they are financially stronger. Thus, while the financial impact of a particular risk may be the same in absolute terms whoever holds that risk, the impact on a typical contractor's business is relatively greater. Turning this around, for an upside risk, or opportunity, it suggests that **for a contractor's business to benefit to the same degree relatively as a client's, the contractor need not receive as much of the benefit in absolute terms to be motivated to perform.** This is good news for clients!

Now, applying this concept to Fig 5.2 and the discussion around it, the obvious question to ask is what should the ratio be for the following:

$$\left.\begin{array}{c} \text{Value to client} \\ \text{minus} \\ \text{incentive payment to contractor} \\ \text{(A minus B)} \end{array}\right\} \text{ to } \left\{\begin{array}{c} \text{Incentive payment to contractor} \\ \text{minus} \\ \text{cost to contractor} \\ \text{(B minus C)} \end{array}\right.$$

or, put another way: return minus plan's cost to plan's cost.

---

‡The following legal judgment is given to help the reader identify the difference between a penalty and damage: 'The distinction between penalties and liquidated damages depends on the intention of the parties to be gathered from the whole of the contract. If the intention is to secure performance of the contract by the imposition of a fine or penalty, then the sum specified is a penalty; but if, on the other hand, the intention is to assess the damage for breach of contract, it is liquidated damages'; see reference 30.

Ibbs and Abu-Hijleh,[28] in their research in the USA, recommended that clients put incentives on 'the project areas in most need of improvement or that yield the highest returns, depending on project objectives' and that when these areas are targeted a 'total return to the owner of five times the plan's cost is not unusual'! In other words, the ratio of the return minus plan cost to plan cost was 4:1.

Ibbs and Abu-Hiljeh[28] later state that, in the USA, between 0.25% and 1% of the contract value under a priced-based contract, or 25–100% of the contractor's fee under a cost- or management-based contract, is sufficient to attract contractor attention. In their research though, the range was from 0.33% to 1.5% for the former and from 25% to 150% for the latter.

However, the ratio chosen will not just depend on the return on investment for the client and the cost to the contractor of achieving that performance, but will also be influenced by:

- the relative size and financial strength of the parties
- the extent of normal profit on capital invested and/or turnover for the contractor
- the degree of risk and likelihood of achieving performance for which incentive will be paid
- the influence of the party offered the incentive in achieving that level of performance over these risks.

5.7.5   Use of caps

A cap can represent either:

- the maximum bonus that the contractor will be paid, in which case the contractor is not motivated to achieve performance beyond this level
- the maximum damage that the contractor will pay, in which case, beyond this point, the contractor loses all motivation to minimize poor performance.

Caps can apply to individual incentives applied to single performance parameters or to the total bonus paid to, or damage paid by, the contractor.

Abu-Hiljeh and Ibbs[15] state that caps on individual incentives can be used 'to provide a check and balance so the contractor does not overemphasise the parameters with the highest bonus return at the expense of others. **A cap on the total bonus may also be used to achieve balance.**'

An overall cap on total bonus to be paid limits the client's exposure to exceptional performance by the contractor. Similarly, a cap on the total damages to be paid as a result of poor performance can be introduced to limit the contractor's exposure and/or if damages on individual incentives are not cumulative. For example, if there are two *inter-related* measures of performance, both of which have damages of £1000 per unit, then if both are not achieved the total damage is not £1000 plus £1000, but, say, £1500.

The general conclusion is that **whenever possible the bonus payment for above average or exceptional performance should exceed the damages for below average performance**, so that the contractor focuses on the former rather than the latter.

5.7.6 Summary

This section can be summarized thus:

- Negative incentives or damages alone do not encourage superior performance and may actually hamper it.
- Positive incentives or bonuses alone do encourage above average or superior performance.
- A combination of positive and negative incentives would appear to be the most likely to be effective, with the added advantage that stating damages caps a contractor's liability.
- Because of the way a typical contractor's finances are structured, a small change in turnover causes a relatively large change in profit and return on investment. Consequently, a typical contractor does not need to be allocated the majority of the benefit to be motivated to pursue an objective with an incentive attached.
- If positive and negative damages are used, the positive incentive should be greater than the corresponding negative incentive so that participants focus on above average to exceptional performance.

5.8 Measuring performance: type, when, by whom and where

5.8.1 Introduction

It is often said that 'what you measure is what you get'. This statement is even more likely to be true in practice if you are also rewarding what you measure!

Before reading this subsection, it is suggested that you read or briefly revisit Appendix 6. Ashley and Workman[12] reiterate some of the essential points by stating that 'performance measures used in an incentive programme should be

- perceived as valid measures
- flexible enough to meet changing conditions and

- easily administered'.

My view is that:

- 'Valid' means that the measures should be realistic, relevant to the project and sufficiently broad or narrow to reflect its true objectives.

> An example of measures that were not valid is given by Ibbs.[9] An incentive was specified based on the amount of labour used, which resulted in the contractor using construction plant and equipment when labour would have been more economic. This resulted in higher overall project costs, when the client's real objective was reduced project costs!

For process/qualitative measures, an example could be 'responsiveness to end-user requirements', measurement of which could result in the contractor becoming over-responsive at the expense of time and cost objectives'.
- 'Flexible' suggests that the definition of measures should reflect the state of technical definition.[31] For instance, there is no point in offering an incentive on the efficiency of a power station once it is in use if the client has already designed it: it is no longer within the contractor's control.
- 'Easily administered' means that employees concentrate on delivering the project rather than measuring, and possibly arguing over, how well they are doing.

5.8.2 Type of measure: quantitative vs. qualitative measures of performance

A quantitative measure is one whereby performance can be relatively easily measured and there is little subjectivity in that measure. A qualitative measure is one for which performance is described and then perhaps given a number or classification. Consequently, there is more subjectivity in that measure. General features of quantitative and qualitative measures are given in Table 5.1.

The subjective nature of qualitative performance measures means that there must be some stimulus for the client to be fair. Contractors, therefore, tend to be averse to them.[9] Their use is most likely to be effective:

- in longer-term relationships, in which the incentive payment is paid on a milestone basis as the project progresses and the parties are more interdependent
- in one-off projects, in which the client is a regular client of the industry, so that, should it be unfair, this will affect other contractors' approach to working with that client; the ensuing publicity then becomes a negative incentive on the client

Table 5.1. A comparison of the features of quantitative and qualitative measures

Quantitative measures	Qualitative measures
Tend to measure the outputs or results of project	Tend to measure the inputs or manner of performance, i.e. process performance
More objective	More subjective
Tend to focus on project objectives	Tend to focus on project processes or behaviours of parties
Tend towards end of project assessment	Tend towards milestone determination
Need precise and credible targets to work	Need pre-established criteria against which to be ranked in order to work

- in projects in which many aspects of performance can be stated or measured objectively, except for one; if this aspect is not allocated an incentive, then the contractor will pursue the objective measures to the exclusion of the subjective performance area.

In general, the more objective the measures can be made, the better. Consequently, I would suggest that, whenever possible, time is spent attempting to make qualitative measures more objective. This has the added advantage that both parties become clearer about what it is that is actually wanted.

An example of too subjective a measure

On one contract in the USA, a construction manager's fee was divided in two, with one-half being guaranteed and the other at risk. However, for exceptional performance this 'fee-at-risk' could be doubled based on the owner's evaluation of performance at completion.

Despite design delays, all the units were completed on schedule, with an 8% improvement in labour productivity compared with the previous benchmark and harmonious labour relationships. The client acknowledged 'high satisfaction' with the construction manager, giving him 140% of the fee-at-risk. However, this left the manager wondering why the remaining potential 60% went unpaid. It was concluded that in future more objective criteria were needed to evaluate client satisfaction.

(Source: reference 32)

5.8.3 *When is performance measured? End of project vs. milestone determination*

Milestone determination means that the contractor's performance is measured and the incentive allocated or paid as the project progresses, rather than at the end of the project. The principal advantages of end of project determination are:

- The measures tend to be quantitative and easily measurable.
- Less administration is required to measure the level of performance obtained. However, it can be argued that measuring performance and giving and receiving feedback as a project progresses is good project management and procurement practice and should be carried out regardless of whether incentives are being used.
- From a business viewpoint, the client is interested in *how* the contractor is performing during the project only to the extent that it gives an indication of whether the end of project objectives will be achieved. Milestone incentives involve the risk that bonuses are paid out yet the client's project objectives have not been met.

> Abu-Hiljeh and Ibbs[15] state that when using milestone determination, the client needs to have 'faith that the intermediate ... targets will add up to the sought-after project completion goal'.

The principal disadvantage of end of project determination is the loss of viability,[15] either because of circumstances beyond the client's or the contractor's control or because an event happened early in the project that puts the achievement of the objective out of the contractor's reach, in which case the contractor has no incentive to pursue the objective. In the former case, it is advisable to have a mechanism for adjusting the particular target (see section 5.5).

The advantages of milestone determination and payment are:

- They force feedback on performance and increase the motivation to improve for all parties.[15] For instance, if the time, cost, safety or quality targets are not being achieved, why not? If a consultant is not being awarded the incentive because of failure to deliver the expected service, why not? And, more importantly, what could be done differently to receive it!
- Their use is more suitable for longer projects in which either the end of project objectives cannot be defined or there is more uncertainty in achieving them:
  - If process incentives — incentives which reward the contractor for

how it is working — are being used, the targets for the next milestone will be based on improving the standard of 'process' at the current milestone. Thus, continuous improvement is encouraged.

— If milestone performance targets — for example, for time and cost — have incentives attached, the targets are developed or refined as the project progresses. This is particularly appropriate if the end of project objectives are not well defined or the process of delivery is subject to high risk. Therefore, if the contractor underperforms in one phase (which is relatively well defined and has low risk), it is still motivated to perform in the next. This both gives the client flexibility in its objectives and/or gives the project team flexibility over how they are achieved while keeping the contractor motivated to perform.

For longer term projects, these two approaches can be combined, with a greater emphasis on process incentives early on in the project, shifting to milestone performance targets and ultimately end of project performance as the project progressively becomes more defined.

In framework or term contracts, the incentive element of the fee should be less for measures taken early in the project as the contractor's initial performance is likely to be poorer, but the improvements should be at their most dramatic as the potential for improvement is at its greatest. Later on, greater effort will be required to achieve the same increases in performance, so it may be necessary to increase the incentive to increase the motivation and the amount invested by the contractor.

Concluding, a 'rule of thumb'[15] is that **projects of less than a year's duration are probably not suitable for milestone determination because of the additional effort required to administer them.** However, if the project performance is being benchmarked as it progresses anyway, then it will be worthwhile on projects of shorter duration. **If end of project performance cannot be defined or is subject to high risk, then milestone determination may be appropriate. This can either be for meeting interim performance measures, which are developed as the project progresses, or, if this is not possible, for achieving defined levels of good process or service.**

The following two subsections predominantly refer to the use of qualitative measures.

5.8.4   *Who assesses the measure: unilateral or bilateral determination*

If qualitative measures are being used to measure performance, it may be worth considering whether they should be unilaterally or bilaterally assessed, that is agreed by a process of negotiation. The former is obviously quicker and results in less immediate surface friction. However, if the assessment is perceived as being unfair by the contractor, then the incentive scheme's value will diminish in the longer term. It is also more likely that the source of underachievement will be discovered during the negotiation and therefore steps can be taken to improve it.

> Ibbs[9] reports that 'experience with joint determination shows a high correspondence between owner and contractor performance ratings.' In some of his case studies, no incentive or a minimum incentive would be paid if no agreement was reached, which, as he noted, 'contractors will hardly consider ... bilateral'.

Particularly if the qualitative measure is of the contractor's performance, as opposed to the project team's performance, I would recommend clients to consult with the contractor on the measure, although they have the final say. This has the advantage of the negotiated approach — it is more likely to lead to consensus over performance and how it can be improved — without the disadvantages.

> The CII study,[11] reported in 1996, concluded that 'feedback and communications that occur between Owner and Contractor during incentive evaluations are a significant part of the overall benefit of incentive plans'. Consequently, it recommends 'periodic meetings between Owner project management and Contractor team for review of performance areas, subjective appraisal and improvement initiatives'.

5.8.5   *Where is performance assessed? Off-site vs. on-site assessment*

When qualitative measures are used, performance ratings can be assessed by on-site or off-site personnel — in the latter case generally by more senior management personnel. The advantage of on-site determination by the client's team is that it is closest to the project and has more information on which to base its judgements. However, its judgement may be coloured by minor relationship, or unimportant, issues. Alternatively, it may not wish to jeopardize relations on site. In my research, one client in the UK felt that its site team's assessment of a consultant's performance had become 'rose tinted' because of their familiarity with each other, yet the objective measures of performance were staying the same.

> Howard and Bell[8] note that 'in long term relationships, scores may artificially trend up because team member's personal relationships inhibit objective performance feedback.'

Off-site determination largely overcomes these considerations and ensures that senior managers are abreast of how the project is doing. However, it is important that the views of those on site are taken into consideration and perceived as valid by the contractor, otherwise contractors' efforts may be more directed at impressing senior client management than at running the project effectively. Ways of gaining feedback from site personnel include use of attitudinal statements, balanced scorecards and informal conversations as well as through monitoring progress towards end of project objectives. A danger of senior management determination, however, is that it may have conflicting agendas, for example the company may now be losing money elsewhere so directors are not inclined to uphold previous agreements.

5.8.6 Summary

This section can be summarized thus:

- The topics associated with performance measurement and improvement link in with the measures of performance used to give incentives to contractors.
- Measures have to be perceived as valid, flexible and easily administered.
- Quantitative or hard measures are easier to administer and are generally suitable for shorter, one-off projects. Where this is the case, they are determined at the end of the project.
- Qualitative or soft measures, which measure process or behaviours, are harder to define and administer. Where possible, they should be used in combination with quantitative measures, although this might not be possible on longer-term or service contracts. Qualitative measures tend to be used in combination with milestone determination as the project progresses.
- Where qualitative measures are used, the author's opinion is that it is generally preferable for the final decision to be taken off-site and unilaterally determined by the client's senior management. However, the decisions should be based both on defined descriptive scales and in consultation with both the client's site team and contractor's management and site team. Otherwise, different views may be left unreconciled, leading to conflict, and the opportunities for continuous improvement lost.

5.9   Types of incentive mechanisms

5.9.1   Gatepost vs. graduated incentives

Gatepost or 'drop dead' incentives are those in which the contractor has to achieve a stated level of performance, otherwise it will not receive any incentive payment for that objective, for example no time incentive will be paid unless the project achieves completion 10 weeks ahead of the contractual date. Graduated incentives are proportional to the level of performance expected, for example a bonus awarded per week of early completion. The advantage of the gatepost incentives is that they can significantly raise the level of expectation of performance and what the contractor is aiming for.

The disadvantage of gatepost incentives is that if the gatepost becomes, in the contractor's view, unachievable, then the balanced emphasis it has put on achieving the client's targets may suddenly narrow in focus and it may pursue some of the client's objectives to the total exclusion of others. For instance, in the example above, what happens if the contractor realizes that it will only be able to achieve completion 8 weeks ahead of the contractual date, rather than the 10 weeks necessary to earn the bonus? It may switch to a least-cost strategy or divert resources to other projects where better rewards can be earned. The contractor becomes motivated by completion date again only when it becomes likely that damages will be deducted, so the project scrapes in, achieving completion on or just before the contractual date.

> Blyth[2] states that 'a multiple incentive arrangement should not only encourage the contractor to strive for outstanding results in all areas, but if during the course of the contract he realises that he will not be able to achieve this, it also encourages him to take the trade-off decision which is in the best interests of the customer.' This was clearly not the case in the example given in section 5.4.

For this reason, **I would generally not encourage the use of gatepost incentives except in special circumstances**, for instance in combination with milestone determination as the project progresses, so that poor performance in one period does not eliminate motivation in other periods.

5.9.2   Conditional and banked awards

Conditional and banked awards are used in multi-incentive plans, and some of the mechanisms identified in Chapter 10 accommodate conditional/banked awards. They are mentioned in this section both to raise awareness and to identify the danger of using them when developing a balanced incentive plan.

Typically, an incentive is paid for achieving a stated level of performance against one objective, irrespective of whether other performance levels and objectives are, or have been, achieved. A conditional award is one in which the contractor earns the award for achieving a given level of performance but payment is conditional upon achieving another target. A banked award is one in which the client keeps the award until a later date. Conditional and banked awards tend to be used together. For instance, any incentive payments for good process or service are financed by savings in the project budget and are, therefore, banked until the end of the project and conditional upon the project coming in under budget. Gatepost and graduated incentives can be used in combination to form conditional awards.

The major advantage of conditional awards is that they tie different incentives, and therefore the achievement of project objectives, together. One cannot be achieved to the exclusion of the others.

The disadvantage is that if the primary condition is not achieved, or looks like not being achieved, then all contractor motivation disappears. In the example mentioned in the first paragraph, once the project is forecast to be over budget, all incentive to perform during the project dissolves.

Ibbs[9] phrases the above disadvantage of conditional/banked awards as they 'may be perceived as reflecting a lesser commitment by the owner. Stated another way, the owner has a second chance to deny paying the bonus. Unknown future circumstances beyond control of the contractor may conspire to void payment as well.'

In the USA, the Cherne Contracting Corporation took part in a contract with an incentive plan. Incentives were placed against the following:

- labour safety: this was jointly funded with payments being made to the workforce
- programme performance against a target completion date
- an overall client satisfaction, funded from project savings.

Although there were programme delays, these were caused by the designer and Cherne managed to pull back 6 of the 14 days delay, which still resulted in loss of operating profit to the client and no incentive payment. Ninety-three per cent of the labour safety incentive was paid out during the contract, with there being no time lost because of accidents, however poor administration by the client's insurers led to post-completion claims being paid out. The net result was that there was no money left to fund the incentive for overall client satisfaction, which was quite high.

(Source: reference 32)

One way round this problem is partially banked awards, in which the contractor is paid a part of any interim payment as the project progresses, with payment of the remainder being conditional upon achieving an end of project objective.

5.10 Conclusion

This chapter has identified terminology and highlighted the basic process and conceptual issues that need to be considered when drawing up a balanced incentive plan that will remain viable throughout the project. The specific conclusions can be found at the end of each subsection. Many of the issues and conclusions are interconnected. I would summarize them as follows:

- Each project is unique, so the incentive plan has to be unique to be effective.
- Define and weight your project objectives.
- Balance the incentive plan, so that:
  - rewards to the contractor for pursuing different objectives match the value-added and weighting of the client's objectives
  - incentives take into account risk and who has influence over it.
- Start from a realistic base from which improved performance is rewarded.
- Develop measures of performance that accurately reflect your objectives.
- Use a combination of positive and negative incentives, with the greater monetary emphasis on the positive incentive/bonus payments.
- To ensure alignment, at the very least consult with the other party when developing the incentive plan. This also promotes realism, understanding and joint ownership.
- On longer-term projects, consider the use of milestone incentives, which are a mix of objective and subjective measures.
- If using qualitative measures, then off-site management determination by the client's more senior staff is recommended, but only in consultation with both the site team and the contractor.
- Despite the above deliberations, the end result should be an incentive plan that is as simple as possible and capable of aligning motivations.
- Communicate the objectives and the incentive plan to all personnel involved or associated with the project.

Before designing a balanced incentive scheme, it is suggested — if you have not done it already — that you first read this chapter, understanding the reasoning and considerations behind this conclusion. Then, having designed your scheme, check that each concept has been adhered to. Finally, at the start of this chapter I suggested that the purpose of an incentive is to more *closely* align the motivations of the contractor, consultant or supplier to those of the client. Perfect commercial alignment will rarely be achieved! Minor misalignment will be more readily accommodated, though, in order not to sacrifice the greater benefits of working together. If superior performance, which is of benefit to the client, is encouraged and achieved, then the incentive plan has served its purpose.

Review question 1   What are the most useful or interesting insights that have come out of reading this chapter?

Review question 2   Imagine you have agreed to give a 15-minute presentation to some colleagues on the contents of this chapter. What slides and diagrams would you develop to illustrate the process and key concepts? What would you say to expand on these?

Either: draw out a learning map to summarize what you have learnt from reading this chapter or, perhaps using Fig. 5.1 as the starting point, draw a detailed flow chart that encompasses all the key concepts and issues necessary to develop a balanced incentive plan.

References

1. Calardine B. *Principles of incentive and performance based contracts in incentive based contracts for win–win solutions.* Construction Productivity Network Workshop Report, King's College London, 16 July 1996, WR 96 14L.
2. Blyth A. H. Design of incentive contracts, basic principles. *Aeronaut. J.*, 1969, **73**, 119–24.
3. Latham M. *Constructing the team: final report of the government/ industry review of procurement and contractual arrangements in the UK construction industries.* HMSO, London, 1994.
4. HM Treasury. *Draft procurement guidance.* London, February 1999.
5. Fincham J. A. Jnr. Expectations of contract incentives. *Nav. Res. Logist. Q.*, June 1972, **A**, No. 2, 389–97.
6. Van Nort P. Executive summary. In *Use of incentives.* Pamphlet and video from Construction Industry Institute Conference, Austin, Texas, 1995.
7. Thompson R. In *Innovative contractor compensation.* Pamphlet and video from Construction Industry Institute Conference, Austin, Texas, 1996.
8. Howard W. E. and Bell L. C. *Innovative strategies for contractor compensation.* CII, Austin, Texas, January 1998, Research Report 114-11.
9. Ibbs C. W. Innovative contract incentive features for construction. *Constr. Mngmnt Econ.*, 1991, **9**, 157–69.
10. Ibbs C. W. and the Contracts Task Force. *Incentive plans: design and application considerations.* CII, Austin, Texas, November 1988, Publication 5-2.
11. Contractor Compensation Research Team. Report. In *Innovative contractor compensation.* Pamphlet and video from Construction Industry Institute Conference, Austin, Texas, 1996.
12. Ashley D. B. and Workman B. W. *Incentives in construction contracts.* CII, Austin, Texas, April 1986, CII Source Document 8.
13. Ibbs C. W. and Ashley D. B. Impact of various construction contract clauses. *Constr. Mngmnt Econ.*, Sept. 1987, **113**, No. 3, 501–27.
14. Stukhart G. Contractual incentives. *J. Const. Engng Mngmnt*, March 1984, **110**, No. 1, 34–42.
15. Abu-Hiljeh S. and Ibbs C. W. Schedule-based construction incentives. *J. Const. Engng Mngmnt*, Sept. 1989, **115**, No. 3, 430–43.
16. Smith S. E. *et al.* Contractual relationships in construction. *J. Constr. Div. ASCE*, Dec. 1975, **101**, No. CO4, 907–21.
17. Richmond-Coggan D. *Construction contract incentive schemes — lessons from experience.* CIRIA, London, Nov. 1999, Funder's Report/CP/76.
18. Schneider M. *Cost reimbursement contracts.* Draft of PhD thesis (photocopied), 1986.

19. Ashley D. B. *et al.* Allocating risk and incentive in construction. *J. Constr. Div. ASCE,* Sept. 1990, **106**, 297–305.
20. Ward S. *et al.* Objectives and performance in construction contracts. *Constr. Mngmnt Econ.,* 1991, **9**, 346.
21. Charvet S. R. *Words that change minds.* Kendall/Hunt Publishing Company, Dubuque, IA, 1997.
22. Hall L. M. and Bodenhamer B. G. *Figuring out people: design engineering with meta-programs.* Crown House Publishing, Carmarthen, Wales, 1997.
23. Carmody D. B. Incentives/penalties for time and cost control: the owner's viewpoint. *Engng Constr. Cntrct. Proc.,* American Institute of Chemical Engineers, 1977, 32–4.
24. Head A. *Incentives in construction contracts.* University of Wolverhampton, Wolverhampton, UK, MSc dissertation, January 2000.
25. Bolton J. Partnering in practice. A presentation organized by *Construction Journal* at the Institution of Civil Engineers, London, June 1998.
26. Uff J. and Capper P. *Construction contract policy — improved procedure and practice.* Centre of Construction Law, King's College, London, 1989.
27. Newman J. J. Bechtel Group implementation feedback. In *Use of incentives.* Pamphlet and video from Construction Industry Institute Conference, Austin, Texas, 1995.
28. Ibbs C. W. and Abu-Hijleh S. F. *Unique features of construction contract incentive plans.* CII, Houston, Texas, 1988, SD40.
29. *Dunlop Pneumatic Tyre Co., Ltd* v. *New Garage and Motor Co., Ltd* [1915] AC 79.
30. *Law* v. *Redditch Local Board* [1892] 1 QB 127.
31. Herten H. J. and Peeters W. A. R. *Incentive contracting as a project management tool, project management.* Butterworth & Co., London, 1986.
32. Hart G. W. The good, the OK and the ugly. In *Use of incentives.* Pamphlet and video from Construction Industry Institute Conference, Austin, Texas, 1995.

6. Single-incentive mechanisms for enhancing value and improving performance

6.1 Introduction

This chapter identifies single types of incentive mechanisms for different performance improvements. For each type of incentive mechanism, guidance is given on its use and the specific considerations needed for successful use. The chapter considers, in order, incentive clauses for:

- Capital expenditure (CapEx) reduction under price-based or management contracts.
- Value enhancement, typically in the form of value engineering clauses that produce savings in whole-life costs or, sometimes, increased income. Both of these are considered. However, innovative thinking is presented on how contractors and consultants can be motivated to increase the functionality of the asset by using a mechanism derived from the value planning phase of value management (see Procurement tool 1 in Chapter 3).
- Improved performance, whereby a monetary sum is allocated against a pre-stated measurable unit of increased performance, for example energy consumption of the asset. Included within this section is the use of incentives to minimize time on site and to encourage improved quality in terms of conformance with specification/number of defects.
- What I term 'process incentives', that is mechanisms by which the contractor or consultant is rewarded for the manner in which the project is delivered, for example higher levels of service, changed behaviour, etc.
- Incentives to stimulate improved health and safety performance.

In some cases, a suggestion might satisfy a number of the above criteria. For instance, there may be ideas about how elements could be prefabricated on the critical path of a commercially driven refurbishment project in which the asset is still partly operational, for example a large retail shop. This suggestion could reduce capital expenditure because, for example, the contractor is on site for a shorter duration, the quality and appearance of the end asset are increased, maintenance costs are decreased, disruption and noise around the shop are reduced, the safety of site workers and the public are safeguarded and the client sees a return on investment earlier.

This section presents and reviews methods for building incentives into each of the above points. Because each succeeding subsection builds on the previous one, I suggest that you at the very least skim through each section reading the highlighted remarks and summaries before reading a section that is of direct relevance to you. **While these are the mechanisms or tools that put the incentives into effect, the effectiveness of any tool depends on how wisely — or intelligently — it is used. Hence, you are referred to the discussion in the previous chapter.** Before proceeding, I would point out that, although the incentive mechanisms presented can be used in many circumstances, unless otherwise stated you should assume that they are being applied to price-based contracts, for either contractors or consultants (be they managers, designers or supervisors).

Applicable to consultants — be they management, design or supervisory — or contractors under a cost-reimbursable contract is the concept of '**fee-at-risk**'. This is a US term describing a standard consultant's or contractor's fee that is divided into two parts: a part that is guaranteed and a part that is at risk. If the consultant's/contractor's and/or the project's performance is substandard then some or all of this fee-at-risk is lost. If it is appalling, none of the fee-at-risk would be paid. If it is average, the normal total fee would be paid. The quid pro quo is that the contractor's or consultant's fee can be increased beyond the standard fee level, normally up to a maximum of double the fee-at-risk, that is the guaranteed fee plus twice the fee-at-risk for exceptional performance.

For a contractor under a cost-reimbursable contract, the amount of fee-at-risk is sometimes defined as in a target cost contract but with the maximum amount payable never exceeding the maximum fee-at-risk element. Alternatively, for both contractors and consultants, it can be calculated on a sliding scale by comparing the out-turn costs with a targeted cost. As yet another alternative, the fee can be linked to cost and other performance criteria through the application of an incentive matrix (see Chapter 10), in which the amount of fee-at-risk is graduated depending on the achievement of project objectives and/or their individual performance.

Preview question   Glance through this chapter. What aspects of project performance do you want to enhance in the projects with which you are involved? How does this affect what you want to gain from reading parts of this chapter?

6.2 Capital expenditure (CapEx) reduction incentives under price-based or management contracts

This section starts by pointing out a fundamental difference between CapEx reductions and value engineering/whole-life savings.[1] CapEx reductions decrease the capital cost of constructing the asset only, whereas *real* value engineering savings predominantly reduce the whole-life costs of an asset, which may actually increase the CapEx. As a result, value engineering saving incentives are considered in the next section.

Price-based contracts or management contracts may have written into them additional clauses that share savings in CapEx. As Standing[1] points out, **no British conditions of contract have standard CapEx reduction incentive clauses written in and, when additional clauses are added, they are often *mis*-referred to as value engineering clauses.** The **procedure** of these CapEx reduction clauses is quite simple, in that:

(a) The contractor, either alone or jointly in a workshop, suggests an idea that may produce a saving in CapEx and that has little or no effect on the functional or performance requirements of the end asset.
(b) At some stage of its development, this idea is formally submitted, normally in a contractually defined form and by a defined procedure, to the client or its agent with a justified *estimate* of the savings in CapEx.
(c) The client has complete discretion over whether this idea is accepted/approved and should respond within a pre-stated timescale.
(d) If it is accepted/approved, the idea is further developed and implemented and the *estimate* of savings in CapEx is split between the parties, normally in a ratio defined in the contract.

> Jergeas *et al.*[2] conclude from their research that 'any changes to the work specified in the contract must be made through a contractually defined change-order process. Changes related to value engineering typically follow the change-order process defined in the contract, with a few additional steps to account for the fact that they originate from the contractor.'

The incentive mechanism works in a similar way to that of shared savings under a target cost contract, except that:

• The shared savings apply only to future innovations that are changes to the contract documents, for example drawings, specifications, and not as a result of improved productivity, non-occurrence of risks included in the target cost etc.

- The shared monetary sums are based on estimated savings, not actual savings.

These reductions in CapEx could come about in several ways:

- by eliminating or refining a procedure such that costs for one or both parties over the duration of the project are reduced
- where the contractor is responsible for design, through
  - a minor change in the contractual functional or performance requirements that has little effect on the operation of the asset in practice
  - a change in the contractor's scheme or outline design that was incorporated into the contract prior to award (the client's functional or performance requirements are maintained)
- similarly, if, under a client- or consultant-designed project, the contractor suggests a revised design for an element of work that still satisfies the client's functional or performance requirements (although these may not be explicitly stated), for example a revised bridge design.

In the last two arrangements, the consultant sometimes receives a share of any savings to compensate for any additional work either in evaluating the contractor's proposal or in redoing the design. Alternatively, consultants are paid for their time. Particularly in the last case, **some clients may object to paying a consultant for redesign work on the grounds that they have already paid for a proper economical design**, so why should they pay for the same work twice! One counter-argument to this is that the lack of buildability etc. is a function more of the procurement route than of the consultant's lack of design expertise. The other counter-argument is more pragmatic: a consultant who is not part of the incentive plan and not paid on a time basis has every reason to be actively hostile to suggestions from the contractor as:

- The consultant's direct costs increase with no benefit to it.
- It wants to avoid professional liability claims resulting from design modifications that are not sufficiently well thought through; equally, the client wants to avoid the need to make claims on its professional liability.[2]

Thus, suggestions are rejected out of hand and the client receives no benefit!

Whether or not the consultant is included in the arrangement, **a view has to be taken on the share of any saving allocated to the contractor.** (The arguments presented in section 8.7.2, particularly in zone 4 for setting the share profile in the five-zone model, are very relevant.) Essentially, for CapEx savings, the client wants, from a business viewpoint, to pay out only the share of any savings that is sufficient to motivate the contractor to look for those savings. This share will be largely dependent on the scope for finding savings: in a fully designed building, less than 50% is unlikely to motivate the contractor. **The less fixed the brief, scheme arrangement or detailed design, the greater the scope for value enhancement, the less effort required to find these enhancements and, therefore, the smaller the contractor's share required for motivation.**

Best practice tip

I have frequently seen contracts that include CapEx reduction clauses in which the contractor identifies savings only when it begins detailed design or programming of a particular element of the project. This has two disadvantages:

- The larger savings that could come about as a result of, for instance, revising the scheme layout are lost.
- Often the timescale for developing and accepting the proposal and then redesigning the element is too short. As a result, either a good idea is not implemented or, if it is, there is insufficient time to check the design, order materials, etc., which results in additional costs that equal or outweigh any savings made.

I therefore suggest that proper structured value engineering studies are conducted as soon as the contractor becomes involved in the project rather than waiting to identify opportunities as the project progresses.

6.3   Value enhancement incentives clauses

Traditional value engineering incentive clauses predominantly focus on reducing whole-life costs. This may result in decreases in CapEx that are outweighed by later savings. However, some suggestions, although not reducing operating costs, may increase the potential income from the investment. Other suggestions may increase the functionality of the asset but not lead directly to increased income or savings. A similar procedure can be used to process all types of value-enhancing suggestions. This section covers the different incentive mechanisms:

(a) for including a losing contractor's ideas in a project that is being implemented by the contractor which won the contract
(b) for whole-life cost savings, in which the implemented ideas only are applied and savings derived on the current project
(c) for situations in which the implemented ideas would increase income to the client on the current project
(d) for suggestions that enhance value by increasing the functionality of the asset but which do not translate directly into increased whole-life income or savings

(e) for situations in which the ideas will have benefit on other similar projects, whether carried out by the same or a different contractor.

For each, **the basis of calculating the incentive is that a baseline estimate of whole-life savings, income and/or functionality is made, there is a process for their submission, the client has absolute discretion over whether the suggestion is implemented and the contractor receives a pre-stated share of any estimated improvement.** In an office building, operating costs typically outweigh CapEx by a ratio of 4:1, although the income derived from such a building is of the order of 200 times the CapEx![3] While this ratio will vary significantly according to the type of asset, the principle should be that a significantly smaller share of any whole-life savings needs to be allocated to a contractor to motivate it compared with reductions in capital expenditure.

6.3.1 Incentive mechanism for including a losing contractor's ideas in a project

Here the winning contractor is selected on the basis of the one that offers 'best value' (see Appendix 4), but **the winning contractor has access to other contractors' ideas to improve the service provided and/or end asset. The protocols for when and how this is done need to be stated up front.** For instance, are all the other ideas given to the winning contractor or only the ones that the client would like to implement or only the ones that losing contractors will allow to be used? Are these ideas released pre-contract, when one contractor gains preferred status, or post-contract? How is it decided, and who decides, which ideas are implemented and which are not?

The general problem with this system *without* an incentive is that, if a contractor knows that all its best and most innovative ideas will be given to another contractor, there is less of an incentive, firstly, to be innovative at tender and, secondly, to declare those innovations. According to Standing,[1] the Australian government has encouraged other contractors' ideas to be used thus:

- An unsuccessful tenderer has the option of submitting a value engineering proposal.
- The government has a set timescale (45 days) to accept or reject the proposal.
- If it is accepted, the net savings are shared in a 50:50 split between the originator and the government.
- The contractor that implements either this or other ideas:
    - is paid any additional cost of implementing the idea
    - has the contract sum reduced by the cost of the any saving
    - has its profit margin, in monetary terms, maintained.

It has to be stated that this system is predominantly used on defence projects in Australia. The timescales for considering and developing ideas probably mean that any project using it for construction needs to have sufficient float planned in for the ideas to be evaluated and then incorporated by the winning contractor into its project.

6.3.2 *Incentive mechanism for whole-life savings**

As well as price-based payment mechanisms, I see no reason why this method cannot be used on cost-based contracts. **The procedure for implementation is similar to that for CapEx reductions** as stated in section 6.2. The difference is that a baseline for operating expenditure (OpEx) is established and added to capital expenditure (CapEx) to give a whole-life baseline from which estimated savings are calculated. This means that an estimate of the 'whole life' of the project has to be stated.

> Jergeas *et al.*[2] state that 'regardless of the length of the owner's involvement, a common definition for the lifetime of the project should exist between everyone involved.'

On a traditional consultant design followed by contractor construct project, it is likely that the consultant will bear the majority of the development or redesign costs. Consequently, the arguments presented in section 6.2 for paying the consultant or including it within the incentive plan are just as relevant here.

> Jergeas *et al.*[2] define a value engineering incentive clause as 'a contractual arrangement where savings from value engineering are apportioned between the owner, engineer [consultant] and contractor. The intent is to motivate everyone to uncover cost effective solutions while still meeting the project's objectives'.

Under procurement routes whereby the contractor is doing the majority of design, **there needs to be clarity over who pays for the development of the idea, how the contract sum (whether lump sum or the target) is adjusted and how the savings or benefits are shared.**

---

*I would like to acknowledge that much of the thinking in this subsection is derived and condensed from the work of Standing in his book *Value management incentive programme: innovations in delivering value.*[1] Credit is hereby given for this work.

The Australian government value engineering scheme

The Australian government scheme was developed from the US Defence Department value engineering scheme. Standing[1] considers it both simpler and superior to its US parent. It functions in this way:

- On a price-based contract, if the contractor develops, submits and implements a proposal without financial assistance, it receives 50% of any savings, with its 'fair and reasonable' development costs being reimbursed without profit. There may be problems in agreeing this cost, if an idea has been developed without the client's knowledge prior to submission. If, however, a contractor's proposal is not accepted, then it would have to bear all these costs.
- If the contractor has an idea but is unwilling to take the risk of developing it on its own, then it can submit an outline proposal to the government. If the proposal is accepted, the net savings, that is after all parties' expenses have been deducted, are shared on a 75:25 basis, with the government taking the majority share. Once again, the contractor is reimbursed its developmental costs.[1]

Any subcontractor proposals have to come through the main contractor, which is allowed to add only an administrative cost. Any sharing arrangement would have to be written into the subcontract. As before, the shared savings are normally based upon estimates of the effect upon whole-life costs.

Let us consider some scenarios under different procurement routes:

On a consultant-designed building, the contractor suggests various ways in which the building can be modified for improved energy efficiency. To work out the incentive, the whole-life savings in energy are estimated, minus the consultant's development and contractor's construction costs of making those improvements, and this is split by the sharing ratio of the value engineering clause. What is presumed here? That there is a baseline figure for energy consumption of the building and, if not, that it can be calculated and agreed.

What would happen if the building was contractor designed under a price-based contract in which there was little cost transparency? Think about it as a sequence before reading on!

What is presumed is that:

- The energy consumption figure would need to be stated as a contractual requirement under predetermined circumstances, for example when all lights are on, inside air temperature is maintained at a set temperature when the outside temperature is either colder (for heating purposes) or warmer (for air conditioning), etc.
- The ideas would be submitted to the client for approval or acceptance, in

accordance with a procedure defined in the contract, before implementation. Otherwise, the client could find itself paying out under the value engineering clause for all sorts of improvements that have no value to it and it does not desire!

- To approve/accept the proposals, the client would want to know the change in whole-life costs so:
    - the 'whole life' of the asset needs to be stated
    - the decreased energy consumption, compared with the contract requirement, needs to be calculated and the improved performance translated into a whole-life monetary saving from which ...
    - the cost of the additional measures needed to exceed the contractual minimum would be deducted.

As the contractor is responsible for design, the client would be probably be comparing a non-existent/hypothetical design for the contractual minimum with an outline design that includes the contractor's proposals for increasing energy efficiency. This is because the contractor is unlikely either to do a detailed design of what it is not planning to build or to do a detailed design until the client has accepted its proposals. In addition, there is the lack of transparency in the contractor's costs under contractor design routes (see section 4.3.2).

What arguments could result?

- Would the contractor's non-existent/hypothetical design satisfy the minimum contractual requirements anyway?
- What change in performance would result from the suggested improvements?
- How much would these improvements increase the construction cost to the contractor?

Are these discussions likely to be conducive to developing a partnering spirit! Probably not. The client may be better advised to define in the contract an incentive payment against energy efficiency as explained in section 6.4.1.

What general conclusion can be drawn from this example? My own conclusion is that the application of how an incentive mechanism is implemented has to be thought through (the 'what if?' questions) and depends on the procurement route adopted.

6.3.3   *Incentive mechanism for increasing income to the client*

This arrangement is very similar to that described in the previous section, except that an estimate of the net whole-life increase in income is made, which is then split in a pre-agreed ratio between the parties. Indeed, the clauses governing this can be combined with the ones governing savings. **The proviso for this is that the suggestion does translate directly into increased income.** An example of this would be a manufacturer building a new production line for a product that is already selling well employing a contractor whose idea allows an increase in production for the same fixed operating costs.

6.3.4 Incentive mechanisms for improved functionality

So far, this chapter has discussed value enhancements in which the increased value affects either whole-life costs or whole-life income. However, some value enhancement ideas will take the form of improved functionality, which may not translate directly into a measurable financial effect. 'Functionality' is used here in the value management context, whereby value equals required functionality over whole-life cost and required functionality is the sum of weighted 'functions' (see Appendix 1). **Presented below is an incentive mechanism for calculating the added value when clients have used value management, and more specifically a weighted value tree, to define the functional requirements and select the best project option. It is a natural development of using value management as the basis for selecting contractors by value** (see Appendix 4). I have not seen this method presented elsewhere in the literature.

If:

$$\text{value} = \frac{\text{functionality}}{\text{whole-life cost}}$$

then a project's value, required functionality and whole-life cost can be expressed as numbers at the start of the project. For instance:

$$\text{original project value} = \frac{68.2}{\text{£10m}} = 6.82^{\dagger}$$

This is the baseline from which any value enhancements are evaluated.

The contractor proposes an enhancement to the project which will cost £0.5 million over the life of the project. This includes the amount paid to the contractor to implement the improvement, as with a normal value engineering saving clause. When assessed against the weighted functions by the client, this increases the required functionality by 8 points. The new 'value' quotient for the project is therefore:

$$\text{new project value} = \frac{68.2 + 8}{\text{£10m} + \text{£0.5m}} = \frac{76.2}{\text{£10.5m}} = 7.26$$

The suggested improvement therefore adds value to the project. This would be fine as a means of evaluating alternative designs at tender to determine best value. However, to stimulate improvements once the contract is let, the contractor needs to have an incentive. Let us now say that the client has

---

$\dagger$Here I have taken the functionality score, which is 68.2 out of a maximum of 100, and divided it by 10 (instead of £10 million). Therefore, the unit of value is functionality per million pounds spent.

specified a similar procedure to that for value engineering savings, except that it has specified a monetary figure to be paid to the contractor for each unit improvement in the required functionality. In the example above, shall we say £2500 per 0.1 unit of improvement in the required functionality. With an 8-point increase:

incentive paid = 8 × 10 × £2500 = £200 000 = £0.2m

The equation then becomes:

$$\text{value} = \frac{76.2}{£10.5m + £0.2m} = \frac{76.2}{£10.7m} = 7.12$$

The functionality improvement still enhances the value quotient after the incentive has been paid. As stated previously, I have not seen this approach to value enhancement in any literature or in practice. Potential points to note about this method are:

- The client has to have used value planning to define the functionality of the project. The weighted value tree and estimated whole-life cost at the time of signing the contract is the baseline for evaluating value enhancement suggestions.
- If this method is used when there has not been some competition in selecting the contractor or consultant, then a danger is that the contractor will hold back on any value enhancement suggestions until the contract is signed in order to be paid the incentive.
- Despite the previous point, I would suggest that this incentive method is of most use when the contractor or consultant has early involvement after the basic scheme arrangement or scope has been decided.
- To a purist, the incentive should perhaps be an increase in 'value' as opposed to 'functionality'. While exactly the same incentive mechanism could then be used for improvements in whole-life costs and income, this would result in iterative calculations as incentive payments were added into the calculation. The method presented in this subsection can work alongside the other methods, with ideas being categorized as either functionality enhancements or whole-life cost/income improvements or being split if they both enhance functionality and improve whole-life costs/income.
- The question arises as to what monetary sum should be stated against each unit increase in functionality. I suggest that the starting point is to ask what payment the consultant or contractor would receive for a whole-life saving that results in the same increase in overall project 'value'. If the project is quality driven, for example a prestige project, then a greater payment could be placed on the enhanced functionality score rather than decreased

whole-life costs, and vice versa for a cost-constrained project. This increases the case for separating out the enhanced functionality incentive from the reduced whole-life cost incentive.

- This weighted value tree and breakdown of whole-life costs needs to be communicated in the contract and to the winning consultant or contractor, so that they understand what is of value to the client and therefore put forward and develop only suggestions that improve value. This saves all parties time and expense.
- Additionally, the contract needs to state the procedure for submission, including time to allow for the client's response.
- It is suggested that after an initial value enhancement/saving workshop, some sort of minimum threshold is set for both enhanced functionality and improved whole-life cost/income suggestions. This is to avoid a constant stream of minor value enhancement suggestions which have to be evaluated by the client's personnel and then cause more disruption to construction than they are worth.
- The client needs to exercise high moral integrity and continuity of personnel in assessing improvements in value enhancements. This is because the evaluation of functional improvements will be, to some extent, subjective. It is not desirable in the medium to long term for the client to assess the functionality improvement with a hidden agenda of minimizing incentive payments. This will undermine the success of the incentive scheme both on this project and, in the longer term, on other projects.

6.3.5 *Incentive mechanism for which the ideas will have benefits for other similar projects, whether carried out by the same or a different contractor*

From the client's viewpoint, **this allows ideas for which the cost of development is not justified on a one-off project to become worthwhile for a series of similar projects. From a contractor's point of view, it allows either a competitive advantage to be maintained or income to be received should another contractor win a subsequent contract.** An example taken from Standing[1] gives an insight into some of the issues:

'A particular VECP [value engineering change proposal] derived for a recent underground station had possible future potential for use elsewhere. The client had to sign a confidentiality agreement prior to the contractor's presentation on the value engineering proposal. The reason for this was to protect this innovation, as there was a large underground rail project where the possibility of using the [same] value engineering proposal existed. The commercial advantage to the contractor would have been lost if the idea had been released. There is also a potential loss of commercial advantage if the alternative is not used on the right project at the right time.'

The issue is that contractors win work and make profit partly through their ability to innovate, rather than through their ownership of intellectual capital, that is trademarks, patents and copyrights. Once an innovation is used it is likely to become common knowledge and their competitive advantage is lost. They may therefore hold back on proposing an innovation on one project, either in the pre-contract phase or once into the project, because the commercial gains will be greater if used elsewhere, for example on a larger project, hence the reason for the confidentiality agreement in the example above. Sometimes these agreements have carried damage clauses to provide for what would happen if the client reveals the innovation to a competitor. If that larger project is for the same client, then the agreements could extend to give the contractor a share of any savings should another contractor win it, as described in section 6.3.1.

If the idea is patent- or copyright-able, then a separate commercial agreement will probably be necessary. The terms of this will vary depending on who bears the cost of developing the idea, the commercial opportunities outside the client company, etc.

I have observed consultancy framework contracts in which the client, while paying for any developmental costs of a proposal, owns all the intellectual rights to an idea or innovation that arises from its projects. Consequently, such ideas and innovations can be used by other consultants under the framework agreement and competitive advantage is lost.

Does this encourage the consultant to innovate actively? Only to the extent that it may be possible to earn extra income from developing the proposal and kudos for having the idea in the first place.

Does this encourage the consultant to declare innovative ideas? The consultant would be well advised not to tell the client, but to give the innovation to its research and development department, patent or licence it and then sell it to the client under a separate contract.

6.3.6   Conclusion

This section has explored various means of enhancing value, in which value is defined as functionality divided by whole-life costs. What are normally referred to as 'value engineering clauses' only motivate the contractor to reduce capital costs (CapEx). This is covered in section 6.2. As a result, most of what has been presented in this section is likely to be quite innovative to the UK reader, as it is covers the following:

- inclusion of ideas from other contractors in both the same project (section 6.3.1) and future projects of the client (section 6.3.5)
- how to put incentives on ideas that:
  - may reduce whole-life costs (section 6.3.2) or increase the income (section 6.3.3) beyond the contractor's involvement in the project
  - enhance the overall functionality of the completed asset, which may increase the CapEx of the project and even, in some cases, increase the whole-life costs (section 6.3.4).

The mechanism chosen will depend on the precise procurement route chosen and the specific contract package, in terms of timing, payment mechanism and scope, under which the part of the project is let. **Whatever mechanism or mix of mechanisms is chosen, common attributes are:**

- A baseline for their evaluation needs to be established.
- The contractor, either alone or jointly in a workshop, may suggest an idea that may produce a value enhancement to the end asset.
- At some stage of its development, this idea is formally submitted to the client or its agent, stating the benefits and/or an approximate estimate of the net whole-life savings, that is after the development and implementation costs have been deducted.
- The client has complete discretion over whether this idea is accepted/ approved and should do so within a pre-stated timescale.
- If it is accepted/approved, then the client normally funds the development of the idea.
- If it produces a saving or increased income, the *estimated* net whole-life savings are split between the parties, normally in a ratio defined in the contract. The share to the contractor is normally less than for a straight CapEx reduction incentive. If it is a functionality enhancement, the reward mechanism also needs to be defined.

If enhanced functionality can be expressed and measured in units of performance, and this improvement is directly related to a core objective of the project, then it is likely to be more appropriate to use a performance incentive, as explained in the next section of this chapter.

Review question 1   In what type of projects with which you are or have been involved, and at what stages of these projects' development, could it be appropriate to consider using the different types of value-enhancing incentives discussed in this chapter so far?

6.4   Performance incentive clauses

Performance incentive clauses place an incentive, usually monetary in form, against a pre-stated measurable unit of end of project performance for the completed asset, for example the energy consumption of the asset or early or late completion per day. This normally, but not always, translates into financial gain to the client.

> Abu-Hiljeh and Ibbs[4] state that, in essence, performance-based 'incentive plans function by
>
> (1) Identifying key project objectives;
> (2) Establishing performance targets for the key project objectives;
> (3) Measuring actual performance against these targets; and
> (4) Rewarding the contractor for performance that achieves set targets and, possibly, penalizing him for those that do not.'

The methods outlined in this section have, from the client's perspective, some **advantages over the value enhancement incentive clauses** outlined in the previous section of this chapter, which include:

(a) As the contractor normally funds any development and implementation costs and is paid the incentive only on actual improved performance, the contractor takes the risk that the expenditure will result in improved performance.
(b) This avoids difficulties in calculating the contractor's development and implementation costs. It is easier to administer. However, because the contractor is now not being reimbursed these costs, it is suggested that the share of savings needed to motivate the contractor is higher than with a general value engineering clause.
(c) The primary advantage is that it focuses the contractor on specific predetermined aspects of performance that are of value to the client. The opposite of this is that it limits the areas in which the contractor seeks improvement to those against which it is directly rewarded.

Table 6.1.   Some performance incentive measures

Main heading	Specific objective
Performance in use with direct financial effects	Facility availability/percentage downtime Power consumption/efficiency at specified outputs Quality of output Production capacity
Performance in use without financial effects	Complaints from general public per time period Number of emissions/leakage incidents to outside site Measurable level of emissions once in use Workers' overall satisfaction as scored on an agreed questionnaire
Time	Hours, days or weeks ahead of or behind contractual date of handover
Quality	Defects per £ spent Ratio of cost of rework–total contract cost
Health and safety	Person-days lost because of accidents per million person-hours worked Notifiable accidents per million person-hours worked

On projects in which the objectives cannot be defined in numbers, use of value enhancement incentive clauses, as defined in the previous section, may be more appropriate (see Table 6.1).

This section considers, in order:

(a) performance incentive clauses that allocate a monetary sum against a pre-stated measurable unit of increased performance, for example the energy consumption of the asset, which results in direct increases in income or savings for the client

(b) performance incentive clauses that allocate a monetary sum against a pre-stated measurable unit of increased performance but which do *not* translate directly into financial gain for the client

(c) the specific case of time incentives for reducing the duration of a project, either in total or in its implementation phase

(d) incentives for improved quality in terms of 'conformance with specification'.

Incentives for improving health and safety improvements will be considered in section 6.6.

6.4.1   Performance incentives that translate into financial gain

This subsection covers a specific incentive amount per unit of measurable performance above or below a stated standard of performance, which translates directly into increased whole savings or income. It can be expressed as a damage as well as a bonus; for example, for a new building, it might be expressed as a monetary value per kWh change in energy efficiency above or below the stated contractual figure.

The key to effective implementation here is fourfold:

(a) The contractor has control over or, at the very least, a strong influence over the level of performance attained. This implies two things:

   (i) for damages still to be valid, the contract needs a method of adjusting the stated performance should there be a breach of contract by the client (see section 5.5)

   (ii) the contractual requirements are expressed as a performance specification!

(b) The unit of performance can be measured accurately, and correctly reflects what the client really wants in terms of improved performance.

(c) The inputs into the process or test conditions are clearly specified, for instance, in a coal-fired power station, the type of coal, range of moisture contents, etc.

(d) These inputs or test conditions can be controlled. For instance, in the case of the energy efficiency of an office building, neither the client nor the contractor can control the outside air temperature. If there is a mild winter or cold summer, it may be several years before the outside temperature rises or falls to the stated levels for comparison. Consequently, both parties have to have their test teams on standby for this time and, until this performance is verified, the contractor is not paid the incentive despite having already incurred extra construction costs.[‡]

These criteria need to be met whether the incentive is a bonus or damage.

> Walker[5] makes the point that 'if performance incentives are included in the contract, these have to be clearly defined, as have the test conditions under which they will be measured. The necessity to demonstrate the value of the increment above or below the target figure requires an increase in accuracy over that required to establish, say, only that a figure is as good as, or better than, the target.'

[‡]One way round this could be that the contractor is paid for the estimated improvement in performance but takes out a performance bond, which the client can call on if it is later disproved.

> One organization operating in the water industry explained why, despite the fact that its contracts included the option of claiming damages for inferior performance in use, this was never exercised, even on price-based contracts. This was because, despite using performance-based specifications:
>
> • The client usually specified the key process to be used.
> • The client did not have any control over the water being put into the process, whether it was sewage or river water.
>
> For similar reasons, the level of care specified in the contract, except for materials used and the work of subcontractors on price-based contracts, was reasonable skill and care, not fitness for purpose.

6.4.2 Performance incentive clauses that do not translate into financial gain

In certain instances, improved performance can be measured directly but does not translate into improved commercial returns to client. **It is likely that the incentive payment will therefore have to be a bonus payment because of difficulties in proving the 'genuine covenanted pre-estimate of likely damage'.** Failure to do this in the UK would result in the courts declaring it a penalty, which the contractor would then not have to pay (see section 5.7.4).

Let us take as an example a project whose central objective is to reduce some sort of environmental pollution. If there is one performance objective, for example reduced noise levels, then a specific incentive can be put against the measure for performance in excess of the contractual minimum. The units of measurement would be decibels, the test conditions could be to take measurements at stated locations around the site when it is working under certain conditions, for example specific weather conditions. Measurements before and after the project is implemented would be used to measure the performance improvement. If there are a number of different pollutants, for example from a chemical factory, then the test conditions can again be stated for each pollutant, with the incentive being paid against an amalgamated measure using one of the incentive mechanisms outlined in Chapter 10.

The above examples could be driven by legal requirements, so that the companies have to meet the minimum legal requirements to avoid fines, subsequent poor publicity and perhaps closure of the facility. Fines can be expressed as a damage. However, the company may also perhaps wish to exceed the legal requirements for environmental, social and positive publicity reasons, as well as to avoid future investment. One question is: how does a client put a monetary figure against each unit increase of performance above the minimum level? One option is to construct an economic model. Another is to use a similar process to that described in section 6.3.4.

6.4.3 Time incentives

Overview

This section considers the use of incentives to improve time performance. It considers in order:

- in this subsection, briefly, alternative procurement routes for different time objectives and use in 'fee-at-risk' incentive plans
- lane or area rental contracts used in conjunction with 'A + B' bidding, which is a method of placing a time incentive on the bidding process
- different types of time incentives that can be applied during the contract.

Much of the literature on incentives is largely drawn from the use of either time or cost incentives. Consequently, the concepts and process presented in Chapter 5 and section 6.4.1 are highly relevant and pertinent. The identified literature which is specifically on time incentives is from the USA,[4] even though it predominantly reviews the experience of the UK Highways Agency 'lane rental' schemes[6,7] and their subsequent application in the USA.[8] I have combined this knowledge with my own formal research and my work with the UK Highways Agency and its consultants and contractors.

Before proceeding, I would like to draw to your attention to the fact that, **particularly with time, the selection of the most appropriate procurement route will have far more impact than 'tacking on' some bonus/damage clauses**. For instance, on one-off projects:

- If the total project duration has to be minimized the client should consider contractor-designed routes, management routes or a project alliance.
- If the client wants minimum implementation time for which the work content is known and chooses the traditional design followed by construction route, then allowing sufficient lead-in time for all the queries to be dealt with and the contractor to plan the works thoroughly, as opposed to hurriedly mobilizing, could have just as much effect as large incentives.
- If the client wants to have high certainty over implementation duration, possibly at the expense of the work content, then a cost-reimbursable or method-related schedule of rates may well be the best route. A good example of this would be a boiler refurbishment project which has a set window of time in which to do the work and for which the extent of the work cannot be predetermined.

'Fee-at-risk' contracts are explained in the introduction to this chapter. Often, this fee-at-risk is tied to a whole raft of measures and calculated using a matrix (see Chapter 10). However, research in the USA indicates that the largest component of that incentive payment is typically based on the project's time performance or the consultant's part in it, for example timeliness of designs, thoroughness of planning. **If clients wish to motivate their consultants to place more emphasis on time performance then the 'fee-at-risk' principle, particularly in conventional routes, is a means of doing so.**

Lane/area rental and 'A + B' bidding

'Lane rental' contracts are those in which the contractor rents a motorway lane to do work on it. This is to circumvent 'damages', which have to be a genuine pre-estimate of likely loss *to the client* (see section 5.7.4 for a full explanation). On motorways it is not the client's loss of time that translates into money, but the inconvenience to the general travelling public, so damages would not be applicable. Renting, however, is a commercial transaction and, providing there is no misrepresentation, the law in the UK will enforce a bargain or rip-off, so the client can charge what it likes for a contractor to rent an area. Obviously this has consequences in terms of premiums added into the contract sum and motivations and behaviours of the parties during the contract.

'A + B' bidding is a form of bidding in which the client asks contractors to tender both a contract sum (A) and duration (B). This duration is multiplied by a monetary sum per unit of time and added to the tendered contract sum to gain a comparative figure that takes account of the time value of money. The contractor with the lowest overall figure is awarded the contract, with the contract duration being that which it tendered. Graduated time incentives, normally both positive and negative, are included in the contract and these are equal to the monetary sum per unit of time used in the tender assessment. The contractor is therefore motivated to be more innovative at tender.

This basic process, together with lane rental, has been used on the UK motorway network and has been credited with progressively achieving 40% reductions in the time taken to resurface sections of motorways since its introduction. The lane rental charge is calculated using an economic model for total economic cost to the travelling public, which is then halved and, at the time of writing, did not exceed a maximum of £20 000 per day. This is to avoid excessive premiums and either contractors becoming bankrupt, in the case of a time over-run, or the Highways Agency paying out excessive amounts for time under-runs. A separate damages clause covers the direct losses to the client, for example continued site presence. Other ancillary work, such as replacing the central reservation and crash barriers, is fitted into the contract. Since its introduction, this process has been progressively modified in a number of ways:

- Rather than, for each tender, 'B' being the implementation period on site tendered by a contractor, the baseline is now the minimum tendered period. In other words, for the contractor that tenders the minimum period,

'B' equals zero. For other tenderers, 'B' then becomes additional days more than this minimum time. The reason for this, as I understand it, is so that the quoted sum of 'A + B' more accurately reflects what will be paid and therefore aids financial forecasting.

- Rather than be applied per lane used per day, the figure above now applies for the time that lane usage is reduced on the motorway, that is because the contractor is using any part of the works. This, I understand, was because contractors were opening and shutting lanes in order to minimize payments, rather than rapidly completing the work. This was causing arguments over whether or not a lane was available and what part of it was available, and led to potentially unsafe practices and, in some cases, increased disruption to the public. In other words, **there has been a tendency to simplify the scheme's operation.**

In order for the scheme to work, high incentives have to be used both at the tender stage and at the implementation stage. This motivates the contractor to perform. However, to win work, the tendency has been for contractors to tender on the optimistic side of reality. Additionally, **if the contractor cannot perform and is given the opportunity to transfer the risk back on to the client through the contract, then it will, and contractors have done so** because the incentive payments, both positive and negative, are so large. **This implies that the scheme has to be well defined with minimal likely changes, both because everything is on or very close to the critical path, so the consequences are considerable in terms of delay and disruption and subsequent cost, and because a lot of money can hinge on who is responsible for any delay.** While this has not stopped work being done on site, because the stakes are so high it has led to long contractual arguments afterwards. Bearing this in mind, and that the objective is minimum time on site, it would also seem sensible that the winning contractor is allowed a sufficient time after award to pre-plan and mobilize, with any technical queries being identified and resolved prior to work on site.

Arditi and Yasamis[8] comment that 'a disadvantage of fixed price contracts (of which unit price contract are a variation …) is that it puts the owner and the contractor in adversarial roles. With the addition of incentive/disincentive provisions and the consequent risk transfer to this scenario, the hostility between the parties is likely to increase.'

In a historical context, 'A + B' bidding and lane rental schemes can be considered a success as they have pushed technology and management of schemes to significantly reduce implementation timescales. However, it could also be argued that the scope for improving timescales is now limited and that real continuous improvement can only be gained by working with contractors in the pre-contract phase. The traditional design followed by construction, 'A + B' bidding and high lane rental charges do not facilitate this. Consequently, the Highways Agency is moving towards regional framework contracts.

Despite this, my view is that **'A + B' bidding plus 'area rental' would seem to have applications outside highways on infrequent (to the client),** *well-defined* **projects with** *low total risk* **in which there is a high benefit from minimizing time.** Note the term 'well-defined': this could mean, on contractor-designed schemes which are well specified, both a performance and a functional specification and what they have to tie into. By 'low total risk', I mean overall risk to the project: if the risks are client owned, then their occurrence will cost the client dear, whereas if they are allocated to the contractor the client will pay a high premium. However, **such risks do not lend themselves to a partnering approach, in terms of encouraging continuous improvement once they become 'live' on site.**

Types of time incentives

This section identifies different types of time incentives. Having identified them, it then discusses the interplay between them by developing a scenario from an imaginary shop refurbishment. To some extent, this is a discussion of the practical effects of the concepts and considerations discussed in the previous chapter. **Critical to the success of any incentive scheme is the realism of the baseline from which improvements are planned to be made, and this applies just as much to time-driven as to cost-driven targets.** This implies that clients or their consultants need knowledge and/or experience of the work to estimate this duration accurately.

On a refurbishment-type project there might be three initial levels of time incentive:

- One for total contract duration, for example from the time the contract is signed and a contractor starts to do some design to the point at which all obligations have been completed, for example all quality documentation has been handed over. Let us say the damage is £100 per day.
- One for implementation/construction time, in situations in which the area is affected by the works. For instance, in a largish prestige department store successive areas may be cordoned off while it is progressively refurbished, meaning that no income is being derived from one particular area at a given time. Let us say the bonus and damage is £1000 per day.
- One for over-running into the opening times of the shop, as work is done overnight because the noise and need for access disrupts customers in other areas of the shop. This is stated on an hourly, or part thereof, basis, with the sum increasing each hour into the opening times because more customers would come in and be put off by the works. Let us say £50 per hour for the first hour with few customers, rising to £100 per hour for the second and £150 per hour thereafter.

It is a 30-week contract, 8 weeks of which are allowed for initial design, followed by a 20-week window for its implementation and a 2-week period at the end for all documentation to be handed over, any defects to be corrected and any outstanding work to be completed.

Will the contractor be focusing on the total project time or starting work on site on time and finishing it within the 20-week implementation time? It will be the latter, which is fine, provided this is in alignment with the client's objectives. It is unlikely, though, that the contractor will be motivated to correct minor defects and complete quality assurance documentation as the project progresses.

Is it in the contractor's interest to over-run by up to an hour if the cumulative time savings add up to days saved? The answer is 'yes' as if the project over-runs by up to 1 hour each day, then the contractor will pay a total damage of: 20 weeks × 6 days per week × £50 per hour = £6000. This will save the contractor 120 hours in total, which with a 10-hour day is equivalent to a 12-day saving in time. If it finishes 12 days early, or alternatively does not finish 12 days late, the bonus/lack of damages is: 12 days × £1000 per day = £12 000.

In other words, it is in the contractor's interests to over-run on a daily basis if it reduces the total time for implementation. If the contractor regularly goes into the second hour, charged at £100 per hour, or part thereof, it is still indifferent. However, once an hour is exceeded, is it in the contractor's interests to stop work as soon as possible? No, because it is per hour or part thereof, so once work has over-run into that hour, it is in its interests to use up all of that hour further disrupting the shop.

Towards the end of the contract, what would the contractor's motivation be if it was running late? The contractor might even decide that it is worth its while going into the £150 band in order to save a day's total time. For instance, if 5 hours of time reduce 1 day's mobilization, then it has spent 5 × £150 = £750 to avoid paying £1000.

The client wants to stop these persistent daily over-runs, but the contractor refuses to agree modifications to the contract that increase the damages per hour of over-run. The only thing it will agree to is a lump sum 'gatepost' incentive, for stopping work and clearing up on time, of £75 for each day (see section 5.9.1 for a full discussion on the use of gatepost *vs.* graduated incentives).

Is it in the contractor's interest to demobilize for the day on time? The answer is 'yes' because, in addition to having £75 bonus each day, it will not be paying a £50 damage, so the total benefit to the contractor is £125. Over 10 days, the benefit to the contractor is £1250, whereas it only loses a day's worth of work, which could translate into a £1000 damage or bonus.

If the contractor does not manage to stop work on time in any one day, is it still worth its while to stop work immediately? The answer is 'no' as we are now back to the situation before the gatepost incentive of £75 was introduced. This is a classic example of the problems associated with gatepost incentives: once the contractor thinks that it will not be awarded it, its motivation switches.

Let us suppose that the client did not introduce the gatepost bonus of £75 per day for stopping work on time. Instead, it broke down the contract into 20 roughly week-long sections, awarding an intermediate bonus of £450 (which is 6 working days × £75) for completing each section according to the contractor's current programme.

How would this motivate the contractor? It would make it even more worth its while to over-run on time on a daily basis to achieve the weekly milestone.

What would the effect on motivation be if it was conditional upon stopping work at the correct time each day? There would be an additional motivation to stop work on time each day and complete each section to programme. However, if the contractor over-ran on one day, then much of its motivation would evaporate: both to hit the section deadline and, as a result, to work overtime each day (except for achieving overall completion in the implementation phase).

Finally, remember that these calculations ignore any savings on the contractor's time-related site overhead costs that would accrue to it for reducing the total duration of the implementation phase. What other modifications can you think of that would improve the operation of the incentive scheme?

These scenarios have been developed from real-life instances, mainly on road projects, in which contractors have occasionally deliberately worked on over time on overnight possessions because they have perceived it to be in their interests to do so. I have heard of instances in which contractors have been ordered off by the resident engineer and have made a counter-claim as a result.

The last incentive that the client introduced in the example of the prestige department store was a milestone plan, in which the contractor was given an incentive to meet short-term schedule dates. This increases the attention that the contractor would pay to monitoring and planning. It can also be developed on a rolling basis as the project unfolds, which is particularly suitable for long-term and ill-defined schemes. There is, however, an increased cost of administration compared with an incentive for final completion on time.[4]

Milestone plans can also be used when completion of an intermediate target is crucial to the overall completion of the project, perhaps because of other contractors having to come within a set time-window. These would probably be specified as **sectional completion dates**. Another use of sectional completion dates/milestone dates is one in which the project has to be in a set state, as opposed to area completed. The costs to the client arising from late completion and therefore the damage that can be passed on are reduced. For instance, in a process plant, the client may be receiving the benefits when everything is installed and working during the testing phase but is still having to have checkers and alternative facilities on standby in case of failure.

Review question 2 Imagine that the above case was a real project. Looking back through the previous chapter, draw out lessons that could be learned, that is what mistakes did they make? What did they not do or should have done?

If you were in charge of the above project, what would you have done differently? You can go right back to redoing the procurement route if you want!

6.4.4 Incentive clauses for improved quality

By quality, I mean that which is expressed as conformance to specification and so can be measured, for instance, in terms of number of defects. As well as undermining their reputation, more enlightened contractors realize that **poor quality that is detected rarely saves a contractor money**. The cost of correcting the defect usually outweighs the cost of 'getting it right first time'. In this sense, a contractor is already motivated to produce high-quality work. Incentives therefore add an additional motivation. This suggests that 'quality' incentives based on measuring the number of defects are used in circumstances in which either:

- high quality is paramount, for example in the nuclear industry
- a project is for a one-off client, so there is no motivation from the possibility of repeat order business
- limited competition means that there is little incentive to improve, for example a housing association in a remote area can only select from a few local contractors for repairs and for their small- to medium-sized projects.

A number of ways of measuring performance can be used, for instance:

- It can be measured as the number of defects detected in the maintenance period.
- It can be measured as the number of uncorrected defects at hand-over or practical/substantial completion. Obviously, the benchmark would vary between projects of different sizes and types. Most experienced clients and consultants could review projects of a similar type to establish a baseline for comparison. While low on administrative cost, this does

not, however, encourage a 'right first time approach' to quality, or the correction of defects as the project progresses. To achieve hand-over or practical/substantial completion, the defects have to prevent the client from using the works and so would be of a minor to medium nature.

- It can be measured in terms of number of defects per stated sum spent over a fixed period as the project progresses, for example over 4 weeks or a month. This has the same disadvantages as the previous approach but, in addition, there is no sorting of minor and major defects. However, it does provide an ongoing evaluation of the contractor's performance, which can then be improved as the project progresses.
- To gain a better idea of the total cost of correcting defects, the measure of performance can be expressed as a percentage of the cost of remedial work required to correct defects over the total expenditure in any period.

The type of measure and incentive used will be determined partly by the client's objectives. For instance, a one-off client with a prestigious building may just want a defect-free building at hand-over to avoid negative press comments. It may therefore design a 'quality' incentive that is a combination of the first two measures, perhaps in combination with an incentive for speed of correcting a defect once notified in the maintenance period. The incentive for defects at hand-over could be banked, with payment being conditional upon performance in the maintenance period. A repeat order client working with a number of framework contractors may measure 'quality' with the last bullet point and reward the better-performing contractors with more work.

A question of significance is 'what is a defect?' Is it only a defect on hand-over or at practical/substantial completion? Is it a piece of work that fails a formal contractual test or inspection during the contract? Or is it that which the contractor's own quality assurance procedure fails to detect but which is later picked up by the client's auditing system? Or is it something that is detected by the contractor's own quality assurance procedure for completed work and then corrected before the client's contractual test or inspection? And does this apply to inspections of temporary works, such as formwork, or only to defects in the permanent works? Or is it even something that workers spend some time putting right as they work, before any formal quality assurance is done? The further back one goes in the construction process, the greater the effort required to monitor the scheme but the greater the potential benefit in terms of total quality management, that is good quality is built in through good process and people, rather than 'poor quality' being detected after the work is done, with a higher cost of remediation. **Whatever it is, thought needs to be given to it and the criteria clearly stated in the contract.**

This leads on to another **fundamental point about measuring and giving incentives for good quality:** in all of the above ways of measuring quality, you are measuring defects or the cost of remedial work. In effect, **you are measuring the extent of poor performance**. Thus, under an incentive plan you are *not* rewarding poor performance, as opposed to measuring and rewarding good performance. The danger is that the motivation for the contractor is to cover up and/or not report poor performance, rather than to perform well. **This can mean that the causes of poor performance are not investigated, which in the medium to long term could lead to poorer performance.**

> The opposite applied on the Channel Tunnel rail link contracts, which were let under a slightly modified version of option C (Target contract with activity schedules) of the NEC Engineering and Construction Contract, with contractors self-certifying the quality of their work. One of the modifications was to state that the cost of correcting defects detected by the client's staff was a disallowed cost and contractors therefore had to bear all the costs of their corrections. In the unamended form, the incentive is that the contractor's costs are increased compared with the target, with any difference being shared. The purpose of the additional clause was to improve quality, encourage contractors' self-certification systems to work and reduce the client's costs of administration. However, the apparent result on some projects was that contractors notified almost everything as a defect, leaving the client's staff to adjudicate over whether it was or was not. This meant more work for the client's staff!

To summarize, my view is that **'quality' incentives should only be used when good quality or improved quality is a specific objective. The type of measure used and their definitions should vary, depending on the specific quality objectives of the client. However, a fundamental flaw of judging quality with a measure related to the number of defects or the cost of correcting them is that you are measuring poor performance, which may mean that poor quality is not reported and/or covered up. Ironically, this could actually encourage poor-quality work in the longer term**. Process measures and incentives, as outlined in the next section, could therefore be a more effective means of encouraging good quality.

6.4.5   *Conclusion*

Summarizing, the threads of the arguments which run through this subsection are:

* Performance improvements can be accommodated by whole-life cost or income incentive clauses as outlined in the previous section. This is likely to be more appropriate under client- or consultant-designed procurement routes.

- If the contractor is doing the design to meet pre-stated minimum performance levels, it is probably wiser to focus the contractor's attention by stating incentives against specific performance measures that are of importance to the client. This has the added advantages that difficulties in calculating changes in the contractor's capital costs are avoided and that, as improved performance is normally measured rather than estimated, the client really is gaining improved performance.
- In projects in which the above is done, a greater share of the benefit (compared with a general value engineering clause) should be allocated to the contractor to compensate it for the lack of direct reimbursement of increased construction costs.
- It is important that what is measured accurately reflects the desired improved performance and that the inputs or test conditions need to be both clearly stated and controllable.

Review question 3 Reviewing the general performance of your contractors or subcontractors, what performance measures could be introduced or modified to improve project performance generally? Pick a specific project, let under a price-based form, that you are familiar with and design a balanced incentive plan to improve this performance.

6.5   Process incentives

'Process incentive' is the term I use to describe an incentive based on a measure of *how* a consultant or contractor delivers a project, for example the level of programming, rather than the achievement of the project's end objectives. The simple rationale behind process incentives is that if project processes are efficient and designed to meet the end of project objectives — that is, effective — then the achievement of the end of project objectives will automatically be ensured. Used in their pure form, under a cost-reimbursable or management contract with no incentive on end objectives, they would be labelled cost-plus-award-fee contracts in the USA.[9,10] Often, they are used with the fee-at-risk concept to reward the consultant or contractor for improved performance. Some examples of process incentives are given in Table 6.2, many of which have been reported in practice. Note the last two points in the table, which typically cover anything not covered elsewhere. The purpose of these categories is to avoid an overemphasis on the other incentivized measures to the exclusion of other more general duties.

Process incentives can be used:

Table 6.2. Some examples of process incentives

Main heading	Specific objective
Cost-related	Quality of estimating submissions
	Timeliness of costing and tracking submissions
	Quality of costing projections and tracking submissions
Time-related	Timeliness of programming revisions
	Quality of programming revisions
	Promptness of early warnings
	Ability to recover from delays
Subcontracting and purchasing	Timeliness of subcontracting and purchasing submissions
	Quality of subcontracting and purchasing submissions
	Subcontractor and supplier relationships
	Speed of subcontractor and supplier payments
	Effectiveness of subcontractor co-ordination
Quality	Quality of method statements
	Implementation of quality assurance procedures
Labour	Quality of labour relationships
	Warning of labour problems
	Communication with workers
Other	Avoidance of unproductive defensive documentation
	Extent of innovation
	Overall contractor performance
	Contractor performance not covered by other measures

- to promote and stimulate good process generally or a specific behaviour in a longer-term relationship
- to motivate the contractor or consultant to perform when the scope is ill-defined and therefore the end objectives of the project cannot be adequately defined
- in projects in which the end objectives, although defined, are subject to a high degree of uncertainty, some of which is beyond the contractor's control, for instance when the intention is to reward the contractor for good project management in minimizing delays, rather than good 'claims management' in justifying them.
- to prevent too much focus on the primary objectives of a project at the expense of secondary objectives, for instance to minimize disruption of an operational facility that is still open to the public.

Process incentives can be used with end of project objectives or intermediate/ milestone incentives or on their own depending on the circumstances of the project. I would argue that:

- If end of project objectives can be defined, process incentives should be used in conjunction with end of project objective incentives.

- Failing this, they should be used in conjunction with intermediate objective incentives.
- In either case, **the rewards available to the contractor from the process objectives should generally be less than those available from the other incentives. Alternatively, payment should be partially or wholly conditional upon achieving them.**

Otherwise, the contractor may concentrate on being seen to do the right process, rather than on achieving the end result. For instance, if the contractor is over-rewarded for its 'responsiveness to end user requirements', it may respond to every changing whim of the end user at the expense of time and cost, which may not have been the intention of senior management.

In one case in the USA,[11] the management contractor's costs were reimbursed monthly, but the quarterly fee (which covered profit and off-site overheads etc. and could be either a bonus or a deduction) was based solely on the client's satisfaction. Some of the contractor's fee could be reclaimed at the end of the project and was conditional on the end results. This provided a strong motivation for the contractor to report accurately. The quarterly payment would be accompanied by a one-page letter explaining what the client was pleased with, what it was not pleased with, and what improvements it wanted in the next quarter.

The likely characteristics of process incentives, compared with end objective incentives, are:

- The measurement of the basis on which the incentive is paid is likely to be more subjective/qualitative, as opposed to objective/quantitative, being based on questionnaires using attitudinal statements and/or scorecards[11] or even on the feelings of the client's senior management. For this reason, they are likely to be less popular with contractors in principle.[10]

> South-West Water (SWW) has used process incentives within a project alliance. In addition to sharing any cost over-run or under-run, the alliance members could be awarded a discretionary bonus of up to 1% by SWW's senior management. While benchmarks are taken into account when determining the size of the bonus, it was entirely at SWW's discretion.[12]

- The measurement is likely to take place periodically throughout the contract, for example monthly or quarterly. This allows feedback to both sides, leading to continuous improvement in process as the project progresses. Indeed, this has been found to be a major benefit of process incentives.[11] This is particularly appropriate if the contractor is involved in a long-term project or a series of projects.

Howard and Bell[11] concluded that process incentives 'would appear to be most applicable in an established relationship in which the parties expect to deal with one another on a repeated basis'.

- Some payment will be released after each assessment, so that the rewards for improved processes are tangible and more immediate. The remainder is banked until the end of the project.

At the time of Ibbs and Ashley's[13] research, reported in 1987, process incentives were fairly new and were generally not written into the contract. They found that 'they generate little additional effort or adversarial attitudes. Although relatively new, this approach received strong endorsements from those individuals, both owner and contract personnel, who had participated in such programmes.'

Summarizing and concluding:

- Process incentives are suitable for use when end project objectives are either ill-defined or distant and/or the path to achieving them is subject to a high degree of uncertainty. They are therefore used more on service- or consultancy-type contract packages, with the contractor or consultant being paid on either an input-/cost-basis or part 'fee-at-risk' basis.
- The rationale for their use is that the more efficient and effective the project processes are, then the more likely it is that the end of project objectives will be achieved.
- A danger of using them is that they can focus too much attention on the process, rather than on the end of project objectives. To counter this, wherever possible they should be used in conjunction with incentives for meeting end of project objectives.
- Usually process incentives are awarded and paid on a regular or milestone basis. Often, though, these are partially or wholly banked and dependent on achieving the end of project objectives.
- A danger of process incentives is that the contractor or consultant only concentrates on the duties that offer incentives to the partial exclusion of other contractual duties. To counter this, a client's 'overall general satisfaction' is also introduced as a criterion.

6.6 Incentives for improved health and safety (H&S) performance

This section is derived from a paper[14] written several years ago for one of the original research sponsors, UKAEA, which asked me to investigate how incentives could be used specifically to promote improved health and safety (H&S) performance. My research found little evidence of incentives being used in practice at a contractual level to promote improved H&S, so I drew upon the literature on the effects of H&S legislation, in particular the impact of fines, and on H&S incentives for workers.

Before proceeding, **some people may object to the use of H&S incentives on ethical grounds, because protection of the workforce and the public *should* be the number one priority of any organization. I agree, and for some it is, in which case it is unnecessary to provide incentives.** But notice the emphasis on the word 'should'. This means that for some organizations it is not a priority. **If, as a client, you are still contracting with unsafe contractors, just saying that in your view 'it should be', when it is obviously not, smacks of both delusion and (having got over this psychological hurdle), if you are not doing anything to make it their priority, hypocrisy!**

> Petersen,[15] in *Safe behaviour reinforcement*, comments that 'in safety, we typically hope for safe behaviour while rewarding unsafe behaviour.'
>
> A report by the UK Health and Safety Executive (HSE), entitled *Factors motivating proactive health and safety performance*,[16] concluded that 'there is little evidence, to date, that UK management are motivated to improve health and safety performance for financial reasons. However, the common perception that health improvements are a "cost" rather than an "investment" does support the case for demonstrating the commercial benefits of health and safety performance.'

Other research on the UK construction industry[17] and subcontracting in the UK and Australian building industries[18] supports this finding. The question then becomes 'how do you stimulate improved H&S performance, of which incentives are only one strategy?' To clarify, **simply providing incentives to improve safety is unlikely to be effective** without training staff and workers, providing support to those without the resources to do it themselves and designing in safety to the end asset and construction process. Indeed, construction companies — smaller contractors and subcontractors — are the ones most likely to respond to a holistic package of H&S improvements.

In general, I would normally recommend using incentives paid for end or intermediate project performance. In the case of health and safety this would be based on the number of incidents, with more serious incidents given a greater weighting than less serious incidents. In order of descending seriousness this might be: fatalities, notifiable incidents (with the person involved being off work for more than 3 days), lost-time incidents (the person involved is taken to hospital and/or takes some time off work), first-aid incidents (the person involved receives first aid on-site), damage to permanent works or machinery and near misses. However, I concluded that **putting incentives on end of project H&S performance is flawed** for the following reasons:

- For more minor incidents, say first-aid incidents and below, what is measured is poor performance. Thus, a likely effect is that those incidents that the contractor thinks that the client will not find out about will not be reported, and consequently only superficial action will be taken to prevent their recurrence. In the longer term, this could lead not only to more minor incidents, but also, because their causes are not identified and preventative action not taken, to more major incidents too. This is because major incidents tend to occur when a series of minor incidents happen together, magnifying their severity.

> Peters,[19] although talking about incentives for employees, thinks that these accidents should be excluded from the incentive scheme 'so that actions can be taken to prevent similar occurrences that may cause great harm'.

- Major incidents, such as fatalities and notifiable accidents, are statistically unlikely to occur on all but the largest of contracts (although large contracts generally mean larger more professional contractors with greater emphasis on H&S). As a result:
  - Contractors will generally expect to be paid this incentive and will perceive the likelihood of not having it paid as low. Not being paid it will be seen as a fine, which, research indicates, is ineffectual in improving proactive H&S performance. Indeed, the smaller the contract, the lower the likelihood and the greater the perception.

> The HSE report published in 1998[16] states that 'there is little evidence that UK firms are generally motivated to proactively comply with health and safety regulations for instrumental purposes, due to the perception that the likelihood of detection and/or prosecution is low'. However, 'subsequent to an incident or enforcement action the firm may seek to achieve a general improvement in health and safety ... due to a realization that its performance is inadequate and not because of any general deterrence effect of penalties.'

- If one of these accidents occur it may just be unfortunate that it happened on that particular contract, for example if a fatality occurs every one in a million person-hours worked and there are ten contracts each involving 100 000 person-hours then, all things being equal, it is likely that a fatality will occur on one of these contracts, but which one is open to chance. Not receiving the incentive is therefore a matter of chance, not poor safety management.
- Alternatively, the reason why the accident happened is because safety management on the individual contract was poor. If it was poor enough to cause a fatality, then this should have been detected prior to the incident.

Consequently, **I do not recommend putting incentives on major incidents either**.

> Calardine[20] states that 'incentive schemes relating to the achievement of safety standards can be controversial and emotive. The rewards are based on the reduction of accidents occurring on site. Such arrangements may be liable to manipulation.'

So how should clients motivate contractors to improve their H&S performance? I concluded that if the client is to offer incentives on H&S performance, it should focus on proactive processes. These include:

- the number and thoroughness of inspections of the site to ensure compliance with H&S guidelines, including inspection of construction plant, and the promptness of action taken when deficiencies are found
- the thoroughness of method statements and risk evaluations for operations
- the extent of ongoing safety training, both of those specifically charged with safety management and of workers
- the orientation and training of new workers
- the provision and extent of use of protective clothing and equipment
- general housekeeping, for example good materials storage and rapid removal of waste from site
- accident record keeping and analysis
- the extent of investigation into all incidents and the action taken as a result of a report's recommendations
- the provision of, and access to, first-aid facilities and trained first-aiders on site.

This is a large number of processes and actions for an individual contractor to suddenly put in place and also for a client or consultant to monitor. It could be argued that all of this is either legally required or best practice and is likely to overawe a small contractor or subcontractor, so prioritization would appear to be sensible. I suggest that the processes and actions to which incentives are attached first are a combination of those which:

- need to be put in place to be legally compliant
- will have the biggest impact on H&S performance; this could be in terms of effectiveness generally, the nature of hazards on the individual project and/or the areas in which the contractor is weakest
- are easiest to put in place
- will have the biggest impact on the contractor's profits, ignoring the effects of the incentive, for instance improved method statements equal better planning while good housekeeping means less double handling and damage to materials, both of which result in less waste, demonstrating to the contractor the commercial benefits of good H&S processes.

The above points suggest that **an H&S incentive plan needs to be tailored not only to the circumstances of the project but also to those of the individual contractor**. This, in turn, suggests that, although the intentions of the client may be stated pre-contract, in terms of total incentive amount and plan outline, it may be better to 'add on' a tailored plan post-contract. If this is developed jointly with an H&S specialist's input, then it is also more likely to be bought in by the contractor (see section 5.6.4). To encourage periodic review and improvement, it is suggested that the contractor is paid on a periodic or milestone basis as the project progresses. Once the contractor has achieved a certain level of competency in the initial processes with incentives, then the level of incentive on these can be reduced and incentives put on other processes. Ultimately, it is in nobody's interest to have poor H&S on site. By promoting it, a client is aligning interests in both the short term and the longer term.

In **summary:**

- Clients should take a pragmatic, rather than moralistic, attitude to the use of incentives to stimulate improved H&S performance.
- Those most likely to benefit from a whole package of H&S initiatives are smaller contractors and subcontractors.
- Using incentives based on the number of incidents is likely to be ineffective and may actually increase the number of incidents.
- Instead, the focus of incentives should be on good H&S processes.
- It is suggested that any H&S incentive plan is tailored to the nature of the work and the contractor's current capabilities. It should be developed in consultation with the contractor, with the client being able to modify the plan as the project progresses.
- Finally, using incentives is not enough. Small contractors and subcontractors will benefit from advice and support in implementing

these processes. Other means of stimulating improved H&S performance which have been found to be effective in practice[21] are the inclusion of past H&S performance and current processes as part of the minimum pre-qualification criteria and qualitative tender selection process, as well as stating minimum requirements in contractual documents.

6.7   Conclusion

This chapter has reviewed the appropriateness and use of incentive clauses for:

- enhancing the value of the project, which includes improving the functionality of the scheme and decreasing whole-life costs (and, it could be argued, includes capital cost reduction clauses). This included a mechanism for using losing contractors' ideas on projects and encouraging the development of ideas by contractors which are not viable on one project but are on a series of projects for the same client
- improving end of project performance by specifying incentive amounts against specific measures of performance, of which time incentive clauses are a major subset
- improving the process of delivery
- improving the health and safety performance on site.

A common theme running through all of these mechanisms is that the baseline, from which changes in value, performance or process are measured, has to be defined, otherwise project participants will be left discussing the extent of improvement and resulting incentive payment. For the incentive scheme to work, this baseline has to be set at a realistic level. In addition, there should be clarity over how the change in value, performance or process is measured.

A difference between value enhancement incentive clauses and other incentives is that in the former, the incentive is typically paid against *estimated* enhancements in functionality or decreased whole-life costs. For both performance and process incentives, the incentive is realized against *actual* improvements. Performance incentives, and in particular end of project performance incentives, have the advantage that improved performance is actually delivered. Their use presumes that project objectives are defined and assumes a greater state of project definition and reduced level of risk that could act on the project compared with either value enhancement or process incentives.

Process incentives are used to encourage improved process and/or changed behaviour in the belief that this improves end of project performance. I prefer incentives to be attached to this end performance, but this is not always possible. Process incentives are therefore generally best used on projects in which end of project objectives are either loosely defined or too distant. An alternative is to use intermediate performance incentives, perhaps developed on a rolling basis in the belief that the sum of these intermediate goals adds up to more than satisfactory end of project performance.

For improved health and safety incentives, I recommend the use of process incentives. This is because, if incentives are put on reducing the number of incidents, then minor incidents will be covered up, leading to a higher likelihood of major incidents, and the likelihood of major incidents is perceived as being too remote to motivate improved process and behaviour.

Review question 4 The line below represents the approximate phases of a project. You may wish to tailor this to your typical project life cycle. For each of the procurement routes presented in Chapter 4, map the typical contract packages on to the line, for example design, management, construction. For each contract package, which type of the incentives discussed in this chapter might be appropriate?

| Concept | Feasibility | Outline design | Detailed design | Construction | Maintenance period | Ongoing operation |

You may wish to further fine tune this to a particular project you are currently involved in, to whatever level of detail is useful to you, to take on the learning you want from this chapter.

Review question 5 Part of the aim of this chapter was to turn the more conceptual considerations outlined in Chapter 5 into specifics. Going through each type of incentive in this chapter, what concepts are used, or lessons drawn, that are (or should have been) stated in Chapter 5?

Now draw a learning map.

References

1. Standing N. A. *Value management incentive programme: innovations in delivering value*. Thomas Telford, London, 2001.
2. Jergeas G. F., Cooke V. G. and Hartman F. T. Value engineering incentive clauses in cost engineering. *J. Am. Assoc. Cost Engrs*, March 1999, **41,** No. 3, 25–34.
3. Evans R. *Opening address. Rethinking the construction client — the national debate*. The Office of Government Commerce, Birmingham, 6 November 2001.
4. Abu-Hiljeh S. F. and Ibbs C. W. Schedule-based construction incentives. *J. Constr. Engng Mngmnt*, Sept. 1989, **115,** No. 3, 430–43.
5. Walker D. The influence of incentive provisions on project management. *Aeronaut. J.,* 1968, **79**, 125–28.
6. Herbsman Z. J. *et al.* Time is money: innovative contracting methods in construction. *J. Constr. Engng Mngmnt*, 1995, **121**, No. 3, 273– 81.
7. Herbsman Z. J. A + B bidding method — hidden success story for highway construction. *J. Constr. Engng Mngmnt*, 1995, **121,** No. 4, 430–37.
8. Arditi D. and Yasamis F. Incentive/disincentive contracts, perceptions of owners and contractors. *J. Constr. Engng Mngmnt*, Sept. 1998, **124,** No. 5, 361–73.
9. Schneider M. *Cost re-imbursement contracts*. Draft of PhD thesis (photocopied), 1986.
10. Herten H. J. and Peeters W. A. R. *Incentive contracting as a project management tool, project management*. Butterworth and Co., London, 1986.
11. Howard W. E. and Bell L. C. *Innovative strategies for contractor compensation*. CII, Austin, Texas, January 1998, Research Report 114-11.
12. Whitehead T. Nice work if you can get it, partner. *Cntrct J.,* 3 Sept. 1997, 16–17.
13. Ibbs C. W. and Ashley D. B. Impact of various construction contract clauses. *J. Constr. Engng Mngmnt*, Sept. 1987, **113**, No. 3, 501–27.
14. Broome J. C. *The use of contractual incentives to stimulate improved health and safety performance*. Paper distributed to industrial sponsors, The University of Birmingham, Birmingham, 1999.
15. Petersen D. *Safe behaviour reinforcement*. Aloray, New York, 1989.
16. Entec UK Ltd. *Factors motivating proactive health and safety performance*. Health and Safety Executive, London, 1998, Contract Research Report 179/1998.
17. Hinksman J. Construction safety: construction safety regs: a money-saver for industry? *Safety Mngmnt*, June 1993, 34–5.

18. Mayhew C. and Quinlain M. Subcontracting and occupational health and safety in the residential building industry. *Indstrl Rltns J.,* 1997, **28**, 3, 192–205.
19. Peters R H. Strategies for encouraging self-protective employee behaviour. *J. Safety Res.,* Summer 1991, **22**, No. 2, 53–70.
20. Calardine B. *Principles of incentive and performance based contracts in incentive based contracts for win–win solutions.* Construction Productivity Network, King's College London, 16 July 1996, Workshop Report WR 96 14L.
21. Lingard H. and Rowlinson S. Construction site safety in Hong Kong. *Constr. Mngmnt Econ.,* 1994, **12**, 501–10.

7. Cost-reimbursable contracts

7.1 Introduction

In the case of both cost-reimbursable and target cost contracts, the contractor is reimbursed its costs plus a fee as the contract progresses, with the difference being that, under the latter, any over- or under-run compared with the target is split in predetermined proportions. Consequently, most, if not all, of **the key implementation points that apply to cost-reimbursable contracts also apply to target cost contracts**. Additional key implementation points for the latter are discussed in the next chapter. This chapter discusses, in order:

- the general advantages and disadvantages of open book/cost-based contracts
- when to use cost-reimbursable contracts, with much of the discussion also relevant to target cost contracts
- degree and type of client involvement in the management of the project
- defining the principal components, namely the reimbursable costs, non-reimbursable costs and the fee, which are also common to target cost contracts
- financial management of the project.

It is worthwhile mentioning that the **key implementation points are different or additional requirements compared with price-based contracts. Knowledge, skills and experience of good contract and project management and of other partnering attitudes and processes are still required for a successful project.**

Before proceeding, I mention, for completeness, a special type of cost-reimbursable contract: a **limit of liability** contract is one under which work will stop when the client reaches its budget limit. In the USA, this is known as a **limit of commitment** contract. Open book accounting allows a more accurate and up-to-date assessment of when this point has been reached compared with price-based contracts. If this point is pre-stated, the contractor may become liable for any over-runs above this point.

In addition, the term **cost-plus-award-fee contract**[1,2] would be used in the USA for a cost-reimbursable contract that includes incentives for performance tied to the *process* of delivery. This could be under a fee-at-risk arrangement.

Preview question   Read the conclusion of this chapter. Express in bullet point format what it is that you want to gain from reading this chapter.

·

·

·

·

·

And, for each bullet point, what level of understanding do you aspire to, for example awareness, familiarity with the key concepts, knowledge so that you can explain it or expertise so that you can put it into action?

And how does this affect how you will read and take notes on this chapter?

7.2   General advantages and disadvantages of cost-based contracts

Under a pure cost-reimbursable contract, the contractor is reimbursed its costs incurred on that project plus a fee. This fee can be expressed either as a percentage of cost incurred or as a fixed fee (see section 7.4.3 for a discussion on the benefits and drawbacks of each). This has two consequences, which could be construed as **disadvantages**:

(a) There is no direct motivation on the contractor to direct attention towards reducing costs incurred. Indeed, under a percentage fee it can be argued that there is a direct motivation to do the opposite. Some surveys in the defence and petrochemical industries have estimated that this lack of motivation could cost the client up to 10% more than with price-based contracts.[1,3,4] However, these comparisons are unfair for two reasons. First, why was a cost-reimbursable contract used in the first place? The answer is probably because the work was time driven, ill-defined and/or subject to high risk. Second, these comparisons ignored post-contract commercial costs, which are likely to be have been significantly higher if price-based contracts were used in those circumstances.

(*b*) The contractor's accounts have to be auditable and transparent, so a system and people need to be in place to audit the accounts on an ongoing basis so that the contractor is reimbursed for costs incurred as the contract progresses.

However, from these potential disadvantages spring two **advantages** of these contracts, if properly used in the right circumstances, namely:

(*a*) They are suitable for use when least cost is not a priority to the client but, for example, time and/or quality are. This is considered in the next section of this chapter.

(*b*) Many benefits can spring from having cost transparency.

Taking the second advantage, more specifically, the **benefits of open book accounting** between the client and contractor can include:

(*a*) Risk contingencies, to varying degrees, can be separated from the basic costs of construction and engineering and become more visible to the client. An immediate benefit of this is that clients realize how much they are paying contractors to take on risk. When this is passed down the supply chain, clients often realize that they are paying a premium on a premium, that is a contractor's risk premium on subcontractors' prices, which also include a premium. All parties are therefore more likely to take a more collaborative approach to risk management and a more informed approach to risk allocation (see section 3.5 for principles of risk allocation and sharing and Appendix 2 for an overview of risk management).

(*b*) A contractor, subcontractor or supplier is generally more aware of market rates than clients or their consultants and is also more aware of the programming implications of different design approaches, which in turn have an impact on cost. Therefore, with earlier involvement of these organizations, it becomes possible to design to a client's budget as opposed to pricing what has been designed.

In a value engineering context, 'value' equals functionality over whole-life costs, and whole-life costs equal capital costs plus operating costs. If a contractor is hiding its true costs to protect or maximize its contractual position, as is often the case under a price-based contract, the effectiveness of value engineering in reducing costs will be undermined. With a cost-reimbursable approach, a contractor has to show its costs to be reimbursed, so there is a big incentive to reveal them!

(*c*) Various approaches can be taken in estimating out-turn costs depending on the state of project definition, known risks, existing relationship between the parties and proposed incentive mechanism. For instance:

(i) applying a cost per unit output based on historical data for a similar size and type of project, for example the unit could be per m^2 of rentable space for an office building or per $m^3 s^{-1}$ of sewage through a treatment plant

    (ii)   applying a multiplication factor — based on historical data — to the cost of principal components, for instance to the tendered costs of generators, turbines and other principal mechanical and electrical components for a power station

    (iii) bill of approximate quantities

    (iv) elemental costing, in which the scheme is progressively broken down into smaller elements that can be costed more accurately

    (v)   open book tendering, in which the contractor reveals all its assumptions, assumed productivities and subcontractor and supplier quotations

    (vi) negotiated bidding

    (vii) competitive bidding.

Under a pure cost-reimbursable contract, it is important to note, if not somewhat obvious, that, whatever estimating method is used, the client pays the contractor's costs plus fee, that is the estimate has no contractual significance. Thus, the last two estimating methods are inappropriate where there is no incentive mechanism. The other approaches lend themselves to a two-stage selection process whereby the contractor is initially selected on a combination of its fee level and various criteria designed to test its potential to 'add value' to the project process and end asset (see Appendix 4).

(*d*) Many good contractors now have the software and expertise to track, on an activity-by-activity basis, forecast cost and progress against actual cost incurred and progress, that is earned value analysis, to an individual operation or subcontract package level. This reconciliation of forecast against planned cost and progress is often done on a weekly basis. The advantage of this is that, as soon as a deviation is detected, the cause can be investigated and steps instigated to bring forecast and actual costs back in line. The deviation could be caused by an identified risk, in which case previously developed risk mitigation strategies can be put in place.

    The advantage of using a cost-based payment mechanism is that the client also has access to this, so if risks do or do not occur, or if greater than anticipated value engineering opportunities arise, then the project can be adjusted or restructured to come in on budget.

One housing association was having seven sets of flats refurbished under a target cost arrangement. Early on, value engineering identified savings that could be made and the residents were asked what they would like done with this money. They opted for a community centre, which was then designed and built to this budget.

Compare this approach with the traditional approach whereby, although the client might be aware of potential claims coming in, until they are submitted it often has little idea of the contractual reasoning and quantum of the claim and it may be several years before this is agreed and paid. I ask you: **How can a project manager effectively manage projects in which there is no transparency of cost?**

(e) The advantages of the different methods of pricing work, the transparency of open book payment and the more up-to-date monitoring of costs is a much more proactive and co-operative approach to cost management. Compare this with the more reactive, confrontational 'contain the contractor's claim/maximize the claim' flavour of price-based contracts.

(f) If there is a mechanism to motivate the contractor, for example a target, then any adjustment to it is relatively easy to make compared with a price-based contract. This is because the client and/or its advisors understand the contractor's initial cost plan much better and so know what is and is not included and therefore what is extra. This adjustment can be made either before the work is done on an agreed estimate or costed up after the work is done using records. If it is made before the work is done, and the contractor consistently exaggerates the upward adjustment to the target, the contractor is much more likely to be found out.

(g) Finally, cost- or input-based payment mechanisms tend to be more appropriate for the use of intermediate performance incentives and process incentives.

These advantages are summarized in Table 7.1. Taken together, **not only does a cost-based payment mechanism lend itself to being used in a partnering environment, but it can also significantly reinforce the partnering culture and ways of working, leading to dramatically improved project results.**

However, all these advantages are lost if there is a poor financial forecasting and monitoring system and if the expertise to administer it is lacking. Indeed, in these circumstances, using cost-based contracts can be a positive disadvantage not only because *all* the advantages will be lost, but also because the administration of the contract will become an expensive and bureaucratic quagmire. So a key implementation point under cost-based contracts is for the client to select consultants and contractors with these systems and expertise, otherwise there is little point in proceeding down this route. Characteristics of this system are discussed later in this chapter in section 7.6.4.

Table 7.1.   A summary of the advantages of cost-based vs. price-based payment mechanisms (developed from reference 5)

Attribute	Open book/cost-based payment mechanisms	Traditional price-based payment mechanisms
Cost visibility	Transparent	Little transparency to client
Risk	Separate from cost	Hidden
Design	Design to cost	Cost the design
Pricing structure	Various approaches	Predominantly competitive
Monitoring/forecasting	More up to date	Wait for 'claim'
Management approach	Proactive cost reduction	Reactive cost containment
Agreeing adjustment to target/contract price	High transparency, so relatively easy	Little transparency, so relatively difficult
Incentives	As appropriate	No real consideration

Schneider,[1] a Swiss lawyer, stated in his draft PhD thesis that: 'The flexibility and frankness in communication which can result from cost reimbursement contracts is likely to have made a major contribution to the success of these projects.'

Ibbs and Ashley,[6] commenting on the situation in the USA, were of the opinion that: 'Cost reimbursable contracts substantially reduce the adversarial relationship between the owner and contractor compared to fixed price contracts.'

The US CII Partnering Task Force[7] found that 'many (participants) feel that projects done on a cost reimbursable basis allow parties to establish a much better working relationship at the beginning of the partnering arrangement.'

Review question 1 Reflect now on some projects you have been involved in. How could the general advantages of cost-based contracts and open book accounting, identified above, be translated into specific benefits on these contracts had they been used?

(a)

(b)

(c)

(d)

(e)

(f)

(g)

(h)

7.3   When to use a cost-reimbursable contract

Cost-reimbursable contracts were traditionally (and still are) suitable for use in four generic situations:

*   Projects in which the time or performance/quality objectives outweigh the cost objectives.
*   Projects that are subject to greater than usual uncertainty whereby the scope or sequence of work is unknown; these can be subdivided into three more specific circumstances:
    −   the *initial* state of the site is unknown, so, although the desired end state is known, the scope of the works is not defined
    −   the *end* state of the works is unknown, so, once again, the scope of the works is not defined
    −   the process of delivery is subject to risk and uncertainty.
    In all three cases, the amount and/or sequence of work to be done is unknown and the contractor is unable to price the works with any degree of accuracy.
*   Projects carried out in buoyant market conditions or where supply is limited.
*   Projects in which there is an existing relationship of trust.

These four situations are explored in more detail below and often overlap. In addition, many of the benefits of partnering and cost-based contracts, as outlined in the previous section, provide benefit to the project, and ultimately to the client, in these same circumstances. Again, because of the lack of incentive to minimize costs, target cost contracts were introduced and used in less extreme circumstances than pure cost-reimbursable contracts. Thus, much of what is said here is relevant to the use of target cost contracts.

7.3.1   *Time or performance objectives dominate*

Typical situations in which the time objective dominates and the use of cost-based contracts may be justified are:

*   In emergency situations, such as cleaning up and repairs of damage after fire, storm or flood and when there is not time to determine the scope of the work. Disaster scenarios are the only circumstances in which cost-reimbursable contracts are allowed to be used under EU procurement rules for the public sector.
*   Projects in which there are commercial benefits to be gained from an early start (leading to earlier completion) before the scope is sufficiently developed for the contractor to price it accurately. This could be in situations in which the cost of repairs or maintenance is outweighed by the loss of revenue, so the emphasis is on speed of repair, for example a factory close-down.

CIRIA Report 85[3] gives other situations in which this was the case:

- the extension of a factory
- the civil works for an oil refinery and construction of an office building
- an urgent development to a tight programme in which the contractor was able to start within 1 week of the first joint meeting.

It should be noted that this general approach has a number of potential risks: lack of established practices and documentation causing contractual problems later on and limiting options in the remaining design or requiring reworking and variations to completed work, which, as one author pointed out,[8] is 'often a precursor to ultimate disaster'. This lack of pre-planning and/or changes in design can lead to the original reasons for using a cost-reimbursable contract being undermined.

- For enabling work, such as diversion of underground services, so as not to delay the main works, which are let on an alternative contract strategy, giving the client greater certainty in the subsequent main package.
- Any combination of the above.

Often, in these circumstances, there is not time for the work to be properly scoped and defined, and for the contractor to price the work accurately.

A time-dominated risky project in the City of London

Towards the end of Bank underground station refurbishment, an artificial roof was taken down to be replaced. Unfortunately, it revealed extensive spalling of the concrete in the slab above. This spalling had exposed the reinforcing bar, much of which was now severely corroded. As this slab was immediately below street level, there was potential for the road to fall in. The client, then London Underground Ltd, immediately brought in a specialist scaffolding contractor to support the slab while a more permanent solution was worked out. The contractor was paid on a cost-reimbursable basis with an agreed fee percentage.

Once the temporary solution was in place, a more permanent solution was sought. The desired end state was known: a replaced slab. The site, however, had numerous constraints and risks:

- It was at a complicated road junction, which was in the commercial centre of London, so traffic management was key to minimizing disruption and noise levels had to be controlled.

- There were various bank vaults nearby with sensitive alarm systems, so vibration from 'pecking' out concrete had to be controlled.
- As well as other services, numerous fibreoptic cables serving financial institutions passed through the site, so the potential for financial loss was large. These had to be located and protected.
- The Lord Major's Procession passed through the site once a year. The works therefore had to be completed within a set timeframe.

Thus, an understanding of these constraints and risks was essential for a successful project, as was good liaison and relations with the financial institutions close to the site. It therefore seemed a good idea to work with a contractor to develop the solution. Because the client had an ongoing relationship with the contractor and its scaffolding was already in place, the same contractor was used. The client's internal designer and contractor worked together to develop the best solution, which included a temporary elevated bridge over the site. When the design was sufficiently complete, the contractor costed up the works, revealing all the assumptions, calculations and subcontractor quotations to the client, to agree a target on which the contract was let.

None of the identified major risks occurred, with the project coming in approximately 5% below the target cost. It was deemed an outstanding success by the client, the institutions around the site and the City of London.

(Source: interviews and reference 9)

A typical situation in which the performance objective dominates is in safety-critical situations. This used to be the case in the nuclear, defence and space industries, in which the consequences of a lack of performance hugely outweighed the costs of doing the work and minimal incentive was wanted for the contractor to skimp on these costs. This is no longer the case as technology has matured.

The European Space Agency[10] used cost-reimbursable contracts because of a desired 'emphasis on technical excellence rather than adherence to budget constraints'.

It could be argued that contracts let early on in the project cycle should virtually always be cost or input based, because the decisions made at this stage have a major impact later on. Therefore, the benefits of taking decisions on quality have a payback many times the cost of employing advisors and consultants to help the client make them.

7.3.2   Scope and/or sequence of work is unknown

The start of this section identified projects that are subject to greater than usual uncertainty as potential candidates for the use of cost-reimbursable contracts. This was subdivided into further situations in which:

(a) the *initial* state of the site is unknown, so that, although the desired end state is known, the scope of the works is not defined
(b) the *end* state of the works is unknown, so, once again, the scope of the works is not defined
(c) the process of delivery is subject to risk and uncertainty.

In all three cases, the amount and/or sequence of work to be done is unknown and the contractor is unable to price the works with any degree of accuracy.

Research has shown that, even when method-related charges are used, conventional bill of quantity contracts typically reach the limits of their applicability when the extent of variations exceeds 20% of the tender price.[11] US literature suggests that at least 40%, and preferably 60%, of design should be complete to set final cost and programme.[12,13] Therefore, if the scope of the works is not defined, under price-based arrangements it is very likely that:

- The client will pay a high risk premium for the contractor to take the risk of not knowing what the initial state is.
- The final asset will not satisfy the client's desired outcomes as these are not accurately defined at the start of the contract.
- When change is introduced as the end state is changed and refined, the client will pay more and the focus of the client's project team will shift to minimizing upward adjustments to the contract price, and vice versa for the contractor's project team, rather than minimizing the consequences of the change. The same applies to a target cost contract, although to a lesser degree.

Situations in which the **initial state of the site is unknown** could include:

(a) Restoration or repair work. An often used alternative to a cost-reimbursable contract, in which the type of work is known but the quantity is not, is to use a method-related schedule of rates (see section 4.4.4).
(b) New process plant has to interface with existing plant, which cannot be inspected prior to contract award therefore its condition is unknown. This is often the situation in the water and power industries.
(c) Ground conditions are uncertain, for example tunnels are a particular case in point,[14] and reservoirs have also been mentioned.[15]
(d) Related to the above point, information for the design, such as ground conditions, can be acquired more economically as part of the works rather than by preliminary studies or tests.

Situations in which the **end state is unknown** could include:

(a) Those in which a client is unsure whether to proceed with the work and a contractor has specialized knowledge or experience. The contractor is paid on a cost-reimbursable basis (or possibly a part-reimbursable basis) until the scope is sufficiently defined for the project to be costed with sufficient accuracy for the client to decide whether it is commercially viable.

> National Power, now Innogy, has used this strategy when working with its framework contractors to develop a scheme. National Power knows and is quite open about what commercial figure has to be reached for the project to be commercially viable. Apart from the ongoing relationship and repeat order motivation, the contractor has the incentive to work with National Power on the outline design to meet this figure, so that the project goes ahead. Once this figure is reached, a target cost contract is signed using a performance-based specification to define the works, with National Power taking a greater percentage of savings as it knows that there is still potential to achieve further cost savings by working together.

(b) Fast-track, time-driven projects in which the scope, quality and/or detail is not finalized. As long ago as 1991, Trench[16] was advocating a similar approach for fast-track construction under the design and build route. He suggested that subcontractors and suppliers should be paid for their involvement on a cost-reimbursable basis until the scope of each part of the works is sufficiently developed to turn it into a target for the work package, which, with the addition of a fee, is added to the main contractor's target. Is this a forerunner of the prime contracting approach (see section 8.11)?

(c) Projects in which statutory authorizations and other third-party influences may alter the details of the design, if not the end performance or look of the project; these could, in turn, alter the process of delivery (see below). A common problem is that clients and consultants often underestimate the extent of design. An alternative approach may be to use a management-based contract (see section 4.3.4).

(d) Projects in which savings generated during the course of the contract, either from value engineering or from risks not materializing, are reinvested in the project, so that the client gains the best asset for its budget, in terms of both performance in use and/or whole-life costs. The ability to do this is significantly enhanced by using a cost-based contract (see section 7.2).

The last three circumstances mean that the process of delivery is subject to risk and uncertainty.

CIRIA Report 85[3] refers to this type of work as projects with 'an expectation of substantial variation in work content'.

Turner[17] refers to it as 'a confused programme subject to unpredictable constraints or disturbances'.

Schneider[1] points out that in price-based contracts 'the costs sustained by the contractor due to such disruption are particularly difficult to assess and disruption claims and their valuation are among the most complicated and disputed issues of construction claims.' The transparency of open book accounting simplifies their assessment.

A danger of using pure cost-reimbursable contracts is that the ease with which variations can be introduced means that discipline is needed in change procedures.[1] This is because there is no contractually meaningful target or price — the client pays what it costs regardless — so people may not fully consider the implications of a change.

Situations in which the **process of delivery is subject to risk and consequent uncertainty** could include:

(*a*) Projects in which possibly small changes in the end state have a potentially large impact on the process of delivery. This links in with the previous situation in which the end state is unknown.

(*b*) Projects involving parallel developments, resulting in difficult or unknown technical interfaces, in which the details of one contract will have an effect on the details of another. An example of this was the case of the civil works for the space shuttle launcher: these were affected by the design of the launch apparatus, which, in turn, was affected by the design of the space shuttle.[1] Again, an alternative approach might be to use a management-based contract (see section 4.3.4).

(*c*) Projects that have a substantial component of research and development, 'undertaken at the frontiers of technology',[18] to satisfy defined functional or performance requirements. Both the expenditure on developing this technology and the technical solution's impact on the rest of the project could vary significantly. Many development contracts in the defence industry are initially undertaken on a pure cost-reimbursable basis. Later, some incentives are introduced to motivate the contractor.

(*d*) Projects in unfamiliar circumstances, either geographically or in term of the conditions encountered. For instance, many of the early oil facilities built in the Middle East were constructed on a cost-reimbursable basis because the trading and commercial environment was not fully understood. In the North Sea, many of the initial contracts in the oil industry were let under cost-reimbursable contracts because the physical conditions and their solutions were unknown. In both circumstances, as contractors came to understand the environment, their use decreased. [1,3]

(e) Projects involving uncertain weather conditions, for example construction of a jetty on an isolated island where access was limited to a few months of the year, because of sea conditions, and most of the cost was in transporting workers and materials to the site.[3]

(f) Projects involving a major unquantifiable risk, which the contractor cannot price accurately and so would put in a large risk premium for something that may not occur. Normally, the client would take the risk out of a price-based contract, but the impact of the risk is so large that it cannot be treated as an 'add-on' to the price-based contract. Examples of this could be where specific or innovative (sometimes specified by the client) plant has to be bought to do the work and the contractor may then be at risk, either because the plant does not work as required or because the circumstances in which it operates change. Tunnel-boring machines are a common example of both categories, although in the latter case this is often because of unexpected ground conditions. Manufacturers' warranties or indemnities against failure of a specific item of plant may be an alternative means of protecting both the contractor and the client.

The net result of the above circumstances is that planning is very complex and/or very fluid as the methods required to complete the works are very changeable. If let on price-based contracts, either the emphasis would tend to be on administering the adjustment to the price, rather than working together to minimize the consequences of change, or the tender price would be, at best, a 'guesstimate' if the risks are included in the price.

According to Schneider,[1] the US Federal Acquisition Regulations System states that 'cost reimbursement contracts are suitable for use … when uncertainties … do not permit costs to be estimated with sufficient accuracy to use any type of fixed price contracts.'

7.3.3 Buoyant market conditions or limited supply of contractors

It may also be appropriate to use cost-based contracts in buoyant market conditions or in situations in which the supply is limited. Often supply is limited because of a recent technical breakthrough or innovation. Therefore:

- only one or a few contractors can do the work
- innovation tends to be risky, so the process of delivery is subject to risk.

A specialist contractor may refuse to work on the project unless paid on a cost-based contract or may charge a high premium for risk, which may not occur.

The client may be unwilling to pay this premium. However, incentives can be used to motivate the contractor.

A case of new technology leading to scarce supply

Directional drilling is a technique whereby a 'mole' digs through the ground laying a pipe. Traditionally, a trench would have to be dug, the pipe laid and the trench back-filled.

When directional drilling first came on the market, only two specialist contractors with the relevant technology existed in Europe; both were busy and used to working on a daily hire rate. A water company needed a new 1.5-km sewerage pipeline to be constructed out to sea, where the dilution factor would be sufficient to satisfy environmental regulations. If no risks occurred, directional drilling could cut the project costs from about £2.5 million to £600000. This would be quite a small contract to the already busy contractors. The client therefore had to entice one of the two contractors to do its work. This was done by using a target cost contract, with the contractor allocated a high share of savings — 50% — and a share of any over-run, which, although low, was sufficient to motivate the minimizing of cost over-runs (20%). Uncontrollable risks, such as bad weather, sea and ground conditions, were excluded from the target, but the risk of the drill breaking down was included because this was predominantly under the control of the contractor.

The initial target was £600000, which was adjusted during the contract to £750000, and the final actual costs to the client were £900000. If the works had been let conventionally under a price-based contract, the client's project manager thought that the contractor would have tendered £1.5 million or more, which would still have been adjusted upwards because of compensation events.

7.3.4 An existing relationship of trust already exists

More recently, cost-reimbursable contracts have been used in strategic partnering relationships in which the above two circumstances (buoyant market conditions and/or a limited supply of contractors) do not exist. However, in strategic partnering:

- There tends to be an existing relationship, which has developed to the extent that the parties trust each other sufficiently to go cost-reimbursable.
- The performance of the contractor and the partnering team is heavily benchmarked to ensure continuous improvement.

- If the contractor did not perform *over time* with respect to these benchmarks, then the relationship would be dissolved; there is therefore a repeat order commercial stimulus to perform.

> The use of cost-reimbursable contracts in partnering-type relationships is not new. Turner,[17] in 1986, noted that 'some employers and contractors enter into it [a cost-reimbursable contract] regularly because they have developed a mutual trust over the years.'
>
> And Schneider,[1] in 1987, noted that 'cost reimbursement contracts allow a degree of co-operation and flexibility which may justify their choice in projects where close and constructive co-operation is essential … provided a mutual relationship of trust is established.'

BAA/Amec's Pavement Team is an example of a strategic partnering relationship that started off on a target cost contract basis for each project and changed to a cost-reimbursable one as the relationship developed. Contracts are heavily benchmarked to ensure continuous improvement (see box in section 3.12).

7.3.5 *Conclusion*

Many of the situations described above overlap. For instance, the project could be *time driven*, so there has not been time to do a proper ground investigation, so the *initial state is undefined*. It could be using innovative technology, which, if it fails, renders the project worthless, so the project is also *quality* or *performance driven*. Because the technology is innovative, there may be only a few suppliers who are unwilling to take on high risks without charging a high premium, so there are *buoyant market conditions* or *a limited supply of contractors*. Or, although the client knows what the end asset has to do, and perhaps look like, as a concept, there also has not been time to develop and finalize these criteria as a performance specification, so the *end state is undefined*. Consequently, the *process of delivery is subject to risk and consequent uncertainty*. Finally, the project may be very definitely one in which working together, or *partnering*, will substantially increase the likelihood of success for all. The client therefore selects a contractor with whom it has had previous good experience and whom it *trusts*.

I put the remainder of this conclusion in the context of the principles of risk allocation and sharing (see section 3.5). Most, if not all, of the circumstances discussed in this section for the use of pure cost-reimbursable contracts fit into one of two fairly extreme circumstances:

- The client is much better able to take the consequences of significant uncontrollable risk occurring. According to principle 1 of risk allocation and sharing, the risk should lie with the party best able to take it, and this is invariably the client.
- The client is much more able to influence the likelihood of major risks occurring, be it through good site investigation, good scope definition, change control, etc. According to principle 2 of risk allocation and sharing, the risk should again, therefore, be allocated to the client.

The benefits of partnering in these circumstances come from working together to mitigate the impact of these risks, if and when they occur. The advantages and benefits of cost-based contracts, discussed in the previous section, mean that the parties are more likely to work together. However, partnering and use of cost-based contracts implies that the client has the expertise and resources to participate in the partnering relationship, which is key implementation point 2 for cost-based contracts and is discussed below. The advantage — and potential disadvantage — of pure cost-reimbursable contracts is that there are no arguments over the adjustment to the target or prices, which makes them particularly appropriate if a high degree of change or risk is expected to materialize.

Trench's[16] summary of when to use cost-based contracts is that they are 'best suited to contracts where there are risks which are unlikely to be borne by contractors at a reasonable premium, where time is of the essence and construction needs to progress before design is completed. It will suit large, complex or innovative projects.'

If the two circumstances in the bullet list above are not present to a degree sufficient to warrant a pure cost-reimbursable contract, a target cost approach may be more appropriate. The share profile — or pain/gain share — and which risks are included in the target and which are excluded should reflect the extent to which these circumstances are present (see section 8.7). Another route may be that of management-based contracts (see section 4.3.4).

Another theme running through this section has been the initial use of pure cost-reimbursable contracts or input-based contracts until the scope of the works has been sufficiently developed for the contract to be converted to a target cost or price-based contract using the same contractor. In these circumstances, it is suggested that a policy is adopted regarding at what point in the project's development the conversion takes place. Again this is discussed later in more detail (see section 8.4).

In summary, **key implementation point 1 is to use cost-based contracts in the right circumstances: projects that are either time or quality/**

performance driven, subject to high risk or scarce supply and/or employing a contractor with which the client has an existing relationship of trust, in which case collaborative working will increase the likelihood of success.

> **Review question 2**   Reflecting on the projects with which you have been directly involved or indirectly associated, or of which you have knowledge, identify and list below those which have some characteristics that may have made them suitable for a cost-based contract. Of those you have listed, which ones were suitable for use with a pure cost-reimbursable contract?

7.4   Defining the principal components of cost-reimbursable contracts

This section briefly explores some definitions relating to types of cost-reimbursable contracts and their principal components, namely reimbursable costs, non-reimbursable costs and the fee.

Reimbursable costs are those for which the contractor is reimbursed directly and are normally defined in a schedule attached to the conditions of contract. Anything listed in this schedule is directly reimbursable. From a contractor's viewpoint, non-reimbursable costs have to be recovered elsewhere, typically in the fee or in another round-up percentage applied to a grouping of items listed in the schedule of reimbursable costs. Before defining this schedule and how these round-up percentages are applied, there are two general considerations that need to be kept in balance, in that the more items directly reimbursed:

* the greater the transparency of costs, which is the principal benefit of cost-based contracts but
* in principle, the more effort needed to administer the contract (Fig. 7.1).

7.4.1   Reimbursable costs

Going down a level, there are two related considerations when defining reimbursable costs:

* The extent of coverage for which items are reimbursed directly, for instance is it only the direct costs of doing the physical work or all costs recorded within the area specified by the client, or this site and any other area specified by the contractor as being exclusively for the works, or does this area also extend to design offices as well? The decisions made

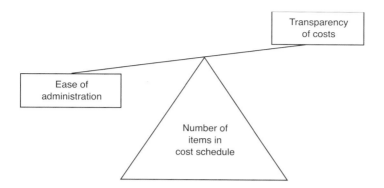

Fig. 7.1.   Balancing the number of items in the cost schedule

on what are reimbursable costs can affect where people and offices are located, for example whether the designer is based on or off site.

- Are items reimbursed at their real costs or on agreed/tendered input rates? An advantage of the former is greater transparency of costs and a disadvantage is the greater initial administrative effort required to work them out. A potential disadvantage of the latter is that the figure derived from using a formula to calculate actual costs can bear little relation to what it costs the site as a cost centre (for example for contractor-owned construction plant under the *NEC Engineering and Construction Contract*, 2nd edn). It is more common for the contractor to have tendered or for the parties to agree market rates for contractor-owned construction plant prior to signing the contract. Under agreed/tendered input rates, the contractor might have, for instance, good rates for people and poor rates for construction plant, and so may have a tendency to use people rather than plant, although the opposite would actually be more economical. In other words, **how actual costs are defined in the detail of a schedule can affect motivations and, if either party finds that it is out of pocket, relationships can be affected, with consequential implications for the project objectives.**

7.4.2   Non-reimbursable costs

Non-reimbursable costs fall into two categories:

- those that are never reimbursed directly because they are not listed as reimbursable costs and are therefore included in a percentage applied to elements or groups of reimbursable costs
- those for which the contractor is normally reimbursed directly but is not because of some default on its part or as a matter of policy.

In terms of reimbursing the contractor's costs directly or by means of a percentage, there is a again a balance between transparency of costs, which favours reimbursing costs directly, and the costs of administration, which favours round-up percentages. Round-up percentages are sometimes applied to cover the cost of items that are funded from head office and used on different sites, for example stationery and computers and surveying equipment not bought exclusively for a project. An additional disadvantage of excessive use of round-up percentages is that the contractor could be tempted to cut any indirect costs included in a rate or percentage, for example the cost of supervision. Again, how these percentages are calculated and what items they are applied to in the schedule can affect motivations; if either party finds that it is out of pocket, relationships can be affected, with consequential implications for the project objectives.

Those costs for which the contractor is normally reimbursed but, because of some default on its part, are deducted could include the cost of correcting defects, extra costs due to not following a procedure stated in the contract, overpaying a subcontractor, etc. If some of these costs — such as correcting defects — are not reimbursed, then the contractor will cover its risk by including an allowance in a round-up percentage, input rate or its fee. In other words, the client will pay somehow, albeit indirectly.

Those costs for which the contractor is normally reimbursed directly but as a matter of policy is not would generally be due to financial irregularities. For instance:

- costs that cannot be properly accounted for
- construction plant and materials that have been ordered and invoiced to the site but have not been used on that site
- paying a wholly or partly owned subcontractor more than it is entitled to under its subcontract
- contractors' own construction plant which has been kept on site when it is no longer needed and which would otherwise be paid for while doing nothing.

7.4.3 The fee

The fee has to include that which is not included in the reimbursable costs and any other percentages applied to reimbursable costs. What the fee covers is often not continually defined, so it is deemed to cover anything not defined as a reimbursable cost or included in a rate or round-up percentage applied to reimbursable costs. This could be profit only or it could include profit, risks, contingencies, interest on capital and overheads on all costs, except direct costs verifiable on site. There are two basic types of fee arrangement:

- *Cost-plus-percentage-fee/percentage of cost contract.* The major disadvantage of this approach, in a pure cost-reimbursable situation, is that it provides an incentive for the contractor to increase costs.
- *Cost-plus-fixed-fee/fixed fee contract.* In this case the level of fee is established as a sum at tender and is normally then adjusted for changes that would give rise to claims under price-based contracts.

These are illustrated diagrammatically in Fig. 7.2.

The advantage of a cost-plus-fixed-fee contract is that, to achieve a higher profit on turnover, a contractor is motivated to reduce costs and, in terms of cash flow, to complete the works quickly. A disadvantage is that, to gain the cash flow advantage, a contractor may accelerate the works at the expense of the client. Additionally, if the scope of the works changes significantly, the contractor may under- (or over-)recover for the turnover and therefore seek adjustment to the fixed fee. Under a target cost contract, it is rare for the contractor to be paid a fixed fee for this reason and because its motivation to perform well is in the extra profit it will gain/lose through the application of the share mechanism.

7.4.4   Conclusion

When using standard forms of contract, reimbursable costs, non-reimbursable costs and the fee, albeit indirectly, will be defined in the contract and in a schedule attached to it. Before entering a contract, clients, consultants and contractors need to understand how costs are defined as this will affect motivations, transparency and administration during the contract. As different contractors account for costs in different ways, it makes sense for the way in which costs are built up under the contract to match how costs are built up in practice. Project participants also need to understand how costs are built up both by the contractor and under the contract to administer the contract properly.

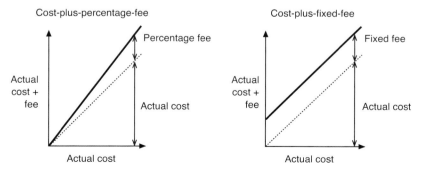

Fig. 7.2.   An illustration of the difference between cost-plus-percentage-fee and cost-plus-fixed-fee approaches

Therefore, **key implementation point 2 is for the client, its consultants and the contractor to understand how costs are built up under the contract prior to signing it, and to make any adjustments necessary, taking into account how the contractor builds up costs in practice. This is because the way in which costs are built up affects motivations, transparency and administration during the project.**

7.5 Degree of client involvement in the *management* of the project

I stress the word 'management' because I mean that and not 'administration'. Partnering implies working together. To gain the most from partnering processes, such as lean construction techniques, value engineering, risk management, etc., the parties need to work together. Under cost-based contracts, the fact that the client is paying on an input basis, as opposed to a pre-defined output basis, implies a more developmental 'hands-on' approach to the project. For instance, if the client has a fixed budget, this might mean developing the scope and detail of the project with the contractor's input at an early stage. Or, during construction, it could mean deciding how to reinvest any savings made or take out some scope if risks occur through working with the contractor to develop and evaluate different construction options.

The above implies that greater client involvement is required for a successful partnership under a cost-based contract, especially compared with, say, a lump sum design and build contract. This has implications for staffing levels and technical and project management expertise of the staff and their willingness to work with what some might consider to be the 'old enemy'. Alternatively, the client could employ a consultant who has these skills and the desired attitude, and who is trusted by the client to make decisions on its behalf. This means that the consultant must fully understand the client's requirements and be delegated sufficient authority to contribute positively and promptly to the team, yet know when to consult or involve the client. **There is a change from *administering* the contract to contributing to the *joint management* of it**. Consequently, **key implementation point 3 is that the client is more involved in the management of the contract, compared with price-based contracts, and staffs the project with a sufficient number of suitably skilled people with the right attitude and authority to partner.**

Walker *et al.*[18] state that: 'Cost reimbursable contracts, whether with or without a target, are not for the risk averse client. Where however *the client has the **expertise** and **confidence** to manage the risks so as to minimize their effect, target cost reimbursable contracts provide a good framework for teamwork* — especially where flexibility is needed.' (emphasis added).

7.6 Financial administration of cost-based contracts

This section focuses on the key implementation points for all cost-based contracts, which are related to their financial administration. **If the project is staffed with sufficiently skilled and experienced quantity surveyors/ cost consultants with a partnering attitude and these people have access to, and know how to use, financial administration software, then all of the advantages of cost-based contracts can flow** (see section 7.2). **If not, then none of them may materialize, and the project may dissolve into a bureaucratic nightmare of matching and chasing orders, receipts of goods, invoices and payments**. This is not in any party's interests.

This section will briefly consider:

- people issues involved in the selection of both cost consultants and the contractor
- when and how payment should be made by the client to the contractor
- specifying and agreeing requirements protocols for auditing purposes.

It will then discuss the main topic of this section: performance requirements for the financial management system of the project. These will vary depending on the size and type of the project and the nature of the relationship — one-off, project alliance or strategic alliance.

7.6.1 People issues

This section starts by making some generalizations about the skills and attitudes of those involved in the financial administration of traditional contracts. Being generalizations, they do not apply to all personnel, but at the extreme:

- The financial skills employed on traditional price-based contracts use retrospective analysis to maximize or minimize the contractor's entitlement. First, the standard conditions of contract are well understood so that their generic weaknesses, loopholes and any areas in which subjectivity can be exploited are known. From a contractor's viewpoint, the contract documentation is analysed — often at tender — to identify opportunities for claims and variations. The design is costed at tender and risks dispersed across the rates and lump sums. Sometimes the work is tendered below cost and the sequence of work, phrasing of communications, etc. are engineered both to create a claim and to maximize the apparent impact of the claim. When a claim occurs, the cost and time associated with the event is assessed by the contractor retrospectively using bills of quantities and records, and many 'benefit of hindsight' arguments. The client's quantity surveyor uses similar skills to refute and minimize the claim. Although the subject area is the same, the skills are not those required to maximize the advantages gained from cost-based contracts, as outlined in section 7.2 and summarized in Table 7.1. A shift from financial *monitoring* and *contract management* to *financial management* is needed.

- The attitude that the use of these traditional skills engenders towards the other party — and which may have been reinforced in the psyche of the personnel over many years of education, practice and rewards — is not exactly conducive to partnering and working together. To reinforce this point, I have gone into numerous partnering workshops as a facilitator, having been made aware that one of the principal stumbling blocks to forming an integrated team is the attitude of the commercial staff.

These comments relate to the need to change culture and skills as processes and teams become more integrated as outlined in my model for partnering (see section 2.4). They are also connected to the point made in section 7.5 about the client's staff generally having more of a management, as opposed to an administrative, focus.

What does this imply when approaching a cost-based contract from a client's perspective? It implies that, to achieve the full benefits of partnering, *both* the consultant's and the contractor's commercial staff who will be involved in the project need to be assessed and selected partly for their skills and attitude (see Appendix 4). From a consultant's and contractor's perspective, it means that **those put forward and selected for the management of cost-based projects should have a more proactive financial management focus and the skills to put this to good use.** Additionally, they need to have the interpersonal skills to preserve and improve the relationship when hard decisions and negotiations take place. If they do not, then training, coaching, and periodic reinforcement are needed. Ultimately, some may not be able to, or may not wish to, make the change and, if all reasonable support measures fail, should be removed from the project. This proactive focus means that **quantity surveyors/cost consultants need to have a working knowledge of programming and resource-based estimating.**

The emphasis on higher quality personnel is an issue found in other partnering literature and from my own previous research on the NEC Engineering and Construction Contract. I would suggest two reasons for this:

- The transparency of actions in partnering relationships, the NEC (with its strong emphasis on programming regardless of which payment option is chosen) and open book accounting under cost-based contracts all expose the source of poor management. Participants therefore have to manage, rather than rely on …
- The traditional approach — 'the one who shouts loudest' or has the biggest contractual/commercial leverage gets its self-centred way — which not only often results in poor decisions, but also causes the partnering and team working ethos to disintegrate.

To emphasize the point: CIRIA Report 85[3] states that 'it is probable that a higher standard of management than that currently applied to lump sum contracts is required from many clients or their engineers'. Consequently 'senior resident staff should be commercially minded' and 'stringent pre-selection of tenderers is essential and particular attention should be paid to the staff nominated by the contractor to run the job'.

Schneider[1] noted in his research that 'the key for success [in a cost-based contract] is not just additional, but proper and adequate management' which 'requires on the purchaser's side not just [technical] supervision of the contractor, but also participation in the decision making process.'

The second quotation in the box above raises the question of the number of management staff. Here the literature is divided on whether more[7,13] or less[1,16] administration is needed. These different views fitted in with my findings in that practitioners' views differed depending on their experience. My own view, based on observations of these projects, is that the extent of administration and management depends on:

- the cultural fit of the partners and the extent of measures taken to build the partnering ethos, for example workshops, social events, etc.
- the degree with which systems are understood and integrated, especially in terms of the financial administration of the project (this is key implementation point 7 in section 7.6.4).

To summarize, **key implementation point 4 is that cost-based contracts should be staffed with adequate numbers of management staff and that those put forward and selected should have a proactive focus and the financial skills to put this into effect. Additionally, they need to have the interpersonal skills to preserve and improve the relationship when hard decisions and negotiations take place.**

Review question 3 As you review this and the previous section, ask yourself, if you were involved in a cost-based contract, what specifically would you do differently, in terms of everyday behaviours, to be more management, as opposed to administration, focused?

7.6.2 When and how should payment be made by the client to the contractor?

It is likely that the client will pay out sooner for costs incurred by the contractor under cost-based contracts than under price-based contracts.

> Rosenfield and Geltner[19] calculated that this earlier release of cash and the higher expenditure resulting from the earlier start to construction and often longer construction period usually more than half offset any commercial benefits of earlier completion. This criticism could also apply to some extent to other fast-track construction methods, such as construction management and design and build. However, the fact that the client, more than the contractor, is financing the contract does have its benefits: CIRIA Report 85[3] considered the consequences of a number of payment scenarios on an idealized contract and found that allocating a lower risk to the contractor resulted in a 4.5% reduction in the tendered target/price and that the contractor was able to increase its internal rate of return on a cost-based contract up to three times because of the prompt payment. This would result in the contractor being prepared to offer a lower mark-up. These factors counteract to some extent — and it may be to a greater or lesser extent — the cash flow and higher expenditure worries expressed by Rosenfield and Geltner.[19]

Regardless of the cash flow arguments, the client needs to take a view on when it will pay out money: before, at the same time or after the contractor has paid it out. Having done this, words need to be written into the contract for this policy to be put into effect.

If it is after, then the client certifies payment after the contractor has paid the money out. The client has the money in the bank for longer, earning interest, and knows that the money has been spent, presumably on the project. It encourages early payment of the subcontractor and suppliers by the contractor. To be paid, the contractor has to keep its accounts up to date. However, this means that the contractor has to finance the works and it may well pay more interest than client, which ultimately costs the client more. This option is therefore sensible only if the client would pay the same interest as, or more interest than, the contractor.

The next option is to certify the amount to be paid to the contractor that it is due to pay out to its employees, suppliers and subcontractors in that accounting period (usually monthly or 4-weekly). Payment is then made to the contractor a few days before these payments are made. In my experience, this is the policy adopted by most major clients and it requires the contractor to pre-plan its payments much earlier. Actual payment is monitored against planned payment, often as a key performance indicator. Sometimes, interest is charged by the client on money certified but not paid out by the contractor.

Sometimes the client decides to pay out money before the contractor has spent it. This may be at the contractor's insistence. However, when this occurs the money is usually paid into a separate bank account set up specifically for the project, referred to as an imprest account. Money paid into this account is based on forecasts, so the contractor knows that money is available to pay for any work before it is done. Sometimes money is paid out of this account directly to subcontractors and suppliers, without going through the contractor's accounts, in which case the signatures of both the contractor and the client are needed. This strategy is also more likely to be used in alliance arrangements, in which there are numerous partners, whose fortunes are all tied, to some extent, to the success of the project. Having an integrated financial management system makes sense and a 'project' bank account is an extension of this.

On some contracts, the money paid to the contractor is based on an agreed project cash flow forecast whether paid out before, when or after the contractor has paid it out. The figures are then reconciled at a later date. The rationale for this is that it simplifies the commercial administration of the project. However, it would be more true to say that it simplifies it at the time. The reconciliation has to be done some time, and if the systems and people are in place not only is it easier to do during the contract, rather than afterwards, but also the advantages of cost-based contracts are more fully realized.

As with costs and the fee, the timing of payment will probably be defined in the selected conditions of contract. However, **key implementation point 5 is to consider when it is most appropriate to reimburse the contractor the actual costs plus fee — before, when or after the contractor has paid out** — and adjust the terms in the conditions of contract if necessary.

7.6.3 Specifying and agreeing requirements for auditing

In order to fully realize the benefits of cost-based contracts (see section 7.2), the client, perhaps through its consultants, may wish to specify the minimum performance requirements of the contractor's financial management system in the contract documents (see section 7.6.4). I am aware of some clients who, now that they have some experience of cost-based contracts, are starting to do this. At the same time, the client may wish to give an indication of the degree of detail which they would wish to audit. For instance:

- Does the client want to physically see every invoice?
- Is the client intending to audit, at random, a certain percentage of the work each month, and if so what percentage?
- Is the client going to look through the contractor's financial system and want to see receipts and invoices for items that appear to be on the high side? or
- Is a combination of the previous two points preferred?

The degree of auditing necessary will depend on the state of the partnering relationship and the amount of trust built up, the financial expertise and systems of the contractor and external auditing requirements. For instance, government requirements tend to be more onerous than those of private companies. **The extent of auditing will have a cost implication for both the client and the contractor, so it is desirable to keep it to the minimum necessary to satisfy the client organization's auditors. Consequently, it is wise to involve the auditors in the whole process of setting up the contract and the financial administration of it**.

Having specified the performance requirements of the financial system and given an indication of the auditing requirements, the client may well evaluate the contractor's system and people's ability to deliver this as part of its contractor selection process (see Appendix 4). For instance, is the contract financially administered on site or from a regional office? Where are the receipts and invoices kept? And so on.

On one contract that I am aware of, although most of the financial information was available on site in the North Midlands, all receipts and invoices were at the contractor's head office in Scotland. This meant at least one overnight stay and trip per month for the client's quantity surveyor.

Having selected and appointed the contractor, it is best that the format for reporting information is agreed and familiarity with the financial systems is gained before costs start to be incurred. The agreed format will depend on, among other things, the capabilities of the financial system, the client's audit requirements and the existing way in which the contractor operates and reports finances. Obviously, the closer the last two of these are, then the less duplication of work will be needed.

Therefore, **key implementation point 6 is to specify and/or agree audit requirements and how these will be implemented up-front.**

7.6.4   *Performance requirements of the financial management system**

Overview

Ideally, the capabilities of the financial management system need to satisfy four requirements:

---

*I wish to thank James Atkinson of Causeway Technologies and acknowledge his contribution in writing this subsection.

- At a minimum, it has to produce and summarize costs incurred or paid by the contractor in a form that is open to audit so that the contractor can be paid.
- It should produce sufficiently up-to-date financial information in a format that enables the parties to the project to monitor planned and actual costs incurred in order to identify any divergence occurring and give predictive capability if corrective measures are not introduced.
- However, monitoring can only identify that something has gone wrong. The system should also ideally have the capability to 'drill down' to detail to help identify the source of discrepancies and also be able to integrate with other partnering and good project management processes, for example integrating time and cost management through earned value analysis, risk management, value engineering, etc.
- It should be easy to understand and operate, avoiding duplication and waste wherever possible, and capable of reporting in different formats that satisfy all parties' audit and operating procedures.

In terms of functionality, the *ideal* system should:

(a) be able to offer integration with each organization's existing software applications, although the extent of integration will depend on the nature of the relationship and requirements of the contract
(b) be able to 'drill down' through cost information from contract level to transaction level
(c) be able to track and assist with the management of labour, plant, suppliers and subcontractors
(d) be able to track and compare estimated, committed, accrued, actual and paid costs
(e) allow the quantity surveyors/cost consultants representing all parties to jointly fulfil their internal financial reporting roles efficiently with minimal additional administration
(f) be able to differentiate between reimbursable and non-reimbursable costs
(g) have additional capabilities when there are meaningful targets
(h) support common partnering processes, such as value engineering and risk management.

To my knowledge these functions are not stated comprehensively elsewhere in the literature and are explored in more detail below.

Detailed performance requirements of the financial management system

The system should be able to offer integration with each organization's existing software applications, although the extent of integration will depend on the nature of the relationship and the requirements of the contract. The nature of the relationship will vary from a one-off project to a framework agreement. If it is a one-off project of medium value, then the most common approach would be to use the contractor's own system. It is unreasonable and unfair to expect the contractor to change its system just for one project, when it already has an established working system, as well as many other clients and projects. If this is the case, then the auditing organization should take time to understand the contractor's system and how costs are built up by that contractor. Following this, protocols need to be agreed on how audits are to be conducted and to what level of detail, and what information is needed and in what form. This is **key implementation point 6** (see section 7.6.3).

On larger projects or framework agreements for a series of projects, it may well become worthwhile to invest in a 'joined-up' system which integrates with the other partners' existing in-house systems. This is again because it is unreasonable to expect the contractor to change its systems just for one client, although over time fuller integration may be realistic. Thus, ideally, the joint system should be able to import information from the separate systems before merging the information and then exporting the relevant updated information. For a contractor, these systems could include its estimating, financial and project planning applications and, for a client, its budgeting and programme management tools. The alternative is that information is entered into the contractor's system, then the joint system and possibly even the client's system. This is time-consuming and will not give as up-to-date or comprehensive information as is desirable.

However, organizations within the project team may be competitors outside the project alliance. If the project system is connected up to the various other partners' in-house systems, then commercially sensitive information is at risk and security of sensitive information needs to be addressed. Therefore, although the system should be able to give any member of the project team the information necessary and desirable for that project, it is also necessary to 'ring fence' an individual project. Such a joint system is illustrated in Fig. 7.3.

Individual users, as well as organizations, will require access to different levels of functionality within the system. For example, the contractor needs the ability to input transactions (employee timesheets, material orders, plant orders, etc.), while the auditing organization needs only to view the information, with the additional ability to 'drill down' through the cost data. The client may need to extract information to a certain level of detail for its cost management and payment systems, but not to the level of individual transactions. A contractor might be unwilling to have this information in a client's cost system, where it could, for example, be accidentally downloaded to a competitor or used against the contractor in later commercial negotiations. It is therefore suggested that individual project participant's needs are thought through and access and functionality controlled on that basis. The system should be able to accommodate this.

Bearing this is in mind, a third-party supplier which installs the system and then manages the financial hard- and software systems only — as opposed to

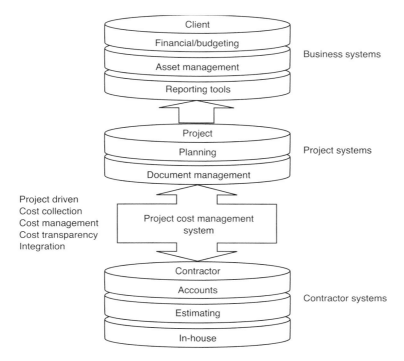

Fig. 7.3.   An illustration of a project-driven financial management system offering integration with existing systems

the finances of the project — may well be deemed to be more independent and trustworthy by the partners than an organization principally employed by the client to represent its financial interests.

The client, when considering the level of integration required within the financial management, needs to weigh up the potential benefits versus the cost and time of putting it in place. It obviously should be in place before the project starts, and installing the system, integrating it with existing applications and training users to the required level will take time. While this may vary greatly depending on the specifics of each project, a 'ball-park' figure given to me in the course of my work is 2 months from purchase to full use, including training. The client needs to allow for this in its project programme.

Lastly, as key performance indicators and benchmarks are now becoming common, clients want to receive information from different contractors in a variety of different formats. A single system offering a standardization of information will drastically reduce the time spent on reconciling information, by allowing for immediate reporting across contracts and suppliers.

The system should be able to 'drill down' through cost information to a transaction level.   Ideally, the system, whether in use by an individual contractor or project team, should be able to 'drill down' through levels of information, starting at an organizational level (although this information would not be shared between different project teams) to:

(a) a contract level
(b) an activity or work package level (however that is defined)
(c) a cost heading level (labour, plant, materials, subcontractors and other)
(d) a cost code level (for instance, concrete, timber, bricks, etc.)
(e) a resource level — exact type of labour, mix of concrete, etc. (for example, 'Concrete-C 20; 20 mm Agg MCC 300 kg m^{-1}, Concrete-C35; 20 mm Agg MCC 310 kg m^{-1}, Common Bricks, Engineering Bricks') and then down to the level of an individual transaction (labour timesheet, goods received note, invoice, etc.)

This is illustrated in Fig. 7.4. A breakdown such as this allows any deviations from that expected at a higher level to be broken down and

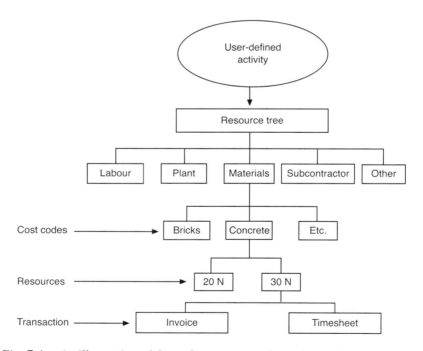

Fig. 7.4.   An illustration of the coding structure that a financial management system should be able to offer

investigated at the lowest level. When performing an audit, whether monthly, at random or to investigate a specific problem, it can be done electronically and the only documentation that needs to be physically checked, if required, would be the paper invoice, which should match that which has been entered into the system. This should much reduce the paper generated and resulting time spent on reconciling and chasing information and, apart from physically checking invoices etc., offer the ability to audit information at any time from any location.

The system should be able to track and assist with the management of labour, plant, suppliers and subcontractors. Under each of these headings, the *ideal* system will be able to assist in tracking and integrating labour, plant, materials and subcontractor costs. The majority of functions that this would entail are listed in Table 7.2.

The system should be able to track estimated, committed, accrued and actual costs. Costs have a cycle from when they are first estimated to when they are finally paid (Fig. 7.5) and it should be possible to offer comparisons in the form of reports and figures to reflect post-contract performance, for example actual vs. estimated cost.

The system should allow the quantity surveyors/cost consultants of all parties to jointly fulfil their internal financial reporting roles efficiently. This means that the system should allow them, at all levels, to:

(a) adjust estimated tender costs to reflect how the project will be constructed, allowing, for example, the reallocation of money across labour, plant, materials, subcontractors and other to create a reworked budget
(b) adjust estimates as a result of both client-initiated changes and, if there is an element of contractor design, contractor-initiated design changes
(c) at any time, compare costs, whether estimated, committed, accrued, actual, certified or paid, with the earlier estimates
(d) flag up any discrepancies between costs and estimates (see the point above), both historical and forecast, so that action can be taken
(e) track and manage any changes and variations that arise in terms of cost and value and through integration with planning systems
(f) ideally, integrate financial management and forecasting with planning and forecasting to give earned value reporting
(g) be able to report and do comparisons in a number of formats, both tabular and graphical, at the touch of button, so that different companies' reporting requirements and procedures can be accommodated, regardless of how the information is entered; this includes collating information for key performance indicators and benchmarks.

Table 7.2. *The desired capabilities of a financial management system for managing cost and value information*

Labour	Plant	Material	Subcontractor
Labour timesheets	Plant requisitions	Enquiry management	Subcontract database
Allow for various payroll profiles, e.g. shift paid, hourly paid, start and finish time, etc.	Plant orders	Requisitions	Package creation and comparison of functionality
	On-hire/off-hire notes	Orders	Subcontract orders
Allow for additional pay codes, e.g. travel allowance, tool money, bonus, etc.	Damages, breakdowns, losses and theft	Goods received notes	Ability to deal with different payment mechanisms
	Swaps	Immediate accruals	Subcontract measures
	Timesheets	Invoices	Payment certificates and export to subcontract ledger if required
Allocation of labour to activities/ work packages giving immediate accruals	Plant accruals		Management of variations, dayworks, contra-charges and attendances
Integration with corporate payroll systems	Detailed reporting highlighting plant costs, overcharges, etc.		
In a joint venture company the ability to integrate to a number of payroll applications			
Labour reports			

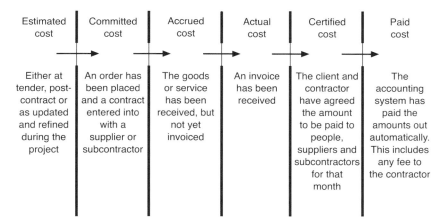

Estimated cost	Committed cost	Accrued cost	Actual cost	Certified cost	Paid cost
Either at tender, post-contract or as updated and refined during the project	An order has been placed and a contract entered into with a supplier or subcontractor	The goods or service has been received, but not yet invoiced	An invoice has been received	The client and contractor have agreed the amount to be paid to people, suppliers and subcontractors for that month	The accounting system has paid the amounts out automatically. This includes any fee to the contractor

Fig. 7.5. An illustration of the cost cycle

The system should be able to differentiate between reimbursable and non-reimbursable costs. (See sections 7.4.1 and 7.4.2 for a full explanation of the considerations in defining these.) Certain costs incurred by the contractor may not be directly reimbursable at cost, but are reimbursed as a percentage applied to another cost heading. For instance, under the cost-based options of the *NEC Engineering and Construction Contract* (options C, D and E), 2nd edn, many of the contractor's preliminaries and site overheads are paid as a percentage applied to the cost of people. Typically, the contractor's head office overheads and profit are covered in a tendered fee percentage, which is applied to the costs incurred on site. The system needs to identify reimbursable and non-reimbursable costs and separate them into two different ledgers:

(a) one is for cost that the contractor has to pay out
(b) the other is for the contractor's income, from which certain cost codes are deleted (as the items under these headings are not directly reimbursed) and then percentages are applied to groupings of non-deleted cost codes to give what the contractor receives.

Likewise, certain costs may be categorized as disallowed costs, for example if the contractor has not followed a procedure and this has resulted in additional expense. The additional expense is disallowed under the contract. Again this needs to appear as a cost for the contractor, but to be excluded from the 'income' paid by the client.

The system should have additional capabilities when there are meaningful targets. These targets could be:

(a) a single figure under a single target cost contract, possibly within a strategic alliance

(b) a single target for a project alliance in which each contract is cost reimbursable or input based

(c) in a project alliance, individual targets for each contract let under a target cost contract with an overarching target for the project alliance; this can involve writing some complex algorithms!

Whatever the targets are, the system should be able to:

(a) differentiate between those changes that adjust the different target(s) and those that do not

(b) provide forecasts of estimated expenditure by the client and income and profit to the contractors, suppliers and/or consultants

(c) depending on how and when the adjustment to what the contractor is paid is made, calculate how much each party is entitled to that month; this will depend on, say, whether the contractor repays the client any cost over-run at the end of the contract or whether payments are adjusted to take account of the projected over-run during the contract or as each over-run is incurred (see section 8.9 for a discussion on this issue).

The system should support common partnering processes, such as value engineering and risk management. When conducting a value engineering exercise that is principally concerned with taking out whole-life costs while maintaining functionality (see Appendix 5), it is common to challenge existing assumptions about how the work is done. Before these can be challenged, they have to be known. It therefore makes sense for the key assumptions behind each costed activity — methods, expected productivity, working conditions, lead-in times, resource costs, availability, etc. — to be visible. The obvious place to record these is on the financial management system, so that they can be easily recalled. If the challenge is successful, a revised forecast can be entered along with the revised assumptions.

Under price-based contracts, the contractor normally distributes its risk contingencies across its rates and lump sums. This means that it is certainly invisible to the client and often to the contractor's site team! Modern risk management methods encourage contingencies for specific identified risks to be separated from base costs, which allow for normal productivity. The financial system should aid this by separating base costs and risk contingencies from each other. This can be done by having an additional activity attached to the main activity or the risk contingency placed under the 'other' heading at the resource level of cost breakdown. If the risk does not occur, then these contingencies can either be reallocated outside the project or reinvested back into the project (see Appendix 2 for a fuller overview of risk management).

7.6.5 Conclusion

This section has described, in fair detail, what I consider to be the *ideal* performance requirements of a financial management system. At the time of writing, I am not aware of any system that completely satisfies these requirements, although some come quite close. As with all computer systems, 'garbage in = garbage out', and poorly trained staff will significantly undermine the benefits of it, while the opposite is also true. This means that, prior to the system becoming live, people have to understand how it operates. If the contractor's system is being used, this means that the client's staff and/or those of its consultant(s) have to gain familiarity with it before serious costs are incurred. While becoming familiar with any system, detailed requirements for reporting, which match the capabilities of the system, can be threshed out (see section 7.6.3).

One last but very important point, **there need to be some checks and balances put in place to ensure that costs allocated by the contractor to the project are actually incurred on the project.** This is because it is always in a contractor's interests to have costs allocated to a cost-based contract rather than to a price-based contract, for example checks on the time put down on labour and plant timesheets, checks that materials delivered to site are used on site, etc. The extent of checks and balances will depend partly on the level of trust between the two parties and partly on the audit requirements of the client.

So **key implementation point 7 is:**

* **Ensure that a good financial management system, as outlined in this subsection, is in place.**
* **Ensure that costs entered into it are actually incurred on that project against which they are entered.**
* **Ensure that it is operated by well-trained, high-quality staff who understand the system.**

Review question 4   Review the contents of section 7.6.4. To the level of detail that is appropriate to your expertise, what functions and attributes do you consider essential, desirable and/or superfluous for financial management of a cost-based contract? (Hint: Use a coloured green '✔', amber '?' or red 'X' to make the text more memorable.) To what extent does the system that your own organization uses or you have seen used on an a project match up to this specification?

7.7   Summary and conclusion

This chapter started by discussing many of the advantages — and some disadvantages — that can flow from the use of cost-based contracts and, therefore, when it is appropriate to use them. It then went on to discuss considerations for defining reimbursable costs, non-reimbursable costs and the fee. Essentially, these need to be defined, and how they are defined can affect the financial administration and the extent of benefits gained.

Seven key implementation points were identified. These are:

(a) Use cost-based contracts in the right circumstances: for projects that are time or quality/performance driven, subject to high risk or scarce supply and/or with a contractor with which there is an existing relationship of trust, in which case collaborative working — partnering — will increase the likelihood of success.

(b) The client, its consultants and the contractor should understand how costs are built up under the contract prior to signing it, and make any adjustments necessary, taking into account how the contractor builds up costs in practice. This is because it affects motivations, transparency and administration during the contract.

(c) The client is more involved in the *management*, as opposed to the administration, of the contract compared with price-based contracts and should staff the project with sufficient numbers of suitably skilled people, with the right attitude and authority to partner.

(d) Staff the project with adequate numbers of financial management personnel; those put forward and selected should have a more proactive focus and financial skills. Additionally, they need to have strong interpersonal skills to preserve and improve the relationship when hard decisions and negotiations take place.

(e) Consider when it is most appropriate to reimburse the contractor its costs plus fee — before, when or after the contractor has paid out costs — and, if necessary, adjust the terms in the conditions of contract.

(f) Audit requirements and how these will be implemented need to be specified and/or agreed up-front in a cost-based contract.

(g) Ensure that a good financial management system is in place, that costs entered into it are actually incurred on that project and that it is operated by well-trained, high-quality staff who understand the system.

I consider the most important of these to be points *(a), (c)* and *(g)*. The net result of these considerations implies that **there is a certain minimum monetary value of contract (or series of contracts) at which the investment needed to properly set up a cost-based contract justifies the potential benefits. In addition, there is a crossover point at which the administrative costs for a properly set up cost-based contract become less, as a percentage of total project costs, compared with a price-based contract. The better**

the project is set up, the lower this point is. The contract value at which the benefits outweigh the costs depends on a number of factors, for instance the degree of desired client control, the extent of change and risk, the potential for value engineering savings, etc. However, if asked to give a ball-park figure, I would say somewhere between a half and one million pounds.

Finally, target cost contracts are traditionally used in less extreme circumstances than pure cost-reimbursable contracts. Because they are essentially cost-reimbursable contracts with additional clauses to share any cost over- or under-run, most, if not all, of the above key implementation points also apply to target cost contracts.

Review question 5 Review what it is you wanted to gain from reading this chapter (see the Preview question at the start of this chapter). Have you obtained the information and level of understanding that you desired? If not, how are you going to obtain it? (Hint: This could mean rereading it, finding someone who does know and discussing your queries with him or her, or even phoning me for a brief talk!)

Now draw a learning map.

References

1. Schneider M. *Cost reimbursable contracts*. Draft of PhD thesis (photocopied), 1986.
2. Herten H. J. and Peeters W. A. R. *Incentive contracting as a project management tool, project management*. Butterworth and Co., London, 1986.
3. Perry J. G. *et al*. *Target and cost reimbursable contracts: Part A: A study of their use and implications; Part B: Management and financial implications*. CIRIA, London, 1982, CIRIA Report 85.
4. Pass I. and Peralta M. Changes in the E/C market. *Hydrocarb. Proc.*, Nov. 1985, 50–4.
5. Cox A. and Townsend M. *Strategic procurement in construction*. Thomas Telford, London, 1998.
6. Ibbs C. W. and Ashley D. B. Impact of various construction contract clauses. *J. Constr. Engng Mngmnt*, Sept. 1987, **113**, No. 3, 501–27.
7. Construction Industry Institute (CII) Partnering Task Force. *In search of partnering excellence*. CII, Austin, Texas, July 1991, Special Publication 17–1.
8. Wallace I. D. Construction contracts from the point of view of the owner. *Int. Constr. Law Rev.*, 1983, **1**, 23.
9. Parker D. *Open all hours. New Civ. Engr*, 23 July 1998.
10. European Space Agency (ESA). *Twenty years of European co-operation in space, an ESA report 1964–1984*. ESA, Paris, p. 222.
11. Barnes N. M. L. and Thompson P. A. *Civil engineering bills of quantities*. CIRIA, London, 1971, CIRIA Report 34.
12. Stukhart G. Contractual incentives. *J. Constr. Engng Mngmnt*, March 1985, **110**, No. 1, 34–42.
13. The Business Roundtable. *Contractual arrangements: a construction industry cost effectiveness project report*. The Business Roundtable, New York, Oct. 1982, Report A-7.
14. Construction Industry Research and Information Association. *Tunnelling – improved contract practices*. CIRIA, London, 1978, CIRIA Report 79.
15. Fordham A. E. *et al*. The Clywedog Reservoir project. *J. Inst. Water Engrs*, Feb. 1970, **24**, Nos. 1, 38, 54, 62 and 72.
16. Trench D. *On target: A design and manage target cost procurement system*. Thomas Telford, London, 1991.
17. Turner D. F. *Design and build contract practice*. Longman, London, 1986.
18. Walker S. C. A. *et al*. *The Thames Water use of the IChemE Green Book*. Photocopied paper.
19. Rosenfield Y. and Geltner D. Cost-plus and incentive contracting: some false benefits and inherent drawbacks. *J. Constr. Mngmnt Econ.*, 1991, **9**, 481–92.

8. Target cost contracts

8.1 Introduction

This chapter builds on the previous chapter by giving four *additional* key implementation points for the successful implementation of target cost contracts as opposed to pure cost-reimbursable contracts. To do this:

- First, it provides some different definitions and terminologies applied to target cost contracts, which vary around the world and depending on how the contract has been set up.
- Second, it gives a brief discussion on the nature of risk sharing within target cost contracts.
- It discusses when to use a target cost contract, identifying the boundary conditions for use, as opposed to a pure cost-reimbursable contract or, at the other extreme, a lump sum or measurement contract.
- It then gives an overview of how the elements of actual cost, the fee, the target and the share profile (pain/gain share) fit together.
- The next section covers setting the target and fee and what risks to include or exclude from the target.
- It then presents the five-zone model for setting the share profile to match the project characteristics.
- Next, it details the four alternatives for deciding when the contractor is paid or pays back its share of any over-run.
- Assuming that the contract has started, the requirements for easily, amicably and accurately adjusting the target during the contract are outlined.
- Finally, two variants of target cost contracts are discussed: guaranteed maximum price contracts and prime contracting.

By the end of this chapter, providing you have also read and understood the previous chapter, you should be able to successfully set up and use target cost contracts to meet the client's, contractor's and other team members' objectives.

Preview question Glance through this chapter and read the conclusion, asking yourself the questions 'What do I know already?' and 'What is it that I do not know?'. Note your answers down.

Now ask yourself 'What specifically do I want to learn from this chapter?'

8.2   Definitions and terminologies

As stated elsewhere, target cost contracts are a development of pure cost-reimbursable contracts in which the contractor is reimbursed the costs plus fee as the project progresses. The development is that a target is stated and any under- or over-run is shared in pre-agreed proportions. However, there are variants within this definition, both around the world and depending on certain characteristics of how the contract has been set up. These are given below.

- In the USA, target cost contracts are often referred to as **cost-plus-incentive-fee contracts**.
- If other incentives are used for targets related to performance or time, these are referred to, in the USA, as **target incentive contracts**.[1] These targets are still predominantly based on inputs to the project. For instance, the target could be based on estimated person-hour content for erection in the process plant industry.
- **Ceiling contracts**, or, in the USA, a **fixed-price incentive contract**, is one in which the contractor takes all the risk of construction costs exceeding the estimated costs and will have to finance the completion of the project. In the UK, this would probably now be termed a **guaranteed maximum price (GMP) contract**. GMP contracts, because of their potential complexity, will be discussed towards the end of this chapter, after an understanding of other issues has been built up (see section 8.10).
- **Prime contracting** is a method of working, not simply procurement and, from a client's viewpoint, is a 'one-stop shop'. The client defines the works using outcome specifications, including a whole-life cost profile, and then selects a prime contractor early in the project cycle. The prime contractor, which, with its supply chain, then develops the project until a target can be agreed. The contractor is still reimbursed its costs, but there is a cap on the client's expenditure. This very brief overview is expanded upon later in this chapter (see section 8.11).

8.3 The nature of risk sharing in target cost contracts

Target cost contracts, in addition to cost-reimbursable contracts, have a target and include a share profile or, in the simplest case, a constant share fraction, which determines the parties' share of any cost over- or under-run relative to the target. Together these produce the effect that **the risks normally carried by the contractor on a price-based contract are now *shared* with the client**. Such risks are traditionally associated with the contractor's productivity, efficiency and expertise in programming. In that context, the client shares the contractor's normal productivity, efficiency and programming risks.

However, by setting different values for the contractor's share of any over- or under-run against the target, a target cost contract can approach either end of the risk spectrum in which either the client or the contractor takes almost all of the normal financial risk. **The main financial motivation is that both parties benefit from a reduction in actual cost** — a unique feature of target cost contracts. This is **provided that each party is given a sufficient share of both the over- and under-run to motivate it**. The client is willing to share risks normally allocated to the contractor to achieve these benefits. Contractors may gain less profit than on their most efficient contracts, but their profit is more secure and they have more protection against large losses. For both parties there is greater satisfaction from working in a collaborative environment and greater prospect of successful longer-term relationships. Thus, **in a partnering context, the principal advantage and main reason for using a target cost contract instead of a pure cost-reimbursable contract is the alignment of motivations caused by the sharing of pain and gain under or over the target. The setting of a contractually meaningful target also gives clients much more comfort than just an estimate, which has no contractual significance.**

Risks that are normally carried by the client on a price-based contract normally remain with the client in that the target is adjusted if they occur. The direct compensation for a client's risk is the reimbursement of the cost incurred in dealing with it. The indirect compensation arises from the adjustment of the base original target to allow for the risk that has occurred. The timing of this adjustment affects whether the client, in reality, shares the risk or carries all of it. In principle:

- the risk is shared if the target adjustment is assessed before the work is done
- the client carries the risk if the adjustment is retrospective and based on the additional actual costs incurred.

This brief analysis shows that, although risk sharing clearly does occur, **target cost contracts do not necessarily sit in the middle of the risk-sharing spectrum of contractual payment mechanisms. The risk allocation**

can, however, be tailored to suit the client's requirements and project characteristics. This can be done by including or excluding risks from the target, allocating a different share of over- and under-runs to the parties and varying how actual costs and the fee are defined. These aspects are covered later in this chapter.

8.4 When to use target cost contracts: boundary conditions

It was consistently stated in the previous chapter that target cost contracts are traditionally used in less extreme circumstances than pure cost-reimbursable contracts (see section 7.3). Indeed, it is far more common for target cost contracts to be used rather than pure cost-reimbursable contracts.* Because of the joint motivation caused by risk sharing (see previous section) target cost contracts are also frequently used as the contractual framework that supports partnering arrangements. So **what are the boundary conditions for using:**

- a target cost contract as opposed to a pure cost-reimbursable contract?
- a target cost contract as opposed to a lump sum or measurement contract?

These questions are answered in generic terms by the degree of risk and opportunity within the contract at the time that the contract comes into existence. If there is a high degree of risk and/or opportunity within the contract, especially if the client can contribute to its management to a higher degree than the contractor, then a pure cost-reimbursable contract is likely to be most appropriate. In addition, the scope of the works has to be defined enough for the contractor to put a price to it, however vague, in order for there to be a target. If, at the other extreme, there is little risk and minimal opportunity for the client to contribute to the management of the contract, then a lump sum contract may be more appropriate. In cases in which the main risk is variation in the quantity of work to be done, a method-related bill of quantities or schedule of rates may be most appropriate (see section 4.4).

As can be gathered from the analysis in the previous section, the target cost contract sits somewhere in between the two extremes of lump sum and cost-reimbursable contracts. Where in the spectrum it sits depends on three factors:

- the risks included and excluded from the target
- the extent of risk allocated to the contractor through the share profile (pain/gain share)

---

*For instance, a survey carried out by Thomas Telford Ltd at the end of 1997 on the use of the NEC Engineering and Construction Contract found that about 27% of the contracts let under it were under the target cost options, whereas less than 3% were let under the cost-reimbursable option.

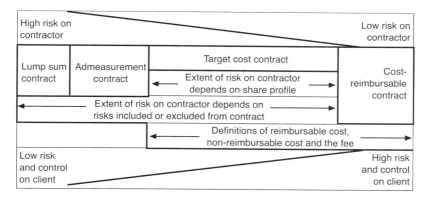

Fig. 8.1. An illustration of how the extent of risk on the contractor and the client depends on the share profile and risk included and excluded from the contract

- the definitions of reimbursable and non-reimbursable costs and the fee (see section 7.4).

The quid pro quo for the client taking more risk is greater control. This is illustrated in Fig. 8.1.

More specifically, the **boundary conditions for using a target cost contract, as opposed to a pure cost-reimbursable contract,** can be identified if the client asks itself the following questions:

(a) *To what extent do I, the client, trust the contractor to be motivated to minimize cost if there is no incentive within the contract?* If there is no incentive then the contractor will be motivated by a combination of professional pride, reputation and the prospect of repeat order business. On the other hand, a contractor may be demotivated to minimize cost by the fee percentage applied to actual costs and other incentives, which put the emphasis on other performance criteria. Large repeat order clients have an advantage in this respect and, as mentioned elsewhere in this book, a number of clients have developed partnering relationships with their contractors under target cost contracts, before changing to cost-reimbursable contracts in which performance is heavily benchmarked.

(b) *Is the scope and quality of the works sufficiently defined for the contractor to estimate an approximate cost for the work?* If the answer is no, then a cost-reimbursable contract should be used, at least initially. If a target cost contract is used, then, in general, the greater the definition of the works, the greater the share of risk and reward allocated to the contractor through the share profile.

(c) *Is the level of risk which is intended to be included within the target and predominantly within the contractor's control at an acceptable level for both the client and the contractor to carry on working together if risks occur (otherwise the whole concept of risk sharing is undermined) and is the contractor able to price it?* If the answer is 'No', then either the particular risk should be excluded from the target or a cost-reimbursable contract should be used.

(d) *Is the level of change that adjusts the target likely to be so high that the target will be continually adjusted by actual cost incurred or forecast, such that what was included in the original target and what is additional becomes so blurred that the contract will effectively revert to a cost-reimbursable contract?* If the answer is 'Yes', then the solution is to use a cost-reimbursable contract initially. Note that this condition also applies to the use of price-based contracts!

I was asked to give a training workshop to a project team using the NEC Engineering and Construction Contract, option C: Target contract with activity schedules. The project team included project managers representing the client, a water company and two contractors who had formed a joint venture: one a civil engineering contractor and another a mechanical and electrical (M&E) contractor specializing in water treatment works. This water company had a requirement for a series of relatively small (£0.5–2.5 million) treatment works which had to be completed and operational by a fixed deadline to satisfy the water regulator and fall within the client's overall programme budget for the series of schemes. As a result, the client had entered into a framework agreement with the civil/M&E joint venture to design and build these works, with the intention that each scheme was let as a target cost contract.

As a result of the need to progress the works, targets were being agreed early in a scheme's development. This target was based on an initial, but fairly limited, investigation of ground conditions and existing plant, and on a performance specification for the end treatment plant. Therefore, an outline scheme design and methodology of delivery could be developed and priced.

However, as the design was developed new information would come to light about the ground and existing plant conditions, the constraints imposed while constructing the works and the features that the operations people wanted included in the new treatment plant. This all led to frequent compensation events (which adjust the target) for redoing the design, which then led to further compensation events as the changed design affected the construction costs. The level of change meant that the project team's efforts were being diverted into agreeing the quantum of the frequent changes, rather than managing the works effectively. As a result, the targets for the different schemes were becoming meaningless in terms of representing what each scheme would cost.

During the course of the workshop, the team identified and developed a number of measures to reduce the level of changes. It was evident during the day that, despite the commercial difficulties encountered so far, there was a high degree of trust and openness between the partners. A project manager concluded that they were entering into contract too early in the project's life cycle. Two alternatives were suggested for further consideration (the first of which was suggested by the project manager):

- The whole works were done under the cost-reimbursable option of the NEC Engineering and Construction Contract (option E).
- The developmental stages of the project were done under the time-based option of the NEC Professional Services Contract — effectively on hours per designer and contractor input — before changing to a target cost contract just before construction started, by which time the degree of change would be much reduced.

Whichever option was selected, it still had to be agreed to by the client programme manager for the series of schemes.

At the other end of the spectrum, what are the **boundary conditions for using target cost contracts as opposed to lump sum or measurement contracts**? To some degree there are no limits to using target cost contracts, but there are circumstances in which the benefits derived are perhaps not worth the extra work. These are:

(a) At the time of entering the contract, the scope and quality of the works are sufficiently defined for the client to be certain of having the end asset it wants and for the contractor to price the works.

(b) The client has little expertise or desire to contribute to the active management of the contract and therefore to improve quality and reduce costs and time during it. The contractor does have the expertise and control to do this, so the best way for the client to minimize its expenditure is to provide a clear and unambiguous statement of what is wanted, have contractors tender competitively on this statement and not change it once the contract is let.

(c) The expected degree of change and/or risks materializing, in terms of both frequency and impact, is within the boundaries so that the means specified within the conditions of contract for adjusting the price or rates can accommodate it. This will depend both on the payment mechanism and on the means of adjustment within the conditions of contract (see section 4.4

for a critique of different payment mechanisms for price-based contracts). Generally, cost-based contracts give greater flexibility and allow changes in scope of design to be more easily accommodated than price-based ones.[2]

An additional factor that may influence the decision is the size of the contract, as the set-up costs tend to be higher for target cost contracts (see the final words in the conclusion to the previous chapter).

In conclusion, **the main reason for using target cost contracts, as opposed to cost-reimbursable contracts, is the introduction of a contractually meaningful target and the alignment of motivations resulting from the sharing of risk and reward. There is also a spectrum, in between the extremes of risk and the degree of control that the client wishes to exert, within which it is appropriate to use target cost contracts:** at one end, cost-reimbursable contracts are more appropriate and, at the other, lump sum or measurement contracts. Therefore, the use of target cost contracts is not a universal panacea and **there is a danger that they are used because it is fashionable, rather than because it is appropriate.** This conclusion is therefore the same as for **key implementation point 1** for cost-reimbursable contracts in the previous chapter: **'Use them in the right circumstances'!**

> **Review question 1**   Recall some recent projects with which you have been involved. Briefly review each one, asking yourself if they fell within the boundary conditions for use of target cost contracts, as outlined in this section. How did these projects go? If they were *not* successful, how much of this can be put down to the contractual framework and how much to other factors? If they were successful, was this despite the contractual framework or because another appropriate strategy was used?

8.5   Overview of how actual cost, the fee, the target and the share profile fit together in a target cost contract

A basic premise of all that is discussed in this chapter and book, and a basic premise for the use of any incentive (see section 5.1), is that, however performance is defined, the contractor makes:

- average profit for average performance
- improved profitability for better than expected performance
- reduced profit, which can mean none, or a loss, for poor performance.

As Blyth[3] states: 'the general principle [of designing incentive contracts] is straightforward. It is simply to take advantage of a contractor's general objective to maximize his profits by giving him the opportunity to earn — and I emphasize earn — a greater profit if he performs the contract efficiently.'

If you do not agree with these principles, then read no further!

In the case of target cost contracts, for these principles to be put into practice implies that:

- The initial actual cost component of the target must be realistic and reflect the costs incurred from the average performance of the individual contractor and not necessarily from a general contractor within the industry. For instance, if you have had a strategic alliance with a contractor for the past 3 years, the benchmark would be its performance in the last contract.
- The initial fee (whether fixed or as a percentage of reimbursable costs) is set at a level at which the contractor is earning returns similar to those on non-target cost contracts.
- The actual cost component of the target plus the fee, then combine to give a realistic target.
- Any share of cost under-run (including any other incentives) will motivate the contractor sufficiently to achieve above average performance.
- Any share of cost over-run will motivate the contractor sufficiently — and ideally the client also — to, at the very least, minimize any cost over-run and achieve the target.

If these criteria are not met, then the fulfilment of the client's objectives may be undermined before construction ever starts. They are therefore explored in more detail in the following sections.

8.6   Setting the target

Much of the thinking and text in this section is based on work done jointly by myself and Professor John Perry of the University of Birmingham. Credit is thereby given.

8.6.1   Accuracy of the target

Literature on target cost contracts, both in the UK and in the USA, consistently emphasizes the need for an accurate initial target.

> **The importance of a realistic target**
>
> Walker[4] states that 'if target costs of purchaser and supplier are close, then there is a good chance of meeting or improving the cost targets with a low risk to both parties', whereas 'if the target costs of the purchaser and the contractor are very different, this must act against both, as the final target cost will be the result of negotiating ability and strength and … may have little or no connection with the true costs.'
>
> CIRIA Report 85[5] stresses the importance of an accurate target throughout the report stating, the 'target cost must be realistic and should be the best estimate of the probable actual cost of completing the work' because 'beating down the target … results in the removal of positive incentive from the Contractor'.

As the CIRIA report states, a low target removes the incentive for the contractor and, not surprisingly, this has been shown by other research to lead to a systematic tendency towards cost over-runs.[6] Equally, if there is a high target then the client will be paying out incentive payments for average performance. When the client realizes that the target is high, especially in a negotiated situation, then it may develop a bad taste, which will undermine both the partnering ethos of the contract and the eventual success, in commercial terms, of the contract.

An additional reason for ensuring that the target is realistic comes from the consequences of the 'adverse selection' problem/theory, put forward by Rosenfield and Geltner.[7] This states that the effects of the share mechanism dilute the profit to the contractor for any cost under-run compared with a price-based contract. The argument is that efficient contractors are likely to tender higher target prices than their estimated actual costs plus fee, to offset the fact that they can earn better rewards elsewhere on price-based contracts, that is all of the savings on price-based contracts are profit, whereas under a target contract they are shared. This would lead, over time, to more efficient contractors focusing on price-based contracts and less efficient ones winning target contracts. This also emphasizes the importance of ensuring a realistic fee percentage.

The result of these deliberations is that **both an unrealistically low and unrealistically high target threaten collaboration from the outset and, in the longer term, will not give the client value for money.** However, the target has two constituents: estimated actual costs and the fee. The actual cost can be further split into another two constituents: the base estimate and specific risk allowances, whereby the base estimate means the estimated costs including allowances for average productivity. **If any of these constituents — base estimate, allowance for specific risks or the fee — is too high or too low, it will have an impact on the realism of the target.** These constituents are therefore explored in more detail below.

8.6.2 Accuracy of the base costs

As stated above, by base estimate the author means the estimated costs of doing the work including allowances for average productivity. **If the target is to be realistic, then the base estimate also needs to be realistic, and therefore steps need to be taken by the client to ensure the realism of these base costs**. The exact method taken will depend on how the contractor is selected.

A timeless quote

CIRIA Report 85[5] suggests that 'the Employer should require, scrutinize and agree the resource programmes and method statements prepared by the Contractor before the contract is signed.' For the client to do this, 'the information required from the Contractor at tender may therefore include a detailed programme, a detailed method statement, cost estimate, the numbers and types of resources to be used and a schedule of costs of labour, plant and materials. Consideration should be given to when the information is required, its contractual status and any resulting obligations on other parties.'

When tendering on the Channel Tunnel rail link, contractors had to return with their tenders a full set of assumptions made in arriving at the target price, for example expected outputs, resource levels, input costs, etc. This was also to ensure that they could complete their contracts both within the financial target and within the allocated timescale. Not only did this impose a heavy workload on the contractors to prepare these tenders, it also imposed a heavy workload on the client's consultants to evaluate them. However, at the time of writing, there were no reported significant time or cost over-runs on the whole project.

In a preferred contractor situation, I do not recommend the positional bargaining approach to negotiation, which means each participant starting at the extreme of its position and applying as much leverage as is possible over the other party to reach agreement over the target. This is both because the figure arrived at may not be realistic and because relationships are more likely to be undermined by this approach, both during and after the negotiation. Modern literature[8,9] suggests that negotiation is best based on a set of agreed principles and/or processes. On a project that has been developed jointly up to the point of signing the contract, whether it is a target cost or lump sum contract, I would suggest open book tendering, in which the contractor reveals its assumptions, methods and resources, etc., as well as its subcontractors' quotations. An example of this is the case study of the project in the City of London in section 7.3.1.

An example of what happens if the target is not realistic

A number of contractors were asked to tender for a dock refurbishment project under a target cost contract. While the largest item of expenditure was a new dock gate, the project involved an extremely intensive month when the dock was closed and the majority of work, and therefore expenditure, was encountered.

The lowest tendered target was £6.25 million when the client's budget was £5.5 million. The client then entered discussions with the lowest tenderer. Half of the difference was taken out by finding genuine savings. This still left a difference of approximately £375 000 between the two parties. The contractor offered to take the difference in exchange for a much reduced share of any over-run and a much increased share of the under-run, which the client accepted.

Therefore, the initial target was too low for the scope of the work. In addition, the client did not have the number and quality of staff to either manage or financially administer the contract, and my impression was that the contractor's financial management system was not as up to date as it could have been, that is the reporting of costs lagged behind their expenditure. Several key implementation points were therefore missing.

As the contract progressed, compensation events, unsurprisingly, occurred, which, while pushing the target up, were not quantified, although it was realized that expenditure was likely to exceed the increased target. However, not having up-to-date financial monitoring meant that the extent was not known until the work had been completed, by which time the parties were unable to separate the costs of doing the original work from the costs of the additional work. This was a result of the short duration of the contract, the frequency of compensation events and a lack of adequate administration, in terms of both quality and quantity.

Consequently, the outcome was a negotiated settlement which both parties could live with but which neither was particularly happy about.

If the client has selected a contractor with which to negotiate, another important decision to make up-front is when to agree the contractual target and enter a contract. The author has noted two unfortunate practices:

- The client appears to want to string along the contractor(s) as the design is developed, gaining the benefit of its (their) input without paying for it. The construction contract is held out as the 'carrot' for this input into what would otherwise be paid for as actual cost if a target cost contract had been entered into earlier. By the point at which the contract is signed, many months after it was originally intended, the vast majority of savings have been taken out and everything is certain. The client has used its leverage to agree a very low target, in which case, it could be argued, why use a target cost contract, when a lump sum contract would be more appropriate? This dishonesty of intention is also counter to the spirit of partnering and may well be counter-productive in the short and, for the repeat order client, long term.

> One contractor encountered this strategy and the client did ask for the agreed target to be transferred into a lump sum. The contractor agreed, but only if the contract sum was increased by 11%, both because the contractor would be taking on increased risk and because a significant proportion of this risk came from a third party over which the client had influence; without the joint incentive the danger was that the client would not be motivated to exercise this influence as the design was being developed, the costing of the design always lagging behind. Consequently, even though the genuine intention had been to enter contract early in the project cycle, agreement was reached only as construction was about to start and the parties had to agree a target.

- Other clients have set out a clear policy of when they intend to enter into contract with the contractor. This can be at a specific time or a specific stage or milestone in the project's development, for example when outline design is defined or when the target plus contingencies is within the client's budget or, better still, on reaching a specific programmed milestone.

> Carmody[10] states that 'it is necessary to include a definitive statement regarding establishment of incentives on even the most ill defined work at the initiation of the contract since the parties must agree to the principles for later establishing specific targets.'

Additionally, it is sensible for clients at the very least to outline what share profile and other incentives they intend to use.

8.6.3   Including risks in the target

Earlier studies of target cost contracts[5] found that a commonly adopted policy was to exclude risks normally carried by the client from the initial target. The actual costs component of the target was simply the best estimate of doing the work known to be required, that is the base cost. When risk occurred, the actual cost was reimbursed and the target adjusted upwards to maintain the equilibrium of the original share profile. One drawback of this approach is that the contractor is motivated to maximize the target adjustment, and the view has been expressed to me, as well as to Professor John Perry, that some contractors have focused more attention on this ploy than on seeking to minimize actual cost. The key implementation points listed and explained in the previous chapter, particularly the clients' showing a keen interest in the contractor's use of resources and their productivities, will mitigate against the worst excesses of this practice.

This may be part of the reason why there has been an increasing trend to include risk within the initial target. There is also a more constructive driver for this trend. This is the increasing use, prior to signing the contract, of risk workshops, jointly held between the client and potential contractors and subcontractors. At these workshops risks are identified and prioritized and initial strategies developed for their avoidance or mitigation should they occur. These risks are then allocated in accordance with the principles of risk allocation and sharing (see section 3.5). This means that **the costs of the agreed preventative, or risk reduction, measures are included in the target as a base cost, because the work is known to be required and is also defined**. The productivity and efficiency risk of providing the measures is then shared within the target, in the same way as other productivity risks. These measures may also shrink the impact of the risk should it occur. The risk is also better understood, and if it is a minor risk, in terms of impact, then the consequences can be included and shared within the target, as it is more time-consuming and costly to agree the adjustment to the target than the impact of the risk is worth. This is all good risk management practice (see Appendix 2).

I welcome the trend to consider risk more thoroughly, as does Professor John Perry, and we are strongly of the view that all risk events that would lead to an adjustment of the target should be identified and listed as such in the contract. This is particularly important to avoid dispute where there might be doubt over whether the target should be adjusted.

Another recent development is the inclusion within the target of specific risks normally carried by the client. The argument for the inclusion of these risks in the target seems to be based, first, on a quid pro quo — the client is sharing the contractor's normal risks, so the contractor should share the client's normal risks; second, on a desire for increased price certainty or, more precisely, a greater certainty in the value of the target; and, third, on the assumption that the contractor is better motivated to try to avoid the risk occurring (if it has any control over this) and to minimize the consequences if the risk does occur.

However, let us consider the consequences of including large risk premiums within the target, in the situation that the risk event itself may or may not occur:

- If it does *not* occur, how is the premium split?
  The client will pay the contractor's share of the amount of risk premium included in the target, so the client is paying out for something that has not happened.
- If the risk does occur, will the risk premium included within the target cover the cost?
  This is unlikely as the premium will be a combination of impact multiplied by likelihood and will therefore be less than it actually costs, perhaps by a large amount.
- What is the consequence of this?
  The extra cost incurred by the contractor over and above the risk premium included within the target will offset efficiency gains made elsewhere, or will worsen any cost over-runs.
- Does this then provide greater price certainty for the client?
  No, it provides greater 'target' certainty, with reduced administration for adjustment, but not price certainty as the over-run will, in any case, be shared by the client.
- Does this threaten the spirit of collaborative working?
  It may actually engender it before the risk occurs as both parties do not want this to happen, but if, having taken preventative measures, the risk still occurs, then this may well seriously undermine collaboration at a time when the parties need to be working together to mitigate the effects. This will be especially so if the occurrence of the risk was more within the control of the client than of the contractor.
- Is the client getting better 'value for money' by including this sort of risk within the target?
  Probably not, because the contractor will find it hard to quantify ill-defined or even unknown risks at tender as their exact impact and likelihood are unknown, so contractors will tend to err on the high side in their premiums.

In our view, the arguments for excluding uncontrollable risks from the target are compelling, and preserving the spirit of collaboration seems more likely to be achieved by excluding such risks from the target. However, we would agree that, if risk reduction and consequence mitigation measures result in the impact of the risk being shrunk to a small amount, then the contractor will be more neutral as to whether or not it takes the risk. An alternative is to set a threshold, for example as for the risk of poor weather or ground conditions in most conditions of contract, so that if the risk occurs in a minor way, then it is shared up to this threshold and both parties then have a motivation to avoid it happening. However, above this threshold, the *additional* actual costs plus fee are added to the target.

Examples of good and bad practice

- Severn Trent Water puts its design and build target cost contract out to tender with three contractors. Included with the tender

> documentation is its risk register. The contractors return their tenders with, among other things, a more developed register of risks, some of which are included in the target and some not. Severn Trent does not want to pay a risk premium for something that might never happen. It therefore 'normalizes' each tendered target price for the purposes of comparison by adjusting it for included and excluded risks.
>
> - A tunnel refurbishment contract had a risk of flooding from heavy rainfall; the maintenance of the existing drains was predominantly within the contractor's control. Traditionally, this would have been a client's risk. The level of risk reduction measures required from the contractor was agreed pre-contract and priced into the target. Although the tunnel did briefly flood during the contract, the contractor was taking the risk reduction measures and there was no dispute.
> - The client's design required, under the contract, that a known and tried production method be applied beyond previous limits in challenging circumstances. The contract was silent on the risk. Productivity was considerably lower than expected, which had a major impact on cost, resulting in the client arguing that this was a normal productivity risk. A major dispute resulted.

Particularly for financially strong clients, I do not recommend including specific identified medium to major risks within the target, as it is unlikely that the client will be gaining value for money in the long term. Instead I recommend that, once specific risks have been identified and prioritized and initial strategies for dealing with them developed, the following points should be considered:

- Identify and develop measures that give value for money in reducing or avoiding the risk (for example, it is not worth spending £50 000 to avoid a risk that has a 1 in 10 chance of occurring and would cost £100 000).
- Clearly state the measures that the contractor is expected to take to avoid or minimize the risks, price these up and include them within the target as a base estimate.
- In general, include contingencies for the occurrence of *minor* risks, especially frequently occurring ones, within the target. Other specific identified risks should generally be excluded from the target.
- Agree plans and contingencies for identified risks should they occur: the contingency level may vary depending on how they are allocated: if within the target, they are shared; if outside, they are taken by the client.

- List and clearly define the boundary conditions for risks that are outside the target as reasons for adjusting the target.
- As a client, include these contingencies within your project budget. If, as the contract progresses, these identified risks do not occur, then the money can either be reinvested in the project to improve its scope or quality or released for use elsewhere in the business.

An example of client contingencies being included: the Eden Project

The £86 million Eden Project in Cornwall, completed in early 2001, is one of the Millennium Commission's landmark projects. Its mission is 'to tell the story of mankind's relationship with plants ... and to inspire positive initiatives that will lead to a sustainable future for us all'. It primarily consists of two large domed 'biomes'— effectively large greenhouses in which temperature and moisture are controlled — with a floor area of $15\,500\,m^2$ and enclosing a total space of $330\,000\,m^3$. These, along with ancillary facilities and gardens, have been constructed in an old clay pit.

Early in the project's life cycle, eight potential contractors were shortlisted to work with the client in developing the scheme. This was reduced to two for final negotiations, with the fundamental requirement being that these two would enter into a design and construct target cost contract with a GMP (see section 8.10) and invest equity in the project. A Sir Robert McAlpine and Alfred McAlpine joint venture was selected as preferred contractor in February 1997 (see section 4.3.3).

Prior to signing the contract, the contractor joint venture insisted that £4.3 million was included as a risk margin in the GMP, and that the client also had £0.75 million outside the contract to finance 'possible fluctuations on provisional sums and the main biomes sub-contract'. There was a 50:50 share split of any savings. As a result of managing risk and value engineering, the contractor reduced costs such that the 50% bonus savings had reached the £1 million limit and the residue of the risk margin served to finance compensation events, which included improvements to the scheme.

(Source: reference 11)

8.6.4 Setting the fee

Perry and Barnes,[12] in their fundamental analysis of the principles of target cost contracts, concluded that **it is always in the contractor's interest to maximize the proportion of the target that is covered by the fee**. This is for two reasons. First, if the target is adjusted by actual cost plus a fee percentage applied to the change in actual costs, then there is greater potential profitability for a contractor with a high fee percentage. Second, it affects how much of a 'hit' the contractor takes for a cost over-run.

Take, as an example, a hypothetical case in which two contractors are tendering for a £1 million project. Both contractors have exactly the same cost base and propose to use the same methods with the same productivities on the project:

- Contractor A tenders accurately, with forecast actual costs of £909k, a fee percentage of 10% and resulting target of £1m.
- Contractor B deliberately tenders an inaccurate 'forecast', £800k for actual costs, a fee percentage of 20% and a resulting target of £960k.

Let us say the contractor's share of any over-run is 50%. Which one, at first glance, would you choose?

Most people would say contractor B. Let us assume that contractor A's forecast of actual costs turns out to be accurate and is what both contractor A and contractor B would have encountered had they won the contract. Using the formula:

Amount paid by client = out-turn actual cost + fee + contractor's share

- For contractor A, this equals £1m (£1000k).
- For contractor B, actual costs plus fee = £909k + 20% × £909k = £1091k. The over-run compared with the target = £1091k – £960k = £131k. So the amount paid by the client = £1091k – (50% × £131k) = £1025.5k. This is £25.5k more than for contractor A, yet the target was £60k lower!

Now let us examine the relative figures if actual costs increased by, say, £200k during the project, as a result of client's risks, and this was added on to the target:

- For contractor A, the new target = £1000k + 200k + 10% × £200k = £1220k, and the amount paid by the client still equals the target = £1220k.
- For contractor B, the new target = £960 + £200k + (20% × £200k) = £1200k. Assuming that the real forecast actual costs were those of contractor A, then actual costs plus fee = (£909k + £200k) + [20% × (£909k + £200k)] = £1330k. So the over-run compared with the target = £1330k – £1200k = £130k and the amount paid by the client = £1330k – (50% × £130k) = £1265k. The difference now is £45k more to be paid to contractor B than to contractor A, yet the original target was £40k lower for contractor B!

Now let us assume the same scenario, but because of risks included in the target actual costs escalate by £150k:

- For contractor A, the amount by which actual costs plus fee exceed the target = £150k + (£150k × 10%) = £165k. This is split between the parties, so the total amount the client pays = £1220k + (50% × £165k) = £1302.5k.
- For contractor B, the *additional* amount by which actual costs plus fee exceed the target = £150k + (£150k × 20%) = £180k. So the actual costs plus fee = (£909k + £200k + £150k) + [20% × (£909k + £200k + £150k)] = £1511k.

This exceeds the target by £1511k – £1200k = £311k. So the amount the client pays = £1511 – (50% × £311k) = £1355k. This is now £52.5k more than for contractor A, yet contractor B has incurred exactly the same costs and had a lower target!

What is the net result of these deliberations? It is this: **if the contractor is being paid a** *fee percentage* **applied to actual costs, the client should do a range of 'what if?' financial calculations to, at the very least, inform, if not select, its contractor. These 'what if?' calculations should not just be on a range of actual cost outcomes compared with the original target, but also on adjustments to the target.[13] This is especially so:**

- **if the client is not evaluating the realism of the actual cost component of the target (see section 8.6.2)**
- **if the contractor is allocated a small percentage of any over-run compared with the target.**

A number of contractors interviewed during the author's research admitted that this ploy has been used, albeit subtly with a 2–3% upward adjustment to their fee percentage. On one project, it was a quite blatant ploy by the contractor, even more so than as outlined in the example above! It emphasizes the need to evaluate not just the realism of the target, but also the forecast actual cost component of the target and the fee.

8.6.5 Conclusion

The conclusion to all of these deliberation is: **key implementation point 2 for target cost contracts** (in addition to those of cost-reimbursable contracts) **is that, in order to satisfy itself with the realism of the overall target, the client should:**

(a) **Evaluate the realism of the actual cost component of the target (the base estimate).**
(b) **Identify, agree contingencies for and clearly allocate specified risks within or outside the target in accordance with the principles of risk allocation and sharing.**
(c) **Only agree a level of fee that is consistent with the returns the contractor would earn under a price-based contract, especially when the fee is expressed as a percentage of actual costs incurred.**

A range of 'what if?' scenarios for out-turn actual cost compared with the original target and adjusted target should be generated to, at the very least, inform the selection of the contractor.

Review question 2   Summarize the generic arguments (outlined in section 8.6.3) for and against including risk in the target.

For   Against

Review question 3   Review the worked examples in section 8.6.4. Check that you understand where the figures come from and agree with them. Derive two algorithms, one for calculating the amount the client pays and the other for calculating the contractor's profit margin for any combination of actual cost, fee percentage and target.

Review question 4   To whatever level of detail is useful for you, as a result of reading this section, how would you alter your company's contractor — or subcontractor — selection procedures?

8.7   Setting the share profile: the five-zone model

8.7.1   Overview

From a client's viewpoint, the optimal share fractions are ones which:

- for a cost under-run, give the client the maximum saving yet still motivate the contractor sufficiently to decrease costs, while not undermining other objectives
- for any cost over-run, allocate the maximum percentage to the contractor yet still sufficiently motivate it to adopt positive rather than adversarial behaviour, again so that other project objectives are met.

The research on which this section is based showed that it is unusual for there to be one continuous share fraction that covers the whole range of outcomes in terms of actual cost plus fee with respect to the target. Normally, there are at least two different share fractions, and sometimes four. Together, these share fractions form what I term a share profile, which covers the whole range of possible outcomes.

When delivering training and attending conferences, many practitioners asked for guidance on setting this share profile. Consequently, I started to develop a model for setting the share profile. It was refined with the help of Professor John Perry. In doing so, **we identified five distinct zones for consideration** (in terms of actual cost plus fee with respect to the target), **with each zone being distinguished by different policy issues and tactical decisions that lead to determining the share fraction within that zone.** This is what we have termed our five-zone model. **Each time a new share fraction is created within a profile it affects the motivation of the parties should a particular circumstance occur, which in turn may affect their attitudes to collaboration and may have second-order effects that are not immediately obvious. Consequently, we are not saying that there should be five different share fractions in any share profile — in practice this is a rarity and we recommend simplicity — just five zones for consideration.** The zones (Fig. 8.2), in the order in which they are discussed, are:

* around the target (zone 1)
* cost over-runs (zone 2)
* significant cost over-runs (zone 3)
* cost under-runs (zone 4); and
* significant cost under-runs (zone 5).

To determine the amount that the contractor is paid for any actual costs, look vertically up from the x-axis (actual costs) axis until the 'share profile line' is reached and then across to the y-axis to find the 'amount paid by

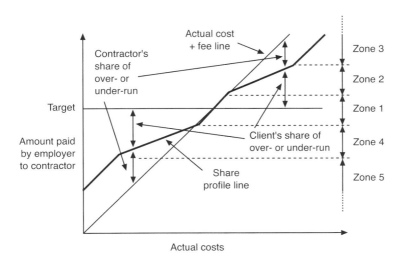

Fig. 8.2. The five-zone model

employer to contractor'. The contractor's additional profit or loss due to the application of the share profile is the difference between the 'share profile' line and the 'actual cost + fee' line.

This section is illustrated with examples of different share profiles taken from real projects and previously published in a paper entitled 'How practitioners set share fractions in target cost contracts' in the *International Journal of Project Management.*[14]

8.7.2   The five-zone model

Zone 1: around the target

A neutral zone, or target band, is the zone within which the contractor is reimbursed its actual costs plus fee only with no share of any over- or under-run compared with the target. This means that the contractor is relatively indifferent about the cost outcome of the contract within the zone. Logically, this means that the zone either straddles the target by up to ±5% of the target or is a band with a range of up to 10% above the target. Technically, it could also be a band with a range of up to 10% below the target. There are a number of potential reasons for having a neutral band:

- The target is negotiated and the two parties cannot agree an exact figure. The band covers the difference. Therefore, in order to gain additional profit, the contractor has to perform better than the client's expectations but will only have its profit margin reduced if it performs worse than its own (the contractor's) expectations. An alternative which has been used in practice is for the elements of work on which agreement cannot be reached to be isolated from the target at tender and for the contractor to be paid on an actual cost plus fee basis only for these elements during the implementation phase.
- The client imposes its estimate on the contractor knowing the likely range of out-turn costs from historical data. Within the zone, the contractor will have turned in an average performance and therefore, so the argument goes, should only be rewarded with average profit, that is that which is already included in the fee. If actual costs plus fee come in above the band, then the contractor starts to lose profit, and it only starts to make additional profit when coming in below the zone.

If these conditions do not exist, then 'zone 1' is a single point, that is the target cost.

This share profile (Fig. 8.3) was used for the purchase of two relatively low-technology school buildings, which were therefore low-risk projects.

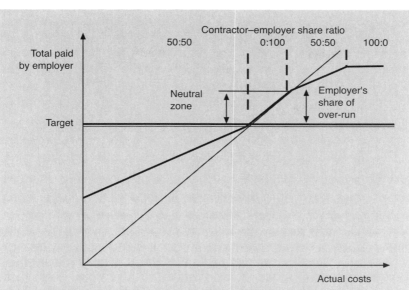

Fig. 8.3. The share profile with a neutral band used on a school building project

An outline design was developed by the client's internal designers and the contractor selected on a number of factors, including its tendered fee percentage but not its tendered target. This was specified by the client because it had good historical data on the cost of similar buildings. Once the contract was entered into, the internal designers were responsible for the detailed design, but the parties value engineered together and the contractor contributed its ideas on buildability. The reasons for the share profile are:

- The neutral band was +5% of the target and, based on good historical data from previous projects, reflected the degree of confidence that the client had in the out-turn costs if procured by a traditional procurement route.
- The scope design was complete and it was a low-complexity building, so the potential for large savings in cost was limited. The contractor was therefore given a large share of any savings below the neutral band in order to provide the motivation for committing sufficient management resources to produce cost savings.
- The client had a fixed budget, so it capped its financial commitment at +10% of the target (although the target could still be adjusted upwards).

> The net result was that this contractual arrangement produced 10% value engineering savings below the target. Because the client and contractor were able to forecast these savings, the client's share, plus much of its contingency, was ploughed back into the project to improve the quality and reduce whole-life costs, for example more durable doors, aluminium- rather than wood-framed windows, etc.

If the contractor's fee is a percentage of actual costs, then the financial motivation will be to have actual costs plus fee at the very top of the zone or band in order to maximize profit. For this reason, one client I know is specifying the contractor's share within zone 1 as the negative of the fee percentage, so that it is genuinely neutral within this zone.

While accepting that the contractor should not suffer unduly within this zone, the client may want to ask itself if it genuinely wishes the contractor to be neutral and, if not, to give some motivation for the contractor to minimize actual costs within this band. It may, therefore, be worthwhile allocating the contractor a comparatively small share of any cost over- or under-run. If the contractor is on a percentage fee then it is suggested that this share should not exceed the contractor's fee percentage by more than 10%.

Zone 2: cost over-runs

This band covers the cost out-turn from the top end of zone 1 to the point at which:

- the client's or the contractor's risk aversion dramatically increases
- cost over-runs, although not desirable, have a realistic likelihood of occurring.

In practice, it is rare for this point to exceed +20% of the target, but it may be considerably less. Within this range, clients will want to allocate the maximum share of any cost over-run to the contractor without:

- The contractor including an excessive risk premium within the target sum; what is judged to be 'excessive' will vary with each client, contractor and project.
- The contractor resorting to traditional adversarial practices, if it becomes apparent that final actual cost plus fee will fall in this zone, by concentrating its efforts into increasing the target through claims and compensation events. It is also worthwhile noting that allocating an excessively high percentage of cost over-run to the contractor may also mean that those representing the client may cease to have the motivation to co-operate. This could lead to other project objectives being undermined.

In section 3.5 the principles of risk sharing and allocation were discussed. Principle 1 of risk allocation and sharing is that 'the extent to which the consequences of a risk are allocated to a party should take into account the overall effect on that party's business, both positive and negative'. A typical contractor is much more risk averse than a typical client, so it implies that the average client should take substantially more of any initial cost over-run than the contractor. However, different contractors are structured differently and make different returns on capital invested, even if they make a similar profit on turnover. This, in turn, affects the amount of risk contingency that different contractors would want included in the target. This suggests that, as a favoured contractor emerges during the tendering process, there may be potential for negotiation between the parties over both the share fractions and the width of zone 2.

So far, the discussion has ignored the next two principles of risk allocation outlined in section 3.5. To recap, these are:

Principle 2. Risk, both positive and negative, should be allocated to a party in proportion to the extent to which it can influence the likelihood of that risk occurring.

Principle 3. Negative risk should be allocated to a party in proportion to the extent to which it can minimize the consequences if that risk occurs, with all things being equal and the second principle taking priority.

If only average productivity risks have been included within the target (which is suggested in section 8.6.3), **this is a good argument for allocating more of any over-run in this zone to the contractor. If, on the other hand, risks predominantly within the control of the client have been included within the target then the opposite is true.**

Zone 2 can effectively be viewed as the 'comfort zone' of cost over-run for both parties. By this we mean that additional expenditure by the client is within acceptable bounds, as is the profit reduction or even loss to the contractor, and the incentive remains to work together to reduce costs.

Much of this comfort is lost in zone 3 as one or the other party may need a cap to protect it from further losses and, in addition, the motivations become less collaborative.

Zone 3: significant cost over-runs

Zone 2 could, at some point, become a significant cost over-run. The point at which this is reached could be determined by a number of factors, for instance:

- The client's risk aversion may suddenly increase, for example in the case of a large one-off project for the client with a fixed budget. In this instance, the client's share of any over-run is often capped at this point, with all normal productivity and neutral risks being taken by the contractor. If this is the case, then the contract might be labelled a GMP contract (see section 8.10 on GMP contracts for a discussion on where to set this cap and the consequences). An example of this is in Fig. 8.3 in the case study of the local authority building two schools. Here, the client had been given sums by government bodies that could not be exceeded, so the client's share of any over-run was capped at this point.

- The contractor's risk aversion increases as, for example, only a certain amount of loss can be absorbed before it starts to have a significant effect on the overall business.
- Prior to signing the contract, neither party expected those risks that are included within the target taking actual costs plus fee beyond this point.

The situation in which the contractor can only absorb a certain amount of loss is not easily compatible with a risk-averse client because the effect of allocating a high percentage of significant cost over-runs to the contractor is that it will include a large risk premium within the target. If the contract is awarded to such a contractor this will not necessarily give the client value for money, although it may be willing to trade this for certainty. A financially strong client may decide to allocate a low share to the contractor, as in the following example (and Fig. 8.4).

The purpose of the works in this case was to install a sewerage pipeline out to sea. Conventionally, this involved digging a trench from a ship, laying the pipe in the trench and then back-filling it. However, the same level of performance could be achieved for potentially a quarter of the cost if directional drilling was used, but this, at the time, was a relatively new technology: indeed there were only two contractors within Europe who offered this service, and both were in strong demand.

However, because the technology was not mature, there was a high risk of equipment breakdowns occurring and, because of the demand and risks associated with the type of work, the contractors were used to working on a cost-reimbursable basis. Despite the technological risk being more within the contractor's control, it was in a strong position to charge a high premium for taking this risk.

The client, however, did not wish to pay a large premium for a risk that might not occur, and recognized that it was in a stronger position financially to take the risk of a cost over-run compared with the contractor, especially as, by the client's standards, it was a relatively small contract. As a result, the client allocated a comparatively small percentage share of any over-run to the contractor, but enough, the client hoped, to motivate the contractor to minimize any over-run. The thinking behind the large share of any savings below the target being allocated to the contractor was that it gave it the opportunity to make

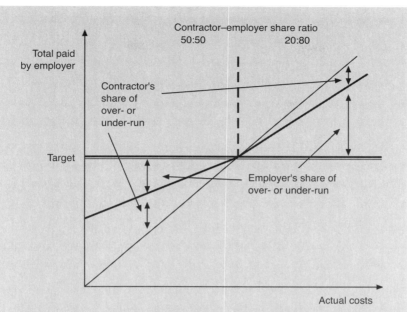

Fig. 8.4. The share profile for a financially strong client and a small contractor

a comparatively large profit if no breakdowns occurred — larger than on a cost-reimbursable contract. This would lead both to a competitive tendered target cost and to the contractor making more effort to prevent equipment breakdowns once the contract was awarded.

Some other interesting nuances of this contract were:

- Up to the physical point at which the rig was set up and ready to drill, the contractor was paid a lump sum. Additionally, at the point at which the drilling was complete, the contractor was paid a lump sum for land-based demobilization. This was because the equipment was coming from Italy and going on to The Netherlands, so it would have been extremely hard to determine where or when actual costs attributable to this project started and finished.
- The client decided to exclude the risk of sea conditions stopping work at the point where the directional drill came up from the seabed and the hole was capped. This was literally expressed as 'sea conditions prevent work being undertaken on the barge'. Consequently, the risk of reduced productivity was shared within the target, while stopped work was an additional risk.

> • There was no bonus for early completion and minimal liquidated damages for delay. This was both because the contractor was given an incentive to finish early as it reduced its time-based costs — and hence gave it a share of the cost savings — and because it had other work to go on to. The contractor therefore did not need additional motivation.

Other clients may decide to limit the downside for the contractor by including a minimum fee, which is designed to cover most or all of the contractor's overheads, but with no profit element. This has been observed where there is an over-riding need to continue working in a collaborative manner with the same contractor. This protection is often viewed as a last resort and is coupled with a strong incentive to achieve cost under-runs in zones 4 and 5.

Finally, there is the issue of including what are normally client risks within the target. These risks have, almost by definition, a low likelihood of occurring to this magnitude and may well be beyond either party's control. As intimated earlier in section 8.6.3, this practice introduces a gamble into the contract, which is best avoided. If clients do insist on including these risks within the target, the relative financial strengths of the parties provide a guide to the appropriate share fraction.

Zone 4: cost under-runs

This band covers the cost out-turn from the low end of zone 1 — which could be the target if there is no neutral zone — to the point at which greater cost savings are made than would normally be expected, that is it covers cost under-runs that have a realistic likelihood of occurring. The general principle is that the contractor is rewarded for better than average performance in reducing costs with better than average profits. On one-off projects, a survey in the USA[15] and another of projects I observed in the UK indicate that savings of 10% are potentially feasible against a realistic target, but that more is unlikely. However, this depends on the stage at which the contractor is brought into the project and the contract signed.

Within zone 4, the client wants to allocate the minimum share of any cost under-run to the contractor without:

• the contractor adding an amount to the target so that it can make a normal profit
• undermining the contractor's motivation to actively pursue cost reductions and inadvertently focusing its efforts on increasing the target and/or increasing actual costs because of a high fee percentage.

However, **too low a contractor's share**, as Perry and Barnes[12] have shown, **will tend to motivate higher values of the fee, which in turn further reduces the contractor's motivation to drive down cost** because the contract approaches a cost-reimbursable one.

All of these points reinforce the argument for ensuring that the actual cost component of the target is realistic and a normal level of profit is included within the fee (see section 8.6).

If the works are already designed, then the contractor will have to work much harder to achieve reductions in actual cost, compared with a design and build contract. In the former case, a 40% share to the contractor is likely to be the minimum to motivate it to commit sufficient resources to look for cost reductions. In the latter, a number of contractors have indicated to us that this could be reduced to 20%, but only if the intention is for any savings to be ploughed back into the project, giving the contractor another 'bite' at earning a share of savings on actual costs.

Zone 5: Significant cost under-runs

This zone starts at the point at which greater cost savings are made than would normally be expected. This could be for a combination of reasons:

- exceptional management, predominantly by the contractor
- high initial or adjusted target
- none or very few of the expected risks included within the target materialize.

In projects in which the cost reductions are expected to be predominantly in the control of the contractor, some clients have held out the promise of a higher share of any savings than in zone 4 in order to encourage contractors to strive for large savings. This could be through good value and risk management, and/or programming. This ploy is sometimes used by clients to balance out a high share fraction given to the contractor for significant over-runs in zone 3. However, we question whether this actually increases the motivation of the contractor in practice.

However, some clients feel that if zone 5 is achieved the most likely reason is not solely, or even mainly, good management by the contractor. For example, on a real tunnelling contract the ground conditions were better than expected, so leading to the lion's share of £4 million savings on a £24 million contract going to the contractor. In other cases, clients negotiate the target with a single contractor. Even when they have attempted to check the realism of the target they lack the comfort of competitive tenders and worry that too high a target has been agreed. Furthermore, I know of some contracts in which the clients have felt that the target cost adjustment has favoured the contractor and, occasionally, run out of control.

This may tempt clients to cap the contractor's share of savings in this zone, but this nullifies *any* motivation to seek further savings. Instead, it is suggested that **for zone 5 an equal or lower share fraction than that used in zone 4 is recommended but with the percentage of savings allocated to the contractor set significantly above its fee percentage.**

The share profile in Fig. 8.5 was used on the project in the City of London described in the case study in section 7.5.1. To recap briefly, the contractor had initially shored up, on a cost-reimbursable basis, a slab below street level and above Bank underground station where the concrete had spalled. The slab was replaced under a target cost contract, with the target agreed between the parties on an 'open book' basis, that is the contractor opened its books to reveal all its calculations and subcontractors' quotations. In reality, although it was client designed, the contractor had a large input into the design as it was method driven. Consequently, the contractor understood the project risks and constraints and the client understood the contractor's problems, methods and costs. It was therefore felt by all parties that:

• Around the target (zones 2 and 4) any over- or under-run should be split equally.

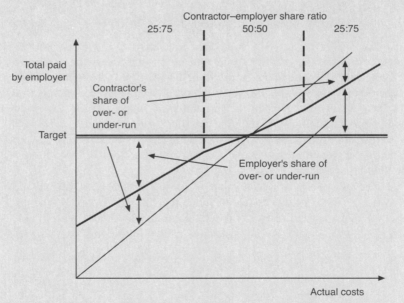

Fig. 8.5.   The share profile for a medium-risk project with a financially strong client

- If actual costs escalated by more than 10% with no adjustment to the target, then both parties had seriously overlooked something, in which case the financially stronger party should bear the majority of the risk in zone 3. In this case, it was London Underground Ltd, which was spending £1 billion or more per annum on construction and engineering compared with the contractor, which, at the time, had a turnover of about £50 million (or say around £1 million profit).
- If circumstances went the other way, and actual costs entered zone 5 by being less than 90% of the target, then the client should take the majority of the benefit.

When agreeing the target, there are, however, two interesting points to note. First, some of the quotations from subcontractors for different packages were higher than expected. The contractor decided to retender these packages in order to get better value for the client, but these costs were not tied down at the signing of the contract and the contractor was taking the risk of high subcontract costs. Second, the parties could not agree costs for certain elements of the works that the contractor was doing itself. Rather than have a neutral band for zone 1, the client agreed to reimburse these items at cost as actual costs could be separated out from other work elements: in effect, they were paid for as a provisional item.

8.7.3 Other issues to consider when setting the share profile

When setting the share profile, we suggest that there are three other issues to consider:

- the effects down the supply chain
- the effects of time
- the perception of sharing.

If it is the client's and/or the contractor's intention to use target cost contracts with their principal subcontractors, then a sufficient share of savings needs to be allocated to the contractor, so that it can in turn share the savings with the subcontractor.

The effects of time may vary the share fractions for two reasons:

- Market conditions will vary between industries and over time. What might motivate a contractor in a depression may not motivate it in a boom.
- The opportunities for cost reductions and the likelihood of the occurrence of downside risk may both reduce over time. For instance, I am aware of one client who entered into 5-year term framework agreements for fairly

standard types of work. Each package was let as a target cost contract with the target built up from a schedule of input rates based on previous contract costs. In the first year, there is good opportunity to innovate, but also more risk. As time progresses each will reduce, so in the first year the client took 80% of cost over- and under-runs; in the second year 65%; in the third year 50%; in the fourth year 35%; and in the final year 20%.

Finally, perception is important. Earlier in this chapter (see sections 8.3 and 8.4), it was discussed how target cost contracts do not necessarily sit in the middle of the risk-sharing spectrum and therefore that the concept of risk sharing does not necessarily equate to sharing in equal proportions.

Particularly when target contracts are used in a partnering arrangement the initial perception may be that cost savings or over-runs should be shared equally. I hope that it has been demonstrated that this is not always realistic, although it may be appropriate in certain circumstances. The parties to a contract, whether or not they are partners in a broader arrangement, need to know and accept the reasons behind the share profile otherwise they may perceive it as unfair, thereby posing a threat to collaboration from the outset. Achieving a commonly accepted perception of the share profile implies that room for negotiation should be accommodated.

8.7.4   Conclusions on setting the share profile

This section has identified five generic zones for building up a share profile in a target cost contract and discussed the considerations within each zone. There has been some discussion of the interplay between the zones. This conclusion draws these considerations together so that the reader can construct a share profile.

Point 1. While the maximum number of share fractions in one share profile observed in practice was four, we suggest that, **in the pursuit of simplicity, the aim should be to have as few share fractions as possible within any share profile**. This is because, as the assessment of the zones has shown, each step change in the share profile produces a different type of motivation. We therefore suggest that the starting point should be a constant share fraction, with new fractions added only when there are sound reasons for doing so. On many contracts the easiest zone to eliminate will be the neutral zone 1. If the two conditions for a neutral zone are not met — that the parties can agree a target or that the client is not specifying the band on a historical basis — then this zone can be eliminated in favour of a single point target cost.

Point 2. For zones 2 and 4, encompassing the normally anticipated variance of cost from target, a 50:50 split is suggested as a good starting point. This provides a strong motivation on both parties to reduce costs, and balances a good motivation on the contractor to manage the work well to produce a reasonable return to the client. However, the exact share fraction within each zone will depend on the capability of each party to minimize cost over-runs in zone 2 and maximize cost savings in zone 4. It is suggested that the contractor's share fraction should therefore be between 30% and 70% in these zones.

Point 3. My own recent research and earlier research by Perry *et al.*[5] indicates that practitioners have used the whole range of share fractions. However, the work by Perry and Barnes[12] showed that both very low and very high values of the contractor's share have adverse effects, for example less motivation to reduce costs, coupled with higher fees in the former case, and fewer benefits from cost reductions to the client, coupled with higher targets in the latter case. Contractor shares of 100% or zero in zone 3 may be judged necessary on some contracts to cap the client's commitment or protect the contractor from large losses respectively. If those conditions are not present, then **it is suggested that the contractor's share fraction within zone 3 for significant over-runs is kept within a band no wider than the extremes of 20–80%.**

A *criticism* of this model has been that the advice and thinking behind it is too general.[†] However, it is much more specific than any other published literature that we have found on setting share profiles,[16] and in particular that based on utility theory.[17–22] We have criticized that approach as having little or no application in practice in a paper published in the *International Journal of Project Management.*[14]

The conclusion to this section is additional **key implementation point 3: think intelligently about the setting of the share fractions that make up the share profile because they affect the risk included within the target and the motivations of the parties once it is awarded. Use the five-zone model as an aid for doing this.**

> **Review question 4**   Identify a project on which it would be suitable to use a target cost contract. Using the guidance in this section, develop a share profile for it. Identify another project with, if possible, markedly different characteristics and develop a share profile for this. [Note: the two profiles should probably not look the same!]

[†]Referees of the *International Journal of Project Management,* to which a paper on which this text is derived was submitted.

8.8 Deciding when the contractor's share of any over-run is paid

This section briefly discusses four alternatives for when the contractor's share of any cost over-run relative to the target is paid. This does not normally need to be considered for a cost under-run, as the contractor is usually paid actual cost plus fee as the project progresses. At the end of the contract, when all actual costs have been accounted for and the final target has been agreed, the contractor is simply paid its share of any under-run.

For each of the four alternatives, the contractor is paid actual costs plus fee up to the point at which the target is reached.

8.8.1 Alternative 1

The contractor continues to be paid all actual costs plus fee even when the target is exceeded. When all actual costs have been accounted for and the final target has been agreed, the contractor simply pays back the client's share of any over-run. This is the policy adopted in the target cost options of the NEC Engineering and Construction Contract. This has the advantage that it is simple to administer but does involve a degree of trust from the client (but, it could be argued, no more than a contractor typically shows to a client when constructing an asset for it). I would suggest that this policy is appropriate when:

(a) The contractor has a good financial management system and people to operate it, so that the final account — actual costs plus fee and target — can be agreed with reasonable speed. Therefore the contractor will not be holding client money for a long time. I would argue that these criteria should be met before entering into a cost-based contract regardless.
(b) The size of any potential over-run will not significantly hurt the contractor, that is it is able to bear it. This suggests that this policy is not suitable for large projects relative to the contractor's size.
(c) The client is a repeat order client, so has the 'carrot' of repeat order business.
(d) The contractor is reputable and so would potentially have its reputation harmed if it did not return the money.

8.8.2 Alternative 2

The other extreme is that, once actual cost plus fee exceeds the target, all excess is held by the client until the 'final account' is agreed, whereupon the contractor's share of any over-run is paid to it. In essence, it is a similar situation to that under a priced-based contract, as the contractor is financing any over-run until agreement is reached. The client will pay for this. It also does not encourage rapid assessment by the client of any adjustments to the target.

8.8.3   Alternative 3

The middle way is one in which the contractor is reimbursed actual cost plus fee minus the contractor's share, that is the client's share, of any over-run compared with the target as the contract is progressing. This has the advantage that neither party, in theory, is holding money that will ultimately be paid back to the other. The 'in theory' is because the adjustment of the target is likely to lag behind the actual costs incurred, so the contractor will be slightly out of pocket on a monthly basis. At each assessment date, there is a reconciliation between the adjusted target (from the previous assessment date) and current actual cost plus fee. This encourages good financial administration of the contract but may be administratively burdensome for smaller projects.

> The Millennium Stadium in Cardiff is the home of the Welsh Rugby Union and was built under the NEC Engineering and Construction Contract, option C: Target contract with activity schedules. It was, in effect, a GMP contract (see section 8.10) as significant risks were transferred to the contractor and the client's share of any over-run was capped. Two other amendments were made to the standard contract:
>
> - The cost consultants representing the Welsh Rugby Union prescribed much more how the contract was to be financially administered by writing in additional clauses, although this could have been done in the specification or 'Works Information' in NEC terminology. This was to ensure that actual costs and the target were as up to date as possible.
> - The contractor was not paid actual cost plus fee above the GMP.
>
> It is common knowledge that this contract over-ran the target of £120 million or so by some £20–25 million and is one of the reasons for the demise of the contractor. Bearing this in mind, the client and its consultants' decision to amend the conditions of contract seem justified!

8.8.4   Alternative 4

Similar to alternative 3 above, but with the following exceptions:

(a) The contractor is paid as the contract progresses according to a pre-agreed cash-flow profile, with the reconciliation coming later. I did not recommend this approach in section 7.6.2 as it does not encourage good financial administration.

(b) Payment of the client's share of any over-run is based on forecast final actual cost plus fee. While it could be argued that it encourages good forecasting, in reality it actually encourages the contractor to exaggerate forecast final actual cost plus fee to improve cash flow.

The author, as the reader might have gathered, is not very much in favour of this approach!

I would recommend either alternative 1 or 3 depending on the project size. Regardless of which is taken, additional **key implementation point 4 is: decide when and how any over-run of the target is paid to or back from the contractor.** However, this only becomes relevant in the case of a cost over-run, which, if all other key implementation points are applied, should not happen!

8.9   Adjusting the target

For changes to cost resulting from client-owned risks or responsibilities, **there is a need to calculate any change in the target,** for two reasons:

- First, to maintain the incentive, as failure to do this can undermine the whole concept of aligned objectives as the contract effectively reverts to a cost-reimbursable one.
- Second, if the target is not changed as a result of breaches of the contract by the client or changes in the scope of the contract, then at the end of the contract the contractor could sue for damages arising from that breach or change!

This is **key implementation point 5: calculate and agree any change in the target as soon as possible after an event that causes an upward adjustment (and ideally before),** for example when new work is added in, quality is changed or a risk materializes.

While there is some incentive for the contractor to maximize any upward changes in the target, evaluation should be easier than in a price-based contract for a number of reasons:

- It allows greater evaluation of the realism of the target (see section 8.6 generally).
- Because all the actual costs are open to scrutiny, the additional actual costs, both already incurred and forecast, are known. However, this presupposes that a good financial management system is in place (see section 7.6.4) and that the client or its consultants understand:
    - how the contractor's actual costs were originally built up (see section 8.6.2)
    - what risks are included within the target (see section 8.6.3).
- As Kahn[23] points out, the adjustment is not as contentious as a price-based contract, because the adjustment to the target affects the financial outcome of the contract only in proportion to the share fractions used. However, this presupposes that the contractor's share of any under- or over-run is sufficient for it to concentrate on reducing costs rather than pushing up the target. This means intelligent setting of the share profile (see section 8.6).

If the above 'presuppositions' are not in place, then the adjustment can become contentious!

Other reasons why the assessment could become contentious include:

- The definitions, which describe the threshold or criteria for adjusting the target, are subjective and therefore open to discussion. The classic example of this is one in which the client's designers are responsible for developing the detail of the design and arguments arise over what are 'design developments' and what are 'changes in scope or quality'. Consequently, **any special risks included or excluded from the target need to be defined sufficiently tightly to avoid arguments** of this sort.
- The method for adjusting the target breaks down as an accurate reflection of how the contractor incurs costs. For instance, bills of quantities are used when there are time effects.
- Once the contract is started, there is insufficient programming information and/or attention paid to the programme to either:
  - understand how the change in permanent works affects methodology, which in turn affects resources used, which in turn affects direct actual costs
  - calculate the time effect of changes and their consequent impact on indirect actual costs, for example time-related preliminaries etc.
- The level of change is too great for the assessment of target adjustment to keep pace. The target therefore loses its significance as the contract reverts to a cost-reimbursable one. In this case, a cost-reimbursable contract should have been chosen initially!

Providing that all the points mentioned so far in this section have been addressed to some extent, then my research has indicated not only that it is relatively easy to administer the adjustment of the target, but also that the overall financial administration of the contract is simplified.

> **Review question 5**   What changes are in the administration of your projects are necessary to enable you to use target cost contracts, or, if you already are using them, to administer them better?

8.10 Guaranteed maximum price contracts

This section discusses what is meant by the term 'guaranteed maximum price (GMP) contract'.

GMP contracts are often used for projects in which there is a developmental aspect to the works and the client has a strictly limited budget. There is no precise definition of what a GMP contract is, but it would seem typically to have the following four characteristics:

(a) At some point, the client's contribution to any over-run is capped. That is, there is a cap above a defined percentage of the target on the client's financial commitment (in zone 3 of the five-zone model; see section 8.7.2).

(b) The more uncontrollable risks, for example weather and ground conditions, or third-party risks, for example access to a third party's property, are included within the target, for which the client will pay a premium (see section 8.6.3).

Birkby,[24] a procurement lawyer, asks readers to 'think hard about a guaranteed maximum price contract. It sounds attractive, but does it really make sense for the supplier to take all the risk? On some projects it will work, and the price will be a good one, but any supplier entering into a GMP will price for the risks, which may be expensive for the client.'

Boultwood,[25] a director of the Turner and Townsend Group's contract services, writes 'The client should not expect a tight fit GMP as this will be reflective of the risk transfer. In current markets (2001) and with recent experiences, the GMP is likely to be inflated. No client would want to be working with his contractor on the wrong side of the pain/gain equation.'

(c) The target is adjusted by the mechanisms of the contract for what would otherwise be breaches of contract (see section 8.9). For example, if the client does not provide something at the agreed time and there is no remedy or compensation provided in the contract, then the contractor could ultimately sue for the effect on its actual costs plus fee, regardless of whether the original GMP is exceeded. This, in turn, increases the GMP.

(d) Increases in the scope or quality of the works are often made only by joint agreement and funded from realized or forecast savings in actual cost. This means that normally the contractor forecasts the savings of which the client has a share. The client reinvests its share in the contract, which increases the target and GMP, and the contractor has another opportunity to earn profit on the turnover and any subsequent savings. There is a balance here for the contractor: if its forecasts of savings are too conservative, then it will potentially lose another opportunity to earn profit. On the other hand, if they are too high, the contractor will have to bear the cost of the over-run relative to the target and GMP. Likewise, before a change is instigated the financial effects have to be forecast accurately so that the change to the target and GMP can be agreed.

The last two points mean that **the term 'guaranteed maximum price' contract is potentially misleading, because there are still mechanisms to adjust the target and GMP for defined, if limited, reasons. The client's maximum final expenditure is not therefore guaranteed.**

A question for practitioners is: at what figure, expressed as a percentage of the target, should the cap or GMP be set? If it is too low, the tendering contractors include a large risk premium in their tendered or negotiated target. If it is too high and any adjustments are made to the target, then the client's budget may be exceeded. Therefore, the client needs to estimate both the target and by how much it will be adjusted. However, the target only becomes known when contractors submit their tenders and so, it could be argued, the cap or GMP may then need to be recalculated. However, because the tenderers are partly basing their target on their exposure to risk, any adjustment to the cap or GMP means that tenderers will then want to revise their target. This suggests that the target and the point at which the client's commitment is capped are likely to be the result of a process of negotiation. This has been observed in practice, but some clients are limited in their ability to do this because of public accountability and procurement law constraints.

An alternative for clients with fixed and/or limited budgets is for the client to state its minimum performance/functional requirements, plus a hierarchical menu of desirable attributes or features, and then ask contractors what they can obtain for the budget. The contractor that offers the best deal is the one chosen.

One final comment on capping a client's commitment, especially for those who have turned straight to this section and not read section 8.7 first: **as soon as it is perceived** by the client and its representatives **that actual costs plus fee will exceed the cap, its financial motivation to help reduce actual costs is minimal**. Once this is lost, and the contractor spots it, it could well be perceived to be more in the contractor's interests to focus attention on increasing the target. Therefore, unless there is an absolute maximum budget, it may be wise for the client to continue taking some share of any significant cost over-run, albeit at a much reduced percentage compared with that for normal cost over-runs (zone 2 of the five-zone model).

With the characteristics identified at the start of this section, it can be seen that 'GMP contracts' are a subset or special case of target cost contracts. From the analysis in the rest of this chapter, **it follows that the management of a GMP contract has the same key implementation points as those required for managing target cost contracts**. An unrealistic target/GMP, as well as failure to agree on forecasts of savings and forecasts of the costs of changes in scope and/or quality, can lead to the whole concept of a GMP contract breaking down.

Review question 6   What are the advantages and disadvantages to a client of the GMP approach? Try and identify a project that is suitable for this procurement route.

8.11 Prime contracting‡

Prime contracting is as much a way of working as a method of procurement. It was initially promoted by the Ministry of Defence (MoD), and in particular its Defence Estates Organization (DEO). A prime contractor has been defined as 'one having overall responsibility for the management and delivery of the project on time, within budget (defined over the lifetime of the project) and fit for the purpose for which it was intended, including demonstrating that operating cost parameters can be met'.[27] In essence, in procurement terms for one-off capital projects, the main features of prime contracting are:

- The prime contractor is selected early on a preferred contractor basis (see section 4.3.3).
- The prime contractor is selected on a management contract basis (see section 4.3.4), so it co-ordinates the design and does very little, if any, design or physical work itself.
- It involves a target cost pricing mechanism with a cap/GMP (see previous section) once the scope of the works is sufficiently defined for a target to be agreed.
- It involves much earlier and greater input into design and programming by the prime contractor's selected supply chain.
- It has a strong emphasis on whole-life costs rather than just capital costs (see Appendices 1 and 5).

Prime contracting therefore brings together other developments in procurement under a single banner.

Prime contracting was trialled by the MoD on two sports facilities projects with approximate capital costs of £10 million and £4 million each. Compared with their benchmarks, both projects achieved time savings (of 2.6% and 20%) and predicted savings on whole-life costs (of 14.3% and 7.18%), as well as greater user satisfaction. However, both projects exceeded their benchmark for capital costs (by 5.51% and 6.02%). Although the overall result is good and to be commended, it is my view that the publicity received and the effect on government procurement policy is out of all proportion to the success and size of the trials!

---

‡The text of this section is predominantly derived from reference 26, although other sources, where used, are cited. I would also like to acknowledge help in preparing this section from Richard Patterson, Senior Contracts Officer with Mott MacDonald.

There are seven stated underlying principles[26] which make up prime contracting, which I have slightly rearranged into an approximate time-based sequence, as well as adding an additional principle/stage, as follows:

(a) *Define client values.* This is done in two ways:
  (i)   It requires the client to define its need in terms of outputs or, more precisely, outcomes and any constraints including aesthetic and/or environmental considerations.
  (ii) The client uses the whole-life cost of the asset, discounted back to a set date, as the most meaningful measure of financial cost, rather than the capital cost of construction alone. Benchmark figures, derived from previous data from previous similar projects, are used as the basis for comparison.

  Effectively, this means using the tools of the value planning phase of value management to produce a statement of requirements and constraints, and using benchmarking to establish a base whole-life cost (see Appendices 1 and 6).

(b) *Compete through superior underlying value.* This means that the prime contractor is selected on its ability to deliver value, as defined by the client in the previous stage. This will be a combination of quality/functionality and cost to the client. This does not mean competition by the lowest tendered price as the prime contractor is selected before the scope and quality of the works is finalized. However, the prime contractor will be partly selected on its margin or fee, as well as its project management capability, technical competence, financial resources and existing supply chain and ability to manage it (see Appendix 4).

(c) *Establish supplier relationships.* Having been chosen partly because of its suppliers' ability to deliver value, the implication is that the prime contractor's longer-term relationship with its supply chain is either in place or being put in place. Initially, the high-level project brief is fleshed out by the prime contractor in consultation with the key supply chain members to give a range of design concepts. The one chosen for further development optimizes functionality and whole-life costs and is signed off by the client and taken on to the next stage at which the next principle is put into effect.

(d) *Integrate project activities.* Once the design concept is chosen, it is then broken down into work elements, for example groundwork, frame and envelope, internal finishes. These elements are then allocated to a 'cluster' of designers, subcontractors and suppliers with the appropriate expertise.

  Initially, the high-level interfaces between elements/clusters are defined by the prime contractor. The interfaces within the cluster are co-ordinated by a cluster leader — a lead designer or principal subcontractor — and by the prime contractor between the clusters. While there is obviously reiteration, the ideal is to define the high-level interfaces first and then work down into the detail.

The cluster members work together to develop the detailed design, with the emphasis switching to joint programming as the time for construction approaches. In addition, the cluster leader becomes responsible for quality assurance of the second-tier suppliers. Once the quality assurance system is in place, the prime contractor audits the system only to check compliance.

(e) *Manage costs collaboratively.* The cluster team works backwards from the functional requirements and maximum market price to develop the design. This is called 'target costing'. Different design options are generated and evaluated to satisfy the functional criteria for the element. Risk management is used to increase certainty, thereby reducing each supply chain member's 'hidden' contingencies, which would ultimately be passed up to — or recirculated — to the client (see Appendix 2). In addition, the client's contingency funds are significantly reduced. Value engineering techniques are used to take out cost without undermining functionality (see Appendix 5). The focus of this approach is to take out whole-life costs and uncertainty during the design stage, rather than once construction has started.

At some point in this stage, when the design is sufficiently developed for the client to be sure that it will have the project with the whole-life cost profile it wants, the target is agreed on an open book basis, that is the client or its consultants have full access to the prime contractor's, subcontractors' and suppliers' calculations etc. (Fig. 8.6). The target therefore appears to evolve rather than to be set at a particular point. Throughout the process, the client will be making decisions, advised by the prime contractor and its

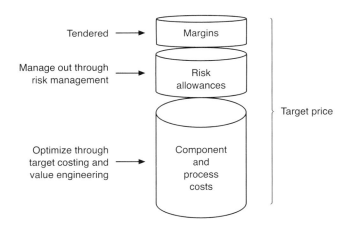

Fig. 8.6.   Agreeing the target price under prime contracting (modified from reference 26)

supply chain, which will trade off higher capital costs with lower whole-life costs and/or increased functionality.

(f) *Develop continuous improvement.* The principles and techniques of total quality management are used to generate continuous improvement. This could involve using process mapping to take out waste both in the building's processes and in the process of delivering it. On one-off projects, the scope for doing this is limited compared with on a series of similar projects undertaken by the same prime contractor and its supply chain. Another aspect of this approach is that it is more participative, seeking to utilize the expertise of the entire supply chain, which helps facilitate the collaborative management of project costs described previously, and is related to the next principle.

(g) *Mobilize and develop people.* This principally involves:
   (i) visible and systematic commitment from the top
   (ii) facilitation for project teams, both in specific techniques, such as value engineering and risk management, and in team-building workshops
   (iii) training in new skills
   (iv) economic incentives, both the use of incentives on the project and the increased likelihood of repeat order business, although these are, it appears, applied to companies rather than individuals.

(h) *Proving.* The last stage and principle of the process is that, after the work is complete, the prime contractor has to prove that the estimated operating costs of the asset are as forecast. This involves the prime contractor being responsible for the facilities management of the asset and monitoring costs for at least an annual cycle of operation, whereupon the asset is handed over to the client.

Many of these and other management issues not listed above are also key implementation points of target and cost-based contracts and common features of partnering. Two additional features not mentioned in this commentary so far are:

• Strong client involvement in the process to ensure that what is designed matches its requirements.
• A series of 'gates' — or management meetings — at which progress is reviewed and the next stage of the project is sanctioned. 'Hard gates' are where the next stage is either sanctioned, because everything in the previous stage is complete, or not. These typically involve contractual commitments. 'Soft gates' allow for the next stage to proceed even though some work in the previous stage may need to be finished or reworked.

In the trial projects, this resulted in minimal client-instigated changes once the contract was under way.

8.11.1 Procurement and contractual issues

The *Handbook of Supply Chain Management*[26] is an excellent guide to the vital 'softer' process elements required to support relationships through the supply chain and prime contracting. It provides criteria to a reasonable level for selecting the prime contractor. It also states that 'normal' bonds and retention were not used and there were not any significant damages for late completion in the trial projects. However, both the *Handbook* and other articles have been remarkably vague on the actual commercial terms used for the two pilot projects. For instance, to my knowledge, it has not been publicly stated:

- how or if the prime contractor's and its supply chains' significant input before the contract sum/target was agreed and paid for
- whether the' target' applies to capital costs or to whole-life costs
- whether a GMP cap on costs was actually used and, if so, how it was set
- when and how savings, whether on capital or whole-life costs, were shared between the client and the prime contractor and then down the supply chain
- the criteria for adjusting the target, which may have applied to capital costs or whole-life costs, and how it was adjusted
- what would have happened if the operational costs had exceeded the forecasts at the end of the proving stage.

A cynic might argue that, were it not for a large repeat order client, which ensured that the two projects had a great deal of publicity, then the projects might not have run as well as they did.

A suggested contractual framework for prime contracting

Patterson[28] suggests that the NEC family of contracts (see Appendix 3) is particularly suited for use as the conditions of contract for prime contracting through the supply chain, with:

- the prime contractor and principal subcontractors employed under option E: Time-based contract of the NEC Professional Services Contract up to the point at which the target can be agreed
- the prime contractor being employed under option C: Target contract with activity schedules of the NEC Engineering and Construction Contract
- the principal subcontractors being employed under the option C: Target contract with activity schedules of the NEC Engineering and Construction Subcontract
- the principal consultants being employed under option C: Target contract of the NEC Professional Services Contract

---

- other subcontractors being employed either under option A: Priced contract with activity schedules of the NEC Engineering and Construction Contract or the NEC Engineering and Construction Short Subcontract.

A simple means of adapting the NEC contracts has been suggested elsewhere[29] to provide for payment on a reimbursable basis up to the point at which a target for future work is agreed and on a target cost basis thereafter.

The fortunes of the client, the prime contractor and the principal subcontractors and consultants can then be tied together into a project alliance (see Chapter 9) by using the NEC Partnering agreement. One of the key performance indicators could be for operational costs against which the parties are jointly rewarded.

My **conclusion on prime contracting** is that, with the exception of delivering to the client's capital cost benchmark, the two pilot projects *were* a success. They incorporated many of the techniques used elsewhere on partnering projects and processes taken from the manufacturing industry. As demonstrated in the manufacturing sector, and on strategic partnering relationships, more significant benefits only come from working together over the long term, rather than on a single project. However, as previously stated, my view is that the publicity received and the effect on government procurement policy was out of all proportion to the success and the size of the trials!

The proponents of prime contracting evangelize it as the only way to integrate the supply chain. Yet the final paragraph of the *Handbook of Supply Chain Management*,[26] produced by the Tavistock Institute, which studied the trial, states: 'single point models and PFI (Private Finance Initiative), strategic partnering, construction management and even traditional forms of procurement all have their contribution to make in achieving integrated construction supply.[§] No single procurement route can be held up as providing the perfect solution.' The good news is that because prime contracting is contractually so vaguely defined, government organizations that are under guidance from the Treasury's Office of Government Commerce to use either the private finance initiative, design and build or prime contracting routes can adapt the last approach to suit their circumstances and project and still call it prime contracting!

[§]The author notes that 'achieving integrated construction supply' is a means to an end and not an end in itself.

Review question 7   What principles of 'best practice' can you take from prime contracting and apply to the projects you are involved in?

8.12 Conclusion

This chapter started off with an overview and defined some terminologies associated with target cost contracts. It then discussed the nature of risk sharing in target cost contracts, concluding that they can cover the full spectrum of risk allocation depending on which risks are included or excluded from the target; how different shares of over- and under-runs are allocated to the parties; and how actual costs and the fee are defined. The risk allocation can, therefore, be tailored to suit the client's requirements and project characteristics.

This led on to the boundary conditions for using target cost contracts. No absolute boundary conditions were established for using price-based contracts instead, although a number of circumstances in which it may be more appropriate were identified. Target cost contracts have traditionally been used in less extreme circumstances than pure cost-reimbursable contracts. The main reason for using target cost contracts, particularly with the rise of partnering, is the introduction of a contractually meaningful target and the alignment of motivations, achieved by the sharing of risk and reward. For a target cost to be agreed, the scope of the works must be sufficiently defined. Therefore, **key implementation point 1 of target cost contracts is to use them in the right circumstances**. This is key implementation point 1 for cost-reimbursable contracts. Subsequent key implementation points are in addition to those for cost-reimbursable contracts (see Chapter 7).

The start of the next section highlighted how other literature had emphasized the importance of an accurate target. By exploring the components of the target — base costs, risk allowances and the fee — this book has been more explicit in that additional **key implementation point 2 for target cost contracts is that the client should satisfy itself with the realism of the overall target, by:**

(a) **Evaluating and being satisfied with the realism of the actual cost component of the target (the base estimate).**

(b) **Identifying, agreeing contingencies for and clearly allocating specified risks within or outside the target in accordance with the principles of risk allocation and sharing.**

(c) **Only agreeing a level of fee that is consistent with the returns that the contractor would earn under a price-based contract, especially when the fee is expressed as a percentage of actual costs incurred.**

A range of 'what if?' scenarios for out-turn actual cost compared with the original target and adjusted target should be generated to, at the very least, inform the selection of the contractor.

The chapter then presented our five-zone model for setting the share fractions that make up a share profile in a target cost contract. It explored the circumstances, effects on motivations and consequences of different share fractions in each of the five zones. Despite there being five zones, our general advice is to have as few share fractions as possible within any share profile. This is because each change in the share profile produces a different type of motivation.

Additional key implementation point 3 is: think intelligently about the setting of the share fractions that make up the share profile because they affect the risk included within the target and the motivations of the parties once it is awarded. Use the five-zone model as an aid for doing this.

Additional key implementation point 4 is: decide when and how any over-run of the target is paid to or back from the contractor. This only becomes relevant if there is a cost over-run relative to the target. Then it can become very relevant, particularly in the case of a significant over-run!

Additional key implementation point 5 is: calculate and agree any change in the target as soon as possible after an event that causes an upward adjustment, and ideally before. This is because failure to do so may mean that the contract effectively reverts to a cost-reimbursable contract, losing the benefit of aligned objectives.

Guaranteed maximum price (GMP) contracts were then discussed. Essentially, they are target cost contracts with a cap or GMP set at some point above the target. At this point, all the risk transfers to the contractor. There were three principal conclusions to this section:

- The key implementation points for target cost contracts also apply for GMP contracts.
- The term can be misleading as the cap can still be adjusted upwards, therefore *not* guaranteeing a maximum price to the client.
- Having a cap can lead to a high risk premium being paid by the client, which may not offer value for money, and may undermine a collaborative approach.

The prime contracting approach was then discussed. It is as much a way of working as it is a procurement route and, as such, incorporates, under one banner, many concepts of partnering best practice. In procurement terms, it essentially consists of:

- the client issuing an outcome specification and whole-life cost profile
- a contractor being selected on the basis of its fee level and expertise, especially with respect to its supply chain management
- the design being developed by the prime contractor and its supply chain with a target cost being agreed prior to construction.

However, much of the commercial details of how the contractor and its supply chain are recompensed and rewarded are still, publicly at least, undefined.

Now draw a learning map.

References

1. Schneider M. *Cost reimbursable contracts*. Draft of PhD thesis (photocopied), 1986.
2. Ibbs C. W. and Ashley D. B. Impact of various construction contract clauses. *J. Constr. Engng Mngmnt*, Sept. 1987, **113**, No. 3, 501–27.
3. Blyth A. H. Design of incentive contracts, basic principles. *Aeronaut. J.*, 1969, **73**, 119–24.
4. Walker D. The influence of incentive provisions on project management. *Aeronaut. J.*, 1969, **79**, 125–8.
5. Perry J. G. *et al. Target and cost reimbursable contracts: Part A: A study of their use and implications; Part B: Management and financial implications*. CIRIA, London, 1982, CIRIA Report 85.
6. Canes M. E. The simple economics of incentive contracting: note. *Am. Econ. Rev.*, 1975, **65**, 478–83.
7. Rosenfield Y. and Geltner D. Cost-plus and incentive contracting: some false benefits and inherent drawbacks. *Constr. Mngmnt Econ.*, 1991, **9**, 481–92.
8. Fisher R. and Ury W. *Getting to yes: negotiating an agreement without giving in*, 2nd edn. The Random House Group, London, 1992.
9. Kamp D. *A guide to better management: how to get to 'win–win'*. Soundfix Audio Publishing, Milton Keynes, UK, 1998.
10. Carmody D. B. Incentives/penalties for time and cost control: the owner's viewpoint. *Engng Constr. Cntrct. Proc.*, American Institute of Chemical Engineers, 1977, 32–4.
11. Carter T. Eden Project — a landmark for the NEC. *NEC Users' Group Newsletter*, No. 16, 2001.
12. Perry J. G. and Barnes M. Target cost contracts: an analysis of the interplay between fee, target, share and price. *J. Engng, Constr. Archtct Mngmnt*, 2000, **7**, No. 2, 202–8.
13. Patterson R. *Financial assessment of target cost tende*rs. Internal document, Mott MacDonald, 2001.
14. Broome J. C. and Perry J. G. How practitioners set share fractions in target cost contracts. *Intl J. Proj. Mngmnt*, 2002, **20**, No. 1, 59–66.
15. Van Nort P. Executive summary. In *Use of incentives*. Pamphlet and video from Construction Industry Institute Conference, Austin, Texas, 1995.
16. Berends T. C. Costs plus incentive fee contracting — experiences and structuring. *Intl J. Proj. Mngmnt*, 2000, **18**, No. 3, 165–71.
17. Al-Subhi Al-Harbi K. M. Sharing fractions in cost-plus-incentive-fee contracts. *Intl J. Proj. Mngmnt*, 1998, **16**, No. 2, 73–80.
18. Weitzman M. L. Efficient incentive contracts. *Q. J. Econ.*, June 1980.
19. Fabel O. Implicit contracts with effort incentives. *Zeitschrift fur Nationalokonomie*, Spring 1990.

20. Baron D. P. and Holmstrom B. The investment banking contract for new issues under asymmetric information: delegation and incentive problem, *J. Fin.*, Dec. 1980, **XXXV**, No. 5, 1115–37.

21. Demski J. S. and Sappington D. Optimal incentive contracts with multiple agents. *J. Econ. Theo.*, 1984, **33**, 152–71.

22. Sappington D. Incentive contracting with asymmetric and imperfect precontractual knowledge, *J. Econ. Theo.*, 1984, **34**, 52–70.

23. Kahn S. G. Partners in risk — cost incentives in development contracts. *ESA Bull.*, May 1981, **26**, 48–53.

24. Birkby G. Making the most of contract relationships. *Project — the Magazine for the Association for Project Management*, Oct. 2001, **14**, No. 5, 12–13.

25. Boultwood J. Choosing the right route. *Project — the Magazine for the Association for Project Management*, Oct. 2001, **14**, No. 5, 10–11.

26. Holti R. Nicolini D. and Smalley M. *The handbook of supply chain management: the essentials.* CIRIA, London, 2000.

27. Lawrence H. *Prime contracting — a step change in UK public sector construction procurement.* Lecture to the Association for Project Management Contracts and Procurement Specific Interest Group, Cambridge, 9 February 2000.

28. Patterson R. *The NEC as a possible support vehicle for 'Prime Contracting'.* Note submitted to the Design and Build Foundation by Mott MacDonald, 2000.

29. Patterson R. Using the NEC for multiple-site, undefined contracts. *Proc. Instn Civ. Engrs*, May 2001, **144**.

9. Project and strategic alliances

(Co-authored by Norman Kerfoot*)

9.1 Introduction

This chapter discusses the use of alliances as a procurement route. At its broadest, alliancing refers to any arrangement in which the contractual arrangements are designed to stimulate trust by aligning commercial objectives. It is often used in general business literature to refer to 'horizontal' arrangements in which two or more suppliers join together to market, manufacture, distribute and/or sell their product(s), so a client is not involved in the arrangement. Over the last couple of years, I have noted that the term 'alliance' has been used rather loosely as an ill-defined subcategory of 'partnering', which in turn can mean many things to many people (see Chapter 2)! This chapter discusses two forms of alliances that are increasingly being used in construction and heavy engineering:

- A project alliance is one which aligns the financial fortunes of the individual parties of the project to its overall success, rather than just to their individual contracts. The parties are therefore more motivated to work together.
- A strategic alliance is one in which a client has a need for a certain type of project over a set length of time, for example sewerage works over a 5-year period, but is unable to define each project at the start of the alliance period. Contractors or consultants work with the client — and each other — to develop and then implement these projects. The main advantage to a contractor should be a more consistent level of repeat order profitable work. To a client, the main advantage should be continuous improvement in overall project performance.

This chapter is therefore split into two principal sections: one on project alliances and one on strategic alliances. Both sections have the same order of subsections:

---

*Norman Kerfoot is managing director of the *Advance* consultancy. He was one of the principal consultants involved in setting up the early project alliances in the North Sea and continues to help clients, consultants and contractors set up and develop project and strategic alliances in both the construction and the oil industries. He can be contacted at *Advance* on +44 (0)1889 561510.

- The first is a brief introduction to their development and what they are at a high level.
- The second is a description of their common characteristics. Like many procurement relationships, alliances are approximations in that their precise nature depends on exactly how they are implemented. However, they have common characteristics that are usually, but not always, present.
- The third is a discussion of when it is appropriate to use them and when it is not. As with all procurement routes, there are certain circumstances to which they are suited and others to which they are not. The section on strategic alliances has a small subsection on their advantages and disadvantages.
- The fourth covers their key implementation points with a focus on the procurement issues.
- The last is a brief conclusion.

Preview question   Glance through this chapter asking yourself: 'What do I want to know more about that I am currently only aware of?'

9.2   Project alliances

9.2.1   Introduction

The concept of a 'project alliance' came from the North Sea oil industry, in which they were used with spectacular results to reduce the time and cost of implementing major projects. The best-known example is the Andrews oilfield, of which a brief overview is given in the case study below. Consequently, we use the definition from the North Sea oil industry,[1] which certainly applies to project alliances, of 'co-operative relationships focused on aligned objectives between two or more parties, which may include an operator, to deliver enhanced business results for all parties and a mechanism for sharing risk and reward'. This definition puts a strong emphasis on the role of procurement because it is only once the commercial terms have 'aligned objectives' that there are the business drivers for cultural, skills and process changes to deliver the 'enhanced business results'.

By the above definition, a target cost contract is an alliance between two parties and a project alliance can be seen as a development of target cost contracts as any cost over- or under-run is split between the parties and cost- or input-based contracts are predominantly used. As a generalization, when people refer to an alliance in the construction and heavy engineering industries, they mean that there are more than two parties to the contract: it could be the client, a civil engineering contractor, a mechanical and electrical contractor and the principal consultant. **As project alliances are a development of target cost contracts, which in turn are a development of cost-reimbursable contracts, what has been said in the previous two chapters is just as relevant,** albeit with some adjustments to take account of the multiparty contractual arrangement.

In terms of contractual project organization, they are likely to have a similar structure to construction management (see section 4.3.4). In essence, the difference is that they have a pain/gain share mechanism that ties the rewards of all alliance members to the success of the project. This promotes a change in how participants work together both culturally and through integrated processes.

The BP Andrews alliance

Andrews was a potential oilfield in the North Sea that had been discovered in 1974. A range of scenarios had been put forward for its development, none of which made commercial sense. In 1991, another conceptual platform design was put forward, which cost £450 million and was still not viable.

BP realized that to make the project viable something radical was required and that innovative technology, although a component of the solution, would not by itself be enough. Two issues were identified as being crucial: aligning the motivations of contractors, firmly linking project performance to their profitability; and cultural change, in order that the parties would work together more efficiently and effectively. BP, in analysing its past projects, also realized that it was far from a perfect client.

The Andrews oilfield would involve seven different types of contractors, consultants and manufacturers; these will be referred to as suppliers from now on. There were many organizations that were technically proficient but, without a scope design, how would they be selected? BP developed a set of ten minimum conditions of satisfaction (MCOS) that potential alliance members would have to sign up to. In effect, eligibility was not an issue and, rather than evaluating suppliers for their suitability (see Appendix 4), BP was reversing the process by asking potential suppliers to commit to a set of cultural values, as well as integrating processes and teams. The first supplier selected was Brown and Root. As well as stating what its MCOS were in order to work with BP, Brown and Root put forward a proposal for the commercial basis of the project. Another six suppliers were selected on a weighted combination of their commitment to the MCOS, cost and technical factors. The higher the risk of a supplier's element of work, the greater the weighting of its commitment to the MCOS.

By February 1993, all alliance members were working in the same office to reduce the cost of the project to one that could be sanctioned. They were all paid on a cost per person-hour basis only, with the motivation being that the project would be sanctioned.

In November 1993, a detailed and much more certain estimate for the project was put forward as the alliance target: a base cost estimate of £334 million with a separate £39 million risk provision, giving a sanctioned target of £373 million and a build time of 3 years. This compared with £450 million in 1991. This was checked independently by BP's cost and risk analysts, and included BP's own internal costs as well as estimated costs for suppliers outside the alliance. The alliance suppliers were to split 54% of any under- and over-run between them, with their over-run being capped at £423 million. This is illustrated below in Fig. 9.1.

The project was sanctioned in February 1994. Only three of the seven alliance members were reimbursed under their separate contracts on an input basis: fixed overhead and profit with person-hours reimbursed at cost. An integrated management team was formed from the most senior personnel of the seven alliance members. This had formulated a high-level strategy for how the alliance would function to reduce costs and time, while maintaining quality.

The key differences that contributed to improved performance, many of which overlapped, were:

- The aligned objectives meant that it was in every alliance member's interest to work together, identifying early any issues that might increase costs or time and then working together to solve them.

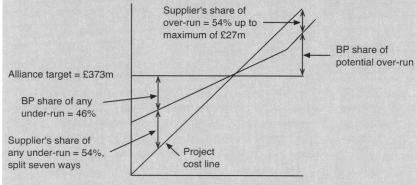

Fig. 9.1. The share profile for the Andrews oilfield alliance

- There was a high investment in training and facilitated 'away days' to drive through the cultural and skill changes required for the project to work.
- The organizational structure was designed to promote a fully integrated team approach throughout the life of the project. This helped to reduce administration costs, such as duplication and person-to-person marking. For instance, there were only 18 BP staff at the central project office out of a total of 350.
- Giving each supplier a broader zone of exclusive control led to reduced contractual interfaces, both of which meant less time administering the interfaces.
- Use of performance and functional specifications, as opposed to detailed technical documents, freed up the expertise of the suppliers to be more innovative and design what they installed.
- Other contracts were awarded on the basis of total acquisition costs, rather than lowest bid price, with a principle of maintaining supplier's profitability.
- The use of risk-management processes was intensive and integrated throughout the alliance members.

Throughout the project, estimates were revised and new targets set. As one interviewee said, 'it became a game to beat a target, re-set it and then beat the new one'. The end result was that the project was completed at a total cost of just under £290 million. This enabled the suppliers to share £45 million between them and gave BP a saving of £115 million, compared with the estimated £450 million of doing the development conventionally. In addition, the project came in 6 months ahead of schedule, allowing BP to start recovering its investment and achieve payback much earlier than expected.

(Sources: interviews and references 2, 3 and 4)

9.2.2 Common characteristics of project alliances

Scott[5] states that the alliance relationship is 'built upon the following principles

- a primary emphasis on the business outcome for all parties (i.e. win–win)
- clear understanding of individual and collective responsibilities and accountabilities
- an equitable balance of risk and reward for the parties

> - encouragement of openness and co-operation between the parties
> - encouragement to develop and apply innovative approaches and continuous improvement
> - access to contribution by the expertise and skills of the parties
> - a commercial basis which offers the opportunity to achieve rewards commensurate with exceptional performance.'

The specific characteristics of project alliances are as follows.

Involvement prior to sanction

Often the potential alliance partners are brought in prior to sanction of the project, with selection based predominantly on qualitative measures of eligibility and suitability (see Appendix 4). This may be because, unless the estimated project cost is brought down, the project is not viable. Usually, the parties are paid for this service on a fee basis. The incentive here is that, if the project becomes viable, then they will win the detailed design and/or construction work. Whatever the arrangement, it also gives the potential partners time to understand the project and each other and to learn to work together. It could be viewed as the 'engagement' before the 'marriage'.

Rewards are predominantly tied to the success of the project, not the individual contracts

This is the number one characteristic of an alliance. Based on the definition of an alliance in the introduction to this section, we would argue that if this characteristic is not satisfied, then it is not an alliance. Because rewards are tied to the success of the project, there is a motivation to work with others to take out time and cost from the project and not to maximize individual contractual and commercial positions at the expense of the others. This is not to say that there is no incentive for those involved to minimize their individual contract costs as, for instance, these are often let as target cost contracts.

> Scott[6] states that: 'Alliancing creates commercial alignment by instituting an incentive scheme that firmly links the returns of all alliance participants to actual performance against specific criteria. These criteria are a direct measure of the overall project outcome rather than just each contractor's individual performance. The "targets" for the performance criteria are derived from jointly developed and agreed data, such as project cost estimates and schedules. It is important that the criteria are regarded by all parties as being achievable. They should not, however, be conservative.'

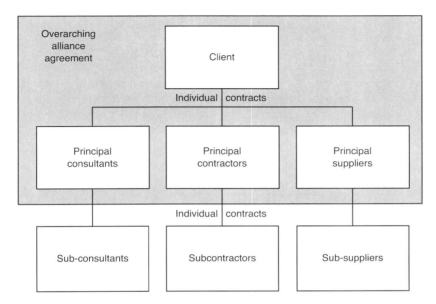

Fig. 9.2. A typical contractual arrangement for a project alliance

Figure 9.2 illustrates the common approach. Here there are individual contracts in place that reflect the nature of the work and state of development of their scope. The overarching alliancing agreement is what ties the fortunes of the project participants together. This is effectively the approach adopted in the NEC Partnering option (which we think should, more accurately, be called the 'Alliancing option'). Here, common additional 'alliancing' clauses are added to each of the contracts for the principal consultants, contractors and suppliers that form an alliance.

Under the PPC 2000 form (see Appendix 7), from what we understand, all key participants sign a multiparty contract at the same time. The disadvantage of this approach is that it is harder to bring in other key consultants, contractors or suppliers as the scope of the works become progressively more defined and the level and type of input becomes known. It also means less flexibility in the terms under which each of the alliance members is appointed.

Employer administration and consultant costs are included in the alliance target and project costs

The other parties to the alliance can see these costs, so it is true 'open book' accounting. The reason for doing this is that it becomes worthwhile for all parties to reduce the costs of both the final asset and the process of delivering it. For instance, a contractor has to satisfy the client that its quality assurance system picks up any defects and does not need additional checking by the consultant. The consultant benefits because its share of the savings is greater than or equal to the profit of employing checkers. However, a balance does have to be struck: many consultants think of one of their roles as protecting the client from inferior performance. If they become too motivated to take out cost, then quality may suffer. Whether to include or exclude a consultant's costs from the alliance target will depend on its role within it. For this reason, cost auditors are often excluded from the arrangement.

Cost- or input-based contracts

Once the project is sanctioned, the partners are often paid for the resource they provide, for example person-hours or actual cost, rather than on outputs, for example units of quantity produced, or by milestones. This is because of the many advantages that open book accounting offers (see section 7.2). An exception is often manufacturing suppliers, for which a significant element of their normal 'price' is in indirect and overhead costs. These costs might be mixed in with other 'non-alliance' orders and could include fixed costs, which have to be written off over a number of years and projects. Consequently, it is much harder to account for them as specific project costs and there is much less variability in them, so it is not worth the bother. However, tying manufacturing suppliers in to the alliance incentive mechanism does provide the motivation for them to be flexible, rather than contractual, when design or delivery time requirements change.

Strategic steering groups

These are set up from senior people, representing each alliance member, who, although involved in the project, are not preoccupied with it on a day-to-day basis. The groups principally set targets, determine strategic direction, sanction extra costs — for instance, groups to investigate and develop potential innovations, or expenditure on major risk avoidance or reduction measures — and settle any disputes. It seems to be quite rare for them to be called upon to perform the last of these functions. The groups meet regularly, but the intervals usually become longer as the project progresses.

The remaining three characteristics are less contractual in nature and more implementation features:

A more 'facilitatory' rather than 'directing' style of management

Project alliances can be seen as a development of management-style contracts, in which the management contractor or construction manager is traditionally employed for its ability to provide strong contractual management and control between the contract interfaces of the project. In alliances, a construction manager may be part of the alliance and the other partners should now be motivated to work together. Rather than resolving interface problems by telling the parties what to do, there is a shift in emphasis towards facilitating the resolution of technical, access and programming problems between the partners. The contractors work 'with' rather than 'for' the client and consultants. This often involves extensive use of facilitation, both to generate changes in culture and skills (see section 2.4.3) and to bring all the partners' expertise to bear on a problem or opportunity.

Integrated processes and teams

As the cultural and organizational barriers are broken down, the partners increasingly use joint systems, co-located offices, etc. (as outlined in section 2.4.4). As mentioned previously, audit teams, particularly financial ones, are often left out of the alliance arrangement in order not to compromise their impartiality.

High start-up costs

The nature of an alliance means that organizations that may have previously worked 'against' each other now have a motivation to work together. This has several consequences: numerous case studies show that unless the people doing the work are educated about the change in contractual motivations, then, unsurprisingly, they carry on working as they always have. Furthermore, in order for the advantages of cultural change and integrated processes to flow, it makes sense to stimulate them, rather than just let them evolve. One means of 'kick starting' this change and rapidly putting in place these processes is running workshops. The literature consistently highlights workshops as an important aspect in achieving change in business. This means paying not only for facilitators, but for the real cost of taking staff out of their day-to-day work. However, **this should be viewed as an investment, rather than a cost, providing the size and duration of the project gives sufficient scope for payback.**

In summary, the essential contractual ingredient of a project alliance is that it aligns the fortunes of all participants to the overall success of the project rather than just to their individual contract. This involves sharing of risk and rewards and the use of cost- or input-based contracts. This means that the key implementation points for cost-reimbursable and target cost contracts also apply to project alliances. Other expected contractual characteristics would be contractors' and suppliers' involvement prior to sanction, project and principal consultants' costs included in the alliance target and an alliance steering group drawn from senior executives of the organizations in the alliance.

A project alliance in the water industry

A water company had a requirement to build ten sewage treatment works along its coastline. The type of treatment works needed to satisfy the EU Directive was originally thought to be primary treatment only. Each project involved the water company's design consultant, a civil engineering contractor and a process contractor, with the contractors working under lump sum contracts. As it happened, the same consultant and contractors were working together on the same projects, with each 'team' having three or four projects each.

However, after construction on these works had started, the interpretation of the EU Directive was reconsidered following consultation with the Environment Agency. This meant that secondary treatment was also needed to treat the outflow from the primary treatment works before it was put out to sea. This entailed building on additional works of similar size to the primary treatment works in half the time, that is from conception to operation the work had to be undertaken in less than 2 years. Something had to be done differently!

The water company decided that it made sense for the same companies working on each scheme to form a project alliance for the secondary treatment works, with each alliance being responsible for three or four projects. Each alliance would therefore consist of the client, its design consultant, a civil engineering contractor and a process contractor. However, the primary treatment works were excluded from the alliance and continued as lump sum contracts. In the same way that the Andrews alliance project members had to sign up to ten MCOS, each potential alliance member had to sign up to an agreement that included behavioural issues. To develop the alliance target, they worked on a cost plus basis. As well as an alliance steering group, there was also a technical steering group made up of representatives from all parties, which set the performance parameters for the design in terms of capability, reliability, design life and operating costs. From this, a suitable outline scheme design was fleshed out, from which the detailed design started to be developed, with input from all members of the team. The client's cost consultants were responsible for running the risk and value engineering processes to help the alliance members take out costs and time. In addition, they had an ongoing role throughout the whole project as independent cost auditors. Finally, there was a separate technical audit carried out on the design by the client's own personnel.

Prior to sanction for each scheme, the design so far and the technical and cost audits were submitted to the main steering group, which then made a recommendation to the water company board for sanction. Before the contracts were signed, much thought was put into the structure of the commercial terms under which the alliance would operate when construction started. Although it was instigated and driven by the client, there was extensive consultation with the contractors and consultants in its development. It worked like this:

- Each contract was let under a member of the NEC family as a target contract with activity schedules. Some amendments were made though: the physical and weather conditions were taken out of the contractors' contracts as a reason for adjustment; the contract was made cash flow neutral; and correcting defects after completion would be paid for by the client. The pain/gain share was:
  - Fifty per cent of any over-run was allocated to the contractor/consultant up to a 15% over-run, at which point it became capped from the client's point of view, that is the contractor's share was 100%. In effect, this was a guaranteed maximum price contract (see section 8.10).
  - Sixty-five per cent of any savings were allocated to the client and 35% to the contractors or consultant.
- The alliance target included the client's costs and would not be changed except if there was a change to the scope of the project ordered by the client. Any savings on the alliance target, which predominantly would come from the 65% share of any savings from the individual target cost contracts, were allocated in the following proportions: 35% went straight to the client, 15% to the design consultant and 25% to each of the contractors.

This whole process of agreeing commercial terms took up considerable management time for all parties, with many 'what if?' questions being asked and resultant adjustments. However, it very much helped gain commitment to the objectives of the project. Linked to these discussions on the sharing proportions were discussions on the amount of risk contingency included within each target. While the processes to identify and manage risk were quite sophisticated, the negotiations were less so, with the amount included being loosely based on the size of the individual contract and the impact and likelihood of the individual risks included within each target.

As the whole reason for forming an alliance was to hit a deadline at the end of April 2001, the client initially did not want to pay out any bonus if the target date for each project was not achieved. However, it accepted that this could potentially be very unfair if a project was, say, a week late. Consequently, it was written in that any bonus to the other alliance members would decrease by 6% per week of over-run.

The basics of these agreements stayed the same whatever the project, although the agreements were continually improved as the contracts were progressively let and tweaked to the individual project circumstances and participant's requirements.

Other important factors highlighted by the interviewees were:

- The team culture was very important. As well as the ongoing risk and value engineering workshops run by the cost consultants, there were two project start-up/partnering workshops, one at the start of design and one at construction. Team morale was further built up and maintained by ongoing social events and co-located offices, during both the pre-construction and construction phases. There was also an unwritten understanding that people could be removed from the projects if there was a personality clash, on a 'no-blame' basis. This was necessary on only two occasions, mainly because of the hangover from working together on the primary treatment works in a traditional form. However, it was found that the degree of cultural change within each alliance depended to a large extent on the existing culture of the participating companies and the top-down commitment to change within each company.
- Each team was made responsible for clearly defining its roles and responsibilities. The main result of this was that checking was much reduced. While it varied from project to project, once the parties were satisfied with each other's own quality assurance procedures, only the critical tests were independently checked.

At the time of the interviews, with just over 6 months left before the date for completion set by the Environment Agency, all projects were on or ahead of schedule. In terms of improving future project alliances, the client was looking at two issues:

- installing a project financial management system, which would completely replace the individual companies' systems
- including the cost consultants within the incentive mechanism without reducing their integrity in terms of auditing.

(Sources: interviews and reference 7)

9.2.3   When to use and not to use project alliances

Project alliances are typically used in larger and more complex projects, and therefore more risky projects, than management-based contracts, in which there is a tight time and/or cost target to achieve. The size and duration of the project has to justify the investment in setting it up, both commercially and culturally.

Sometimes the arrangement flounders when the project is too constrained, in terms of project definition and/or the ability of the parties to act independently or differently. This leaves little opportunity for innovation in terms of both the end product and how it is to be achieved, and therefore allows little scope for savings and additional profit to be generated. The realization of this fact can sometimes have a serious impact on the project morale and the willingness of the parties to continue working together. Therefore, initial project briefs lend themselves much more to a performance or functional specification with minimal constraints.

Another important factor is that the client needs to be actively involved in the project so that good decisions can be made promptly, yet not in a dictatorial manner. It has to tread a fine line between giving direction and setting an example in terms of behaviours, yet facilitate the active involvement of all parties in the decision-making and project processes. This is a fine line requiring exceptional leadership. The client has to supply it.

9.2.4   Key implementation points

This subsection focuses on the key implementation points from a procurement aspect. For a more substantive text on how to implement a project alliance once it is off the contractual ground, we would refer the reader to *Partnering in Europe: incentive based alliancing for projects*.[6] Many of the key implementation points have already been mentioned in the previous two chapters. While some adaptation may be necessary, exactly the same principles apply. Others were covered in section 9.2.3. Put in place these characteristics and the project has a much higher likelihood of being successful.

We would highlight four additional issues:

(a) *Be truthful and clear to yourself and others about your and their ability to collaborate*. In the same way that there is a spectrum of partnering (see Fig. 2.3) there is also a spectrum of alliancing model that can be adapted. Ensure that the scope and scale of the project and the model used is a reasonable fit for the parties, based on their experience and capabilities of partnering and alliancing.

(b) *As a client, design a robust selection process to assess the technical and collaborative capabilities of your potential partners* (see Appendix 4).

(c) *As a potential alliance partner, bravely avoid those clients who have aspirations beyond their capabilities on a single project.*

Failure to follow either or both of the points in *(b)* and *(c)* may still deliver a reasonable project to the client, as long as the commitment is there, but with some bruising to all concerned in terms of corporate image and profitability. At worst it may destroy the alliance.

(d) *Design the incentive arrangements so that individual parties make more profit by saving project cost than by increasing the price paid by the client under their individual contracts.* For instance, in the water company case study, the contractors would receive 35% of any savings under the target cost contract. Of the remaining 65%, they would still receive 25% (or 16.25%), which is still more than they would make by uplifting the target on their individual contracts. Even for an over-run on their target up to the 15% GMP, 25% of the project savings multiplied by their 50% share of the over-run on their individual contract (or 12.5%) was still more than they would receive on any increases to the target. Factors to take into account include each party's normal profit, the size of its contract, the degree of risks and opportunities included within its contract and its influence on the project out-turns. **The more partners to the alliance there are, the more complex the process and the greater the split of project cost savings, which means less profit and therefore less motivation for the individual organizations to work together**. **This** *does* **place a limit on the numbers that are included in the alliance.**

Halman and Braks[8] state that 'to realize a win–win situation all parties involved will have to negotiate about the interest they are to have in taking and sharing the project risks and rewards. This requires openness on objectives, understanding each others' business drivers and alignment of individual interest of all parties involved.'

Thomson,[9] an Australian lawyer, has stated his views on the commercial drivers of an alliance:

- 'It is particularly important that the best commercial drivers are put in place in the alliance documentation. Each of the participants will have different factors motivating them, and it is worth spending considerable time ensuring the right motivators have been identified and that realistic targets (albeit stretch targets) are agreed' with 'the margins determined on how well the final performance compared with the planned performance'.
- 'Another very important question is the extent of "pain" which is appropriate for the alliance participants if the project does not perform to expectations'.
- 'There should be only very limited grounds for adjustment of the risk/reward regime' so that 'the parties should be focussed on performance, and not on reasons for non-performance'.

9.2.5 Conclusion

Project alliancing is currently towards the far end of the partnering spectrum (see Fig. 2.3). It has the greatest complexity in terms of aligning objectives, calls for the greatest change in the culture and behaviours of project participants and integrates the greatest number of teams and processes, compared with any other procurement route.

> Thomson[9] states that 'of all the new approaches to delivery of construction projects, project alliancing is the most innovative and it challenges many attitudes and practices which have long been entrenched in the industry.'

Unlike strategic alliances, participants only have one large project to make it work. Consequently, a large up-front investment is needed. For the client to receive payback, the projects need to be large. However, as the Andrews oilfield case study illustrates, the returns can be immense!

Review question 1 Quickly review Chapter 5 (perhaps by re-reading the conclusion to the chapter). What principles or concepts can you see applied in the two case studies in this section? Reviewing Chapter 2, what other common features of partnering can you identify in these case studies?

Review question 2 Imagine you are a procurement consultant brought in to design an alliance incentive plan which would motivate all participants. Assume that client internal costs account for 5% of project costs and that there are:

- two contractors, each of which typically makes 10% profit on the cost of any contract, including any uplift, and accounts for 35% of project costs
- a key manufacturer, which typically makes 15% on the cost of any contract and accounts for 20% of the project costs
- a consultant, which accounts for the remainder and has 20% profitability.

It is a 100-week contract, with the client increasing its return on capital by 1% for every 2 weeks it is brought in early for the first 10 weeks and vice versa for any over-run. Make up any details that are missing.

In real life, how would you know if this motivated the parties to work together?

9.3 Strategic alliances

9.3.1 Introduction

A strategic alliance is one in which an agreement or contract has been reached between a client and contractor(s) or consultant(s) to carry out projects of a similar type over a number of years. However, the client is unable to define its exact requirements at the start of the alliance. Under a **framework agreement**, each project is let as a separate contract, but governed by the terms of the alliance agreement. The contracts can therefore be modified over the duration of the alliance, but, if subject to EU procurement legislation, only to the extent that they still reflect the requirement or specification in the contract notice and documents that set up the framework. Under a **framework contract**, each project is a separate task or scheme governed by the original contract for the duration of the alliance. The advantage of a framework agreement is therefore increased flexibility and there is no commitment to buy anything, as contracts are only formed once a project is called off. We have heard it said that public sector clients are allowed to use only framework contracts under EU procurement legislation. According to a source within the Office of Government Commerce, which represents the UK on these matters, this is a fallacy: providing all other requirements are met, both routes are legal.

9.3.2 Common characteristics of strategic alliances

Limited number of alliance members selected

The number of contractors or consultants in a strategic alliance for a specific type of work is generally reduced compared with open market competition. One advantage to the contractor is therefore less competition and a more consistent stream of work. One of the principal advantages for the client is the benefit of continuous improvement that comes from working together more often. If the number of strategic partners is too large, then these benefits are reduced. However, it is rare for only one partner to be selected as:

(a) this may mean the incumbent becomes complacent as there is both no means of comparison and no internal competition within the alliance framework

(b) it could mean that, at the end of the strategic alliance, there is effectively no competition.

Instead of coming from a situation of outright competition and going to a monopoly, clients are more inclined to move to a position of *managed* competition. Normally, the number is three, although BAA unusually has only one partner for each type of work, while other clients may have two, but rarely more than four.

Selection is on quality and input costs

The contractors and/or consultants are normally selected on a combination of factors, which break down into:

(a) Quality, which is measured in terms of eligibility — technical competence, experience, systems in place and financial size — and suitability — cultural fit, commitment to continuous improvement, etc. (see Appendix 4).

(b) Cost, in terms of inputs, plus a fee for head office overheads and profit, for example the cost of an employee who is part of the team doing an activity and the material and construction plant costs and expected productivities, rather than output prices, for example the price per unit of output. This is to provide greater transparency of cost and understanding at various stages:

   (i) At selection. For the financial comparison, often a contractor is asked to cost a number of outline 'ghost' schemes of different sizes using these figures, separating out its method-related charges and risk allowances. Thus, the tendered figures represent base costs only. The fee percentage is added to this. As contractors and consultants no longer have to market themselves or tender in competition to win work, their overheads are reduced.

  (ii) Building up the contract sum for each project. Because risk and method-related charges are not included in the input rates, methods and risks can be identified, discussed and priced separately for each scheme, leading to realistic targets, which is one of target cost contracts' key implementation points (see section 8.7). It is quite common in strategic alliances, particularly for construction, that each project is awarded on a target cost basis.

 (iii) As the starting point for continuous improvement in implementation, whereby teams work on the sources of base costs, risks and method-related costs, which leads to reductions in what the client pays. If a benchmark of productivity is beaten on one scheme, then this becomes the new benchmark and is used to build up the contract sum for the subsequent schemes. If the project is let in a target cost format, the contractor receives a share of any innovation on each project, while the client takes the long-term benefit of each improvement.

One large client uses output rates as the basis for the financial selection on framework contracts, in which each project or scheme is let as a separate task in a target cost format. As a result, its consultants have had to develop a huge bill of quantities to cover every possible item that might be required for the duration of the framework. With no defined schemes, contractors have put a high risk premium in each rate to cover for uncertainties over the methods that will be used. This means that risk and base costs are not separated out and there is little transparency of cost (see sections 4.4.1–4.4.4 for an explanation). The contract also allows for extra costs which are method related to be added in to form the target for each scheme.

Consequently, once into the contract, some contractors have argued that their tendered rates do not reflect the methods that will be used or risks that are inherent in that particular scheme and as a result, the target cost for the scheme is artificially high. Savings of 15% are apparently commonly being achieved on the scheme target once implemented. This is much higher than would be expected for quite well-developed schemes using well-developed technology. Other, more honest, contractors have adopted a policy of realism, saying that they do not want artificially high targets. While they score highly on the predictability benchmark, they could be penalized on a cost reduction benchmark.

Finally, as there is little transparency and the client is tied into the tendered output rates, the author suggests that there is little scope for continuous improvement over the duration of these frameworks.

Input-based contracts

As with project alliances, and leading on from the basis of their selection, the method of payment is normally based on the cost of inputs, rather than on output prices.

One client's method of payment is to ask its consultants to give a daily rate for different pay bands of designers plus a mark-up for design office overheads. Where possible, a target is built up for each design assignment, with each assignment treated as a target cost contract. Any over- or under-run for the consultant is capped, so the client takes all the savings or over-run beyond a certain point, rather than the consultant. This is to ensure that design is not skimped on, which would have a greater effect once into the construction phase. The consultant's overall performance is measured through a series of benchmarks, which includes its cost performance.

Contractors or consultants are allocated projects

Rather than compete for each individual project with others in a strategic alliance, projects are assigned by the client to an individual contractor or consultant based on its costs, suitability for the work and/or geographical position.

Alliance members are expected to work in teams with others to develop and implement the project

This highlights the importance of cultural suitability when working in teams. Once allocated, this often takes on the form of a project alliance in that:

(a) Partners are paid on an input or cost basis.
(b) Partners work up the project brief and budget jointly before sanction.
(c) Once the project is sanctioned there is a project target to work together to achieve with cost over- and under-runs split between the alliance partners.

Some clients adopt a policy of mixing up consultants and contractors on different projects, so that there is a continuous cross-pollination of ideas from one project to another. Others adopt a policy of predominantly having the same teams working together on subsequent projects so that successes and lessons learnt from one project are incorporated by the same team in the next project, with changes being made only occasionally.

Steering boards

In the same way that project alliances have boards to provide direction, strategic alliances have them too. Often these are at two levels: an operational or regional board, consisting of senior people with day-to-day involvement in the strategic alliance, and a national-level board, which deals with more strategic issues.

Performance is heavily benchmarked

Performance on a number of parameters is benchmarked both over time and against other consultants/contractors in the client's strategic alliance. Depending on the alliancing arrangements, this can be for each company and/or each project delivery team. For instance, if work is divided up regionally with only one consultant/contractor of a particular type in each area, then one area's performance is compared with another's. This is to encourage continuous improvement over time compared both with partners' own previous performance and with the performance of others.

Best-performing teams and companies have a greater share of future work

At the start of a strategic alliance, each company is normally given a chance to perform on at least one project. From then on, the better its performance as a project delivery team and/or company, as measured by benchmarks, then the greater its likely share of any future work. For instance, in regional alliances, the area in which a team works may be expanded into that of a team with poorer performance. This is managed competition. If a team consistently underperforms then it may not be given any more work. **The provision to terminate the framework or, at the very least, not give an organization any more work, possibly giving it to an organization outside the alliance, seems always to be written into the framework agreement or contract**. This is just good business sense, as it increases motivation and reduces dependence on any poorly performing contractors or consultants.

Opportunities to learn from others and to be learnt from

Benchmarks identify areas of top performance. Benchmarking goes behind the number to find out why (see Appendix 6). While being in competition with others, alliance participants are also expected to share their knowledge and the reasons for their successes with others. This could be by working with other alliance members or more directly briefing them. This has both advantages and disadvantages, but what it means is that…

The ability to continually improve is the only sustainable competitive advantage

Essentially, the preceding point means that two things are necessary from a contractor's or consultant's perspective to be consistently successful in a strategic alliance:

(a) An organization has to rapidly understand and apply lessons from others in the client's strategic alliance so that it is always up to speed and 'on the pace'.

(*b*) To be ahead of others, it has to consistently innovate and lead innovation.

The more alliances of a particular type that a company is involved in, the greater its ability to continuously improve should be, as it can also bring in knowledge and experience from outside the client's alliancing arrangement. This has obvious benefits for the client also. This suggests that **knowledge management, creativity and innovation are key implementation points, from a contractor's or consultant's viewpoint, for success in strategic alliances**, in which the client is managing the competition.

9.3.3 *Advantages and disadvantages of strategic alliances*

At the start of a strategic alliance, participants are likely to be motivated and energized, both at a company/organizational level and at a personal level. Therefore, initial performance may well improve significantly. Indeed, the initial results may be spectacular simply because of the 'bulk purchase' effect. For instance, we were told that when BAA, the airports operator, set up its framework agreement for runway and airport pavements, it immediately saved 7% on contracts procured through the traditional route. This was because the contractor was not incurring marketing and abortive tendering costs and, with a long-term commitment of work at each airport, was gaining greater utilization of its construction plant as well as not having to mobilize and demobilize sites. However, there are some potential disadvantages with long-term arrangements:

- For a client, there is a risk that, when it approaches the market again at the end of the alliance period, potential replacement suppliers have gone elsewhere or cannot match the current incumbent in terms of costs. While this means the existing alliance has been successful, over a period of time it means that the client becomes increasingly dependent on fewer and fewer suppliers. It could be argued that BAA, by selecting only one supplier for any particular type of work, is now in this position for airport-specific types of work.
- Over time, the framework arrangement may become too 'cosy' despite the performance measurement through benchmarks, with the negative incentives of reduced workload, and even of being expelled, not enough to galvanize continuous improvement and innovation.

In the North Sea, many of the first phase of long-term alliancing arrangements were either terminated or awarded to competitors as clients complained of growing complacency.

In terms of the current arrangements let in the construction industry, the jury is still out. In some relationships, we have certainly detected a sense of complacency in terms of a lack of urgency in implementing improvements.

Consequently, **at both an individual and an organizational level, there is a need to keep the arrangement fresh and dynamic**, through bringing in new blood and setting specific targets on a project-by-project basis and possibly by rewarding teams through positive incentives for achieving them.

9.3.4   When to use strategic alliances?

It is appropriate to form strategic alliances in the following circumstances:

- The client has a portfolio of difficult-to-scope work of a similar type, which can be let over a number of years.
- The client and its potential partners in industry are sufficiently mature, particularly at the board and operational level, to collaborate and work together (or at the very least to learn to do so). Some experience of each other is usually necessary to evaluate this properly.

Aligning the parties' objectives is key to driving this relationship and, if this is not possible, it is essential to have mechanisms in place to deal with non-aligned events. Some framework agreements insist that the demands of the contract take precedence over any informal procedures and arrangements.

We are aware that some clients have been sufficiently honest with themselves to realize that their organization is not yet mature enough to enter into a formal strategic alliance. Consequently, they have selected contractors with a reputation for collaboration for their projects in order to both learn from them initially and then later grow together. This is known as a **collaborative escalator** — although there is no formal strategic alliancing agreement and so the award of each successive project is not taken for granted, each project builds on the previous one in terms of a collaborative culture and integration of processes and skills. At some point, the parties may decide to formalize the arrangement into a strategic alliance.

9.3.5   Key implementation points

The first two key implementation points for project alliances in section 9.2.4 are just as relevant for strategic alliances. In addition:

Be clear about your criteria for selecting a partner, in terms of
both technical eligibility and cultural suitability, before you begin
discussions and design the selection process

This is the second key implementation point in section 9.2.4. As a client, you may have to accept that that your supply chain is not adequately mature to engage in a strategic alliance. This is the opposite of the collaborative escalator mentioned in the previous subsection, which applies if the client recognizes that it is not mature enough to partner properly. Therefore, start partnering at a point on the spectrum (see Fig. 2.3) at which you and your partner are sufficiently mature. To use a courting analogy, know what sort of partner you want and play the field until you find the right one. In doing so, you will learn about yourself and your potential partner, and grow together until you reach the point at which you are both happy to commit.

Be informed by objective experience of your potential partner, but
put it into context

A key issue in the selection process for clients is how much the client relies on previous experience of a potential partner. Bear in mind that potential partners also have previous experience of you! We believe that, within any procurement constraints, you should take into account any information as long as it is objective. It presents an opportunity to inform you of how well a candidate can partner and of how it could react to adverse events and/or respond to less than favourable feedback. Having done this, realize that:

(a) Although a corporate culture is made up of individual attitudes and the two interact, an experience of one individual or of one project does not mean that the whole company is the same.
(b) **In selecting a strategic partner, you are selecting not only where it is now, but also its potential to improve continuously over the duration of the alliance.** If it acknowledges previous 'misdemeanours' and is actively and demonstratively taking steps to change, for instance, corporate culture, then it could be a far better potential partner than another existing organization resting on its laurels from past glories.

Approach the deal with pragmatic humility

By pragmatic, we mean be clear about what work is within and what is outside the scope of the alliance, how it will be compensated and the incentives offered, and what you want to happen should the alliance succeed or fail. Contractors seem to have often been given the impression that more work will become available sooner than it actually does in order to attract them to working with a client. Once the contract is awarded, a big project is always just around the corner. Consequently, contractors and consultants invest in and allocate people to the alliance, only to have them to hang around waiting for work. This is bad for their businesses, reduces trust and kills off the initial enthusiasm.

By humility, we mean be willing to learn from others both in the negotiation stage and once the alliance has formed. Treat your partner as an equal with its own expectations and expertise to offer: if you could do what it does better, why are you not doing it yourself?

Forming a strategic alliance is not an excuse for poor project or contract management

We are aware of a number of clients who view alliancing almost as another form of outsourcing in order to reduce internal numbers and transfer risk. Their alliance partners are given poorly defined briefs to work with and unrealistic timescales in which to implement those briefs (often because a client has used up all available float), and are not given sufficient project management leadership during each project's development and implementation. This could be due to staff cut-backs as construction has now been 'outsourced' by the procurement department. **As each project is usually let in a target cost format, more client involvement is actually required** (see sections 7.5, 7.6.1 and 8.9). Consequently, the alliances do not achieve their potential or, as we know has happened in a few examples, out-turn costs actually increase! **Each scheme is a project in itself, so the principles of good project management still need to be applied to it for a successful outcome.**

Related to the above, if expressed positively, the contractual terms define the rules of the game in terms of how the parties will work together, certainly at the start of the relationship. If, for instance, how and when each scheme is priced, how risks are allocated or shared, the extent of cost and programme transparency, how and why a target is adjusted, etc., is poorly or inappropriately expressed, then the parties will initially focus on sorting these out, rather than working together. By poorly expressed, we mean that there is a lack of clarity so that the parties are arguing over what the contract means. By inappropriately expressed, we mean that the contract terms do not facilitate working together, for example allocating uncontrollable or even client-controlled risk to a contractor. We would encourage the contract terms to be evolved over time as part of the process of continuous improvement (see sections 2.4.5 and 3.12) and have no problem with certain contract terms being waived in unique circumstances. However, **contract terms do need to be clearly expressed and intelligently thought through, so that the relationship has a good base to develop from.**

Extra incentives may be necessary as the rate of continuous improvement drops off over time

In section 9.3.3, it was noted that the stimulus of less or even no work is not always enough to prevent the relationship from becoming too cosy and therefore fresh blood and incentives may be needed to stimulate continuous improvement. However, it has to be accepted that, over time, finding areas for improvement becomes progressively harder as those areas of poorest performance that are tackled initially are those with the greatest returns. Areas identified later have diminished returns by comparison and, in the later stages of the alliance, may not produce a payback before the alliance period ends. Paradoxically, if these had been identified early on in the alliance, improvements would have had sufficient time to achieve payback. The effect of this is that more and more effort has to be put in for decreasing returns, which in itself can be demoralizing. If the contractor or consultant is partly rewarded on the basis of the extent of continuous improvement per period of time or per project, then it is also receiving less return on its investment. For it, staffing the alliance with its most motivated, creative and innovative personnel becomes less attractive, as better returns can be found elsewhere. This has two possible consequences:

(a) It is accepted that most of the waste has been weeded out of the processes, which are now very 'lean' (efficient) and goal directed (effective). Consequently, it is sensible that the psychological profile of the typical team member changes from one who, at the start, is most effective and happy thinking up and implementing innovation and change to one who, at the end, is most effective and happy operating defined, but very refined, processes. Any changeover should be gradual, so that the innovations and culture are still embedded in the teams.

(b) If each project is let in a target cost format, then the contractor would receive a share of any savings for that project. If the target is built up by using the best benchmarks from past projects, then the rate of improvement and therefore the amount of any cost savings should progressively decrease. Consequently, the contractor's rewards progressively diminish. Either the contractor's share of any savings needs to increase or an extra incentive mechanism can be added in to stimulate continuous improvement, which focuses attention on a specific area for each project. The incentives could be for good process or achievement of other client objectives. The danger, of course, is that this diverts attention from other important areas where performance then suffers.

9.3.6   Conclusion

The common characteristics and key implementation points of strategic alliances have been identified in this section. These can be reviewed by reading the italicized words at the start of each point in the lists in sections 9.3.2 and 9.3.5. Common themes have been the importance of selecting the right partner for the client, honest and clear communication with each other (both of intention and at a contractual level) and the difficulties and importance of keeping the partners motivated to improve continually. For the last point, client attention and leadership is needed. As in project alliances, this leadership should not be dictatorial, otherwise it constrains the partners and therefore the results achieved. Because strategic alliances develop projects, they are based on relationships. This means there needs to be client's staff to partner and work with. Strategic alliances should therefore not be confused with preferred supplier relationships or used as a means of reducing client staff numbers.

Review question 3 If you are in a client organization or represent one as a consultant, think about how you might set up a strategic alliance in terms of selecting partners, rewarding them and nurturing the relationship so that it does not become cosy. If you are a contractor, do the same with your subcontractors, but think about the differences needed because of your circumstances.

Review question 4 If you are involved in a strategic alliance, what characteristics listed in this section are shared by your alliance? How does it differ? How could it be improved as a result of reading this chapter? How could it be done differently next time?

9.4   Conclusion

Project alliances are suitable for use on large, complex and risky projects, in which innovation is needed to produce step changes in results.

Strategic alliances are used in cases in which the client has a portfolio of difficult-to-scope work of a similar type, which can be let over a number of years. Continuous improvement is therefore more evolutionary than revolutionary.

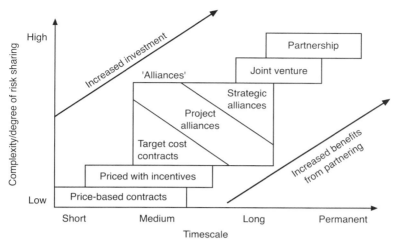

Fig. 9.3. The relationship between procurement route, level of investment needed and potential returns (adapted from reference 8)

Both of these approaches are at the extremes of the partnering spectrum. Common themes of both are the importance of selecting the right partner that is appropriate for the client and its project(s), and creating — and, in strategic alliances, maintaining — commercial motivation and cultural change. Both of these require client involvement, leadership and investment to drive them. Equally, the other partners need to be committed to the alliance at a senior and an operational level. As these changes take place and a relationship grows, cost and time savings and an improved end asset should result. Any investment, in business terms, has to achieve payback and a return. Project and strategic alliances require a large investment, but can equally produce a large return. This is illustrated in Fig. 9.3.

As project alliances can be viewed as a development of target cost contracts and the method of delivering a project within a strategic alliance is often through a target cost contract or project alliance, the key implementation points identified in the previous two chapters also apply.

Now draw a learning map.

References

1. CRINE (Cost Reduction in the New Era) Secretariat. *Guidelines for alliancing, issue no. 2*. CRINE, London, August 1996.
2. Knott T. *No business as usual: an extraordinary North Sea result*. The British Petroleum Company, London, 1996.
3. Barlow J. *et al. Towards positive partnering: Revealing the realities for the construction industry*. The Policy Press, Bristol, 1997.
4. Bakshi A. Alliances change economics of Andrew field development. *Offshore Engr,* Jan. 1995, 30–4.
5. Scott B. Partnering and alliance contracts: a company's viewpoint. April 1994.
6. Scott B. with the European Construction Institute Task Force 23. *Partnering in Europe: incentive based alliancing for projects*. Thomas Telford, London, 2001.
7. Whitelaw J. All for one and one for all. *New Civ. Engr*, 2000.
8. Halman J. I. M. and Braks B. F. M. Project alliancing in the offshore industry. *Intl J. Proj. Mngmnt*, April 1999, **17**, No. 2, 71–6.
9. Thomson G. Project alliances. Paper delivered at *AMPLA 21st Annual Conference*, Brisbane, July 1997.

10. Mechanisms for multi-incentive plans and other incentives

10.1 Introduction

In this chapter, I have attempted to identify the mechanisms for combining different types of incentive. The sources are my own research and other literature, which can be found elsewhere in this book. The mechanisms for multi-incentive plans described in this chapter are:

- the standard method for combining cost and other incentives, in which a monetary bonus and/or damage is put against each measure of performance (the use of time incentives under a target cost is explored in detail as the most pertinent example)
- sliding scales, in which the incentive payment is paid against a sliding scale, which, although usually stated mathematically, is often illustrated for clarity
- trade-off diagrams, which take the sliding scale concept further by adding in an additional performance measure
- incentive matrices, which take two basic forms: a two-performance-measures incentive matrix and a weighted incentive matrix
- multipliers, in which a base incentive sum is multiplied by the 'multiplier', which is derived from another measure of performance.

Depending on the project circumstances, these different multi-incentive mechanisms can be combined in almost any way. However, the principal advantages and disadvantages of each are discussed.

The last section of this chapter briefly identifies other indirect incentives, that is methods apart from the stimulus of repeat order business that do not result in the contractor receiving more money. These are improved cash flow, enhanced reputation and bonus flow-down.

Preview question   Glance through this chapter to gain a brief impression of it. From this, prioritize below which multi-incentive mechanisms you currently think will be most applicable to you as a client, consultant or contractor. What detail do you need to know to put them into effect?

Priority	Multi-incentive mechanism	Detail
(1)		
(2)		
(3)		
(4)		
(5)		

10.2 Standard method for combining cost and other incentives

The standard method for combining cost and other incentives is just to pay a bonus and/or damage against a specific performance measure. This could be for any sort of performance: end project, intermediate/milestone or process. The most common measure is against time in the form of liquidated delay damages and this, together with time bonuses in the specific case of target cost contracts, is considered in detail below.

It could be said that, in terms of time and cost, any project has four quadrants into which the project outcome can fall:

(a) over budget and under time

(b) over budget and over time
(c) under budget and under time
(d) under budget and over time.

This is illustrated in Fig. 10.1. For the time being, ignore the shaded area in the figure.

The easiest way to combine time and cost incentives under a target cost format is just to specify time bonuses or damages in the normal way as a monetary sum per day. However, care is needed not to overemphasize time. Consider the example below:

A priced lump sum contract of £1 million is let with time bonuses and liquidated damages calculated at £20 000 per day. How much would the contractor be prepared to spend to bring contractual completion forward by 1 day? The answer is, fairly obviously, up to £20 000.

Now take the same contract, but let in a target cost format with a 50% share of any under- or over-run allocated to the contractor. Again, how much would the contractor be prepared to spend to bring practical/substantial completion forward by 1 day?

The answer is not quite the same. Say the contractor is exactly on budget with the forecast out-turn costs predicted to be £1 million but is facing a 1-day delay over the contractual completion date. Half of any cost over-run is borne by the client, so the contractor is therefore willing to over-run by up to £40 000 — of which it contributes half — to avoid £20 000 damages. The client, meanwhile,

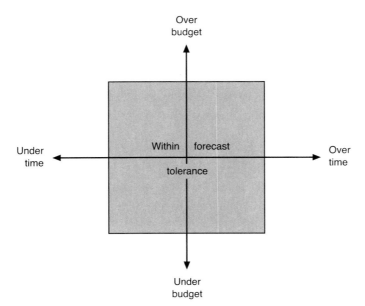

Fig. 10.1. An illustration of the four project outcome zones

is matching the contractor's share of any over-run, rather than receive £20 000 in damages for a 1-day delay. The opportunity cost to the client of finishing on time is therefore £40 000, whereas the benefit is only £20 000. The contractor, by comparison with a lump sum contract, is therefore 'over' motivated to spend money to save time if damages are set at the same level. This will apply whatever the delay is.

Will the same apply in the case of a time under-run? The answer is 'Yes'. The contractor will be willing to increase its share of a cost over-run by up to £20 000 to gain a day, so that it receives a £20 000 bonus. The client matches this, so the total amount spent to achieve completion a day early is up to £40 000. The contractor receives the £20 000 bonus that the client pays out in addition to contributing up to £20 000 for the cost over-run, while only receiving £20 000 in benefit. The same logic applies however far ahead of time the contractor is, as well as for cost under-runs. Again, the contractor is 'over' motivated to spend money to save time if damages are at the same level as that of a lump sum contract.

At what level, then, should the daily bonus/damages be set? The level in this case should be £10 000. In this case, the contractor will contribute £10 000 to save a day. The client will effectively contribute the same whether it is a cost over- or under-run and pay out a £10 000 bonus or, alternatively, not receive £10 000 in damages. The opportunity cost to the client is therefore £20 000, which is the same as the benefit of £20 000 it is receiving from a day's earlier completion.

What can be taken from this example? That, under a target cost contract or project alliance arrangement, the bonus/damage per unit of time that would be charged under a priced contract should be multiplied by the contractor's share of any under- or over-run, so that it puts the same emphasis on time as the client. For instance, in the example above, if the contractor's share of any under- or over-run was 25%, then the bonus/damage should have been set at 25% of £20 000.

All of the above presumes that the share profile is linear, which is rare. The client may well take the view that for a significant time and/or cost over-run — that is outside the shaded box in Fig. 10.1 — the contractor should take a greater or lesser share of any pain or gain. Outside this zone, in terms of cost, would be zones 3 and 5 in the five-zone model, that is significant cost over-runs and significant cost under-runs respectively (see section 8.7.2). Because time and cost are linked, a project that is over budget is also likely to be over time, and vice versa for a project that is under budget. Consequently, having taken a stance on its policy towards significant cost over- or under-run in the five-zone model, a client is likely to adopt a similar policy in principle for significant time and cost over- or under-runs.

The net result of these deliberations is that clients need to think through their policies in this respect before they design the incentive plan, which includes the share profile, risks within the target, etc.

A well-thought-out incentive plan that combines time and cost incentives

The first phase of the Channel Tunnel rail link comprised 60 or so contracts on a project costing more than £2.5 billion. A major risk to the client was that, if one work package was late, then the opening of the whole asset would be delayed, so the client would be having no return on its £2.5 billion plus investment. Each contract package was substantially designed prior to putting it out to tender on a competitive basis, with the target price being a major factor in the selection of the contractor. However, the client took many steps to evaluate the realism of the contractors' target costs and programmes, asking the tendering contractors to provide detailed programmes with method statements and resources, expected productivities, risk allowances, etc., which were then scrutinized by the client (see section 8.6). The ground conditions risk was included within the target and the fee percentage was capped at 10% on the civil engineering projects. The share profile shown in Fig. 10.2 was used.

The share profile was decided upon for the following reasons:

- As the ground conditions risk was included within the target and there was a high degree of confidence that the final actual costs plus

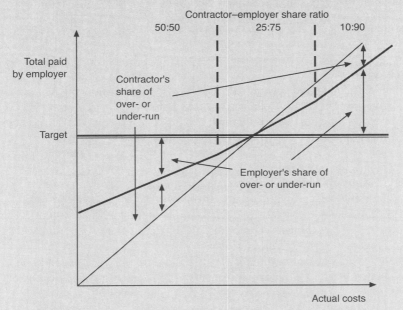

Fig. 10.2. *The share profile for a multicontract project*

fee would be in the vicinity of the target, a share of only 25% was allocated to the contractor if the actual cost plus fee was between 90% and 120% of the target. Although this share is quite low, it was deemed sufficient to motivate the contractor.

- For savings of more than 10% of the target, the contractor was allocated a 50% share in order to motivate it to strive for large savings.*
- If the target was exceeded by more than 20%, then it was recognized that something had gone seriously wrong with a contract, and on contract packages of this size — in some cases over £200 million — the contractor may well be unable to bear a significant loss. If allocated this loss, then the contractor would probably become adversarial and, in extreme circumstances, bankrupt. Neither scenario would aid the timely opening of the whole project. For these reasons a comparatively small percentage — 10% — was allocated to the contractor for over-runs exceeding 20% of the target. In taking a 25% share of any over-run up to more than 20% of the target, all of the contractor's profit and some of its contribution to head office overheads would have been eaten up. From there on, the contractor would be comparatively neutral about actual costs once this share fraction was reached. However, the damages for delay would still motivate the contractor to spend money in order to reduce time. This was in alignment with the client's objectives.

To summarize:

- When combining time and cost incentives, the client needs to consider four quadrants for time and cost and under- or over-runs. However, because time and cost are linked, it is likely that the project outcome will fall into two of the four quadrants: a time and cost under-run or a time and cost over-run. There is therefore a danger of doubly rewarding or punishing the contractor.
- If using straight bonuses or damages per unit of time, then under a target cost contract or alliance arrangement, the bonus/damage that would be charged under a priced contract should be multiplied by the contractor's share of any under- or over-run so that the contractor puts the same emphasis on time as the client.
- The client needs to think about its policy towards risk allocation at the extremes, especially for significant time and cost over-runs, as with zones

---

*Given the considerations outlined in section 8.7.2 for zone 5, I would question whether this is necessary.

3 and 5 in the five-zone model for setting the share profile under target cost contracts.

While perhaps a little more abstract, the same principles and logic apply to any other performance measure used. Therefore, clients need to think about the combined effect and motivations of their incentives on specific performance measures, particularly at the extremes of cost and performance parameters. That is the 'what if?' questions need to be asked so that the plan is intelligently designed and balanced.

10.3 Sliding scales

A sliding scale is used in cases in which there is a mathematical relationship between the performance measure and the incentive. This can usually be represented more easily visually. These are normally used to moderate the contractor's or consultant's fee under a cost-based contract. A sliding scale for a contractor's fee is illustrated in Fig. 10.3.

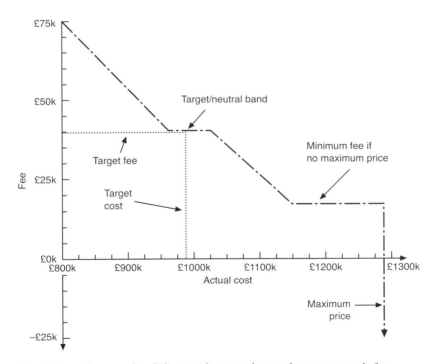

Fig. 10.3.   The use of a sliding scale to moderate the contractor's fee (derived from Fig. 4 in reference 1)

313

This method is often used to illustrate the pain/gain under target cost contracts, although, as illustrated, the scale tends to go into free-fall off the bottom of the diagram when the contractor will be taking a significant share of any over-run.

The scale on the x-axis can be any parameter of performance, not just cost, for example, for a consultant, a measure of its overall performance as scaled on a combination of process, intermediate/milestone and end of project performance measures. The drawback of a sliding scale is that it is has to be precisely drawn. Therefore, it is used to illustrate the incentive mechanism, with the exact payments described in writing or by formulae in the conditions of contract.

10.4 Trade-off diagram

A trade-off diagram is effectively a sliding scale, but with a second performance parameter introduced. The contractor is potentially trading off two measures of performance against each other to maximize its incentive payment. An example of a trade-off diagram is given in Fig. 10.4. This was used for determining the contractor's fee for the construction of a satellite, for which weight and time were of critical importance.

To use it, first read off how many months after the contract was signed the asset was delivered, then look up along the rightward-slanting near-vertical

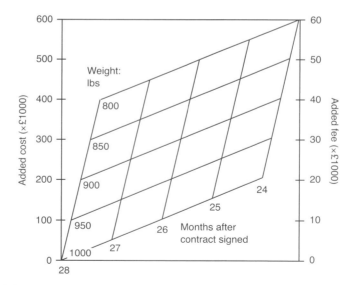

Fig. 10.4. A trade-off diagram used to determine the contractor's fee for a construction project in which weight and delivery time were critical (taken from reference 2)

314

line until it meets the weight of the satellite. Then draw a horizontal line towards the right-hand vertical axis to determine the additional fee that is paid to the contractor. The left-hand vertical axis shows how much these savings in weight and time are worth to the client. It is purely for the purposes of comparison, but in this case the design and build contractor is effectively receiving 10% of the total benefit to the client.

Like a sliding scale, a trade-off diagram has to be precisely drawn so that incentive payments can be taken off.

10.5 Incentive matrices

Using an incentive matrix appears to be the most common mechanism for motivating consultants in a multi-incentive plan. For consultants, it would predominantly be used in cases in which the basic payment mechanism is a lump sum contract, with part of the fee at risk, that is the fee-at-risk concept (see section 6.1). It can also be used in a cost-plus-incentive fee arrangement with a contractor. The basis of an incentive matrix is quite simply that a consultant's performance is broken down into various measures of performance which, when combined in a matrix, give the incentive payment.

Before proceeding, I would point out that, while pleased that better than average performance is recognized, **some consultants are a little wary of this approach on the grounds that it could undermine their professional role. There is some justification for this.** For instance, as a cost consultant, if the amount you are paid is partially dependent on project out-turn costs, you may be overmotivated to reduce the settlement of claims from contractors that are truly justifiable. Equally, if you are similarly motivated in a quality checking role, the boundary of what is and is not a defect may shift. The checks and counter-arguments are:

- The client needs to distinguish between pure audit roles, such as cost and quality checking, and the roles in which its consultants can be given incentives. For the latter, a well-thought-through plan will more closely align motivations.
- In some cases, the same individual consultant will be expected to 'wear two hats', having some role ambiguity. For example, a cost consultant may both be actively contributing to reducing costs by driving a value engineering initiative on a project and be responsible for agreeing adjustments, which are normally increases, to the contract sum. Designing the incentive plan so that only the specific measures of performance which do not compromise his or her professional role are rewarded reduces the motivation to act 'unprofessionally'.
- Most incentive plans that the author has seen for consultants have a subjective portion in their evaluation, such as overall client satisfaction on other matters, to counter any overemphasis on other more specific measures.

An **incentive matrix for two measures of performance**, in this case time and cost, is shown in Table 10.1. Here, the client can calculate its benefit in monetary terms for any combination of time and cost shown and decide, in the matrix, how much of this benefit to pass on to the contractor in order to motivate it. In an alliance situation in which the design and construction management professionals are not taking any of the construction risks an incentive matrix can be used to modify their fee depending on the project outcome.

In this example, it is the targeted cost, after adjustments to the budget for variations etc. of the construction contracts, that is the fulcrum around which the incentive operates. If the contractor or professional organization was involved in the definition of the project before the construction budget was agreed, then this could be the original budget figure.

A weighted incentive matrix can be expanded to include many components of performance — such as time, cost, quality and including performance in use and health and safety — which are then broken down into more specific measures. Some of these measures may be specific to the supplier's contract, while others are linked to the overall performance of the project. Some of the measures will be pure process measures, others linked to milestone or intermediate assessments and others to end project performance. Normally, the consultant has a chance to double its fee-at-risk for exceptional performance, so the maximum score would be 2 and the minimum zero. The fee-at-risk is then multiplied by this score. An example of a matrix for a completed project is given in Table 10.2.

Obviously, for each specific measure the scoring would be defined more precisely, with, in this case, a score of 0.5 being average performance. Notice how, in this project, the consultant seems to have put more emphasis on the user satisfaction and operating costs (OpEx) than on the variations on project time and capital cost (CapEx) performance compared with the original forecasts. As this is in line with the weighting of the client, this should be fine.

Table 10.1.   Time and cost incentive matrix for adjustment of construction management company's fee (taken from case study 2 in reference 3)

		Final cost of construction contract as a percentage of target cost				
Completion date	90–100	88–89.99	86–87.99	84–85.99	82–83.99	80–81.99
		Percentage adjustment to construction manager's fee				
2 months early	+10	+28	+46	+64	+82	+100
1 month early	+5	+19	+33	+47	+61	+75
On time	0	+10	+20	+30	+40	+50
1 month late	−5	+1	+7	+13	+19	+25
2 months late	−10	−8	−6	−4	−2	0

Table 10.2. *Weighted incentive matrix for a consultant's performance on a completed project*

General heading	Specific measure	(A) Weighting	(B) Score out of 1.0	(C) = (A) × (B)
Time	Quality of programming	0.10	0.7	0.070
	Percentage compliance with schedule dates and response times	0.14	0.6	0.084
	Overall project schedule performance vs. forecast	0.20	0.6	0.120
Cost	Adjustment to consultant's own costs vs. original forecast	0.10	0.8	0.080
	Variation of total project CapEx costs vs. forecast CapEx	0.15	0.5	0.075
Quality/performance in use	Number of defects reported by others in 10 weeks after handover	0.05	0.8	0.040
	User satisfaction with building as measured by agreed questionnaire	0.35	0.95	0.333
	Predicted OpEx vs. target OpEx	0.25	0.8	0.200
Service	Responsiveness to current user requirements	0.10	0.5	0.050
	Overall client/sponsor satisfaction with other factors	0.25	0.8	0.200
Health and safety	Contribution to good H&S in design and construction	0.10	0.6	0.060
	Overall impression of good H&S process on site	0.15	0.8	0.120
	No. of major incidents	0.06	1.0	0.060
	Maximum total =	2.0	Weighted score =	1.492

The overall mark is 1.492 out of a maximum of 2. Therefore, the fee-at-risk element would be multiplied by 1.492. If the consultant had put half its fee at risk, then the payment it would receive is $0.5 + (0.5 \times 1.492) = 1.246$ or close to 25% more than its normal fee.

This weighted incentive matrix can be added on to a construction contract, be it conventional, cost-reimbursable, target or alliance. Effectively, the client specifies a sum that can be paid out over and above the contract sum, which is dependent on other factors such as those in Table 10.2. The difference between this matrix and the one illustrated in Table 10.1 is that the maximum score would be 1. Typically, payment of this sum would be conditional upon the project coming in under a declared total budget figure.

If you have read about the value planning process, then the linkage of this approach should be obvious (see Appendix 1).

10.6 Multipliers

Multipliers are used to determine incentives as follows: an incentive amount has already been established by one incentive mechanism, such as a matrix, which is then multiplied by a multiplier figure, which is established through another measure of performance and is normally between 0 and 2. They are typically used to multiply the incentive amount under a fee-at-risk concept.

Use of a multiplier to adjust an incentive matrix

For the UKAEA, safety is obviously of paramount importance. It employed a consultant at one of its decommissioning sites and 20% of the consultant's fee was put at risk depending on a range of measures primarily related to good project management, with its performance being assessed every 3 months. However, safety and quality assurance were excluded from this matrix. Instead, a safety multiplier was made up of a comprehensive mixture of process measures and periodic safety performance measures (as the decommissioning is ongoing). Exceptional health and safety performance would give the consultant a multiplier of 1.5, so the maximum that it could receive was 110% of its standard fee. While project management performance gave the consultant's base fee-at-risk incentive payment, it could not be at the expense of health and safety, as it was the multiplier that had the biggest effect on its total incentive payment. Equally, there was no incentive for the consultant to compromise on its quality assurance role in checking contractors' work as this was not part of the incentive scheme. Despite some difficulties in application, the overall effect of the incentive plan was deemed to be worthwhile.

In a sense, **a multiplier is a less extreme gatepost or conditional incentive**, as the multiplier figure is usually dependent on an important measure of performance, as in the case study above. **Its advantage is that it decreases or increases already earned payments, rather than reducing them at a stroke to zero. Consequently, the client is less likely to witness a sudden change in focus by the consultant** when it realizes that it will not reach a measure that releases the gatepost or conditional incentive.

Multipliers can, in theory, be used to adjust the share of cost under- or over-run paid to a contractor or contractors in an alliance arrangement. However, in practice, I have not seen this happen, presumably for the following reasons:

- There are simpler, more obvious ways.
- Time and cost are interdependent, so the greater the cost over-run, the greater the likely time over-run too. If the multiplier is derived from the contractor's time performance, then the contractor's share of any over-run would progressively become more and more exaggerated by the time multiplier. The danger is that it would exceed the actual damage suffered by the client, that is it is a penalty, which is inadmissible in the UK and much of the world. Alternatively, the bonus payment for a time and budget under-run becomes more and more exaggerated until it exceeds the benefit to the client.

Use of a multi-incentive plan in a co-generation scheme

'Co-generation scheme' is the label given to projects in which a small to medium power station is built to sell electricity to one company. The buyer gains electricity at a guaranteed price compared with the variability of taking it from the national grid. The power company has a guaranteed price and customer to form the basic business case, plus the opportunity to sell excess electricity back to the grid at a higher profit.

Before sanctioning the project, the scope is developed to the point of identifying the main capital plant and how it will be put together, having identified the various technical interfaces. This typically gives sanctioned CapEx figure with between ±5 and 10% certainty. The whole process of firming this up and agreeing the contract sum under a price-based contract typically takes 3 months. A power company wanted to develop these schemes with much greater input from the principal contractor in order to gain greater maximum price certainty, and ideally cheaper projects, before sanctioning the projects and also to shorten the project duration from concept to operation. One such project's multi-incentive plan is presented and assessed below.

The project's sanctioned total budget was £57 million, of which approximately £46 million was for the main detailed engineering, management and construction contract. Of the remainder, £7 million was accounted for in the client's own costs and other construction contracts to tie the development into the national grid, leaving a risk allowance outside the main contract of some £4 million.

Following a period of joint development, the main contract was let as a target cost contract essentially with two components:

- £41.5 million was reimbursed on the basis of a rapidly agreed 'S' curve payment profile for the procurement of plant suppliers and subcontractors. This would be reconciled at completion with actual costs. The normal target cost sharing of risk and reward mechanisms applied. In terms of pain/gain:
  - The contractor took none of the pain as the client bore all risk above the target. This was because the contractor was a large US company used to working, at the time, on an hourly fee basis.
  - For the first £1 million of any savings, the contractor took 80% as this approximately corresponded to the a price certainty of ±5% on £41.5 million.
  - Any greater savings were shared in equal proportions.

  For a contractor used to working on an hourly fee only basis, this meant that there was a substantial positive incentive to save costs. The intention was that it would motivate the contractor to spend more of its fixed fee (see below) in order to gain a share of savings in reimbursable costs.
- A fixed sum, paid for against a payment profile of £4.5 million, which included all the contractor's own internal costs for designing, managing, procuring, testing and commissioning the works. This could only be varied for a specific compensation event. Of this fixed fee, approximately £700 000 was profit, and this was all put at risk. No positive incentives were put on this, with the contractor able only to lose this fee and not to gain an additional fee. The incentive mechanism for this fee-at-risk was broken down into:
  - A £300 000 sum, from which £1 was deducted for every £10 overspend on the target of £46 million up to £1 million — which again corresponded to the ±5% price certainty range — and £2 per £10 overspend on the target for the next £1 million up to a maximum of £2 million overspend. This fee would be paid on completion of the project.
  - A £300 000 sum paid according to whether the contract was on schedule. The 22-month programme was split into six intermediate milestones of roughly 3–4 months' duration, for

which the contractor was paid £45000 if it was on schedule, and a final payment of £30000. If the contractor missed a milestone, then it was able to reclaim the £45000 only once it was back on schedule.

- A £100000 sum 'service' incentive split into eight payments of £12500, seven paid every 3 months and one on completion of the project. This was paid on a fairly subjective scoring basis, whereby, providing a certain threshold score was achieved, the full £12500 was paid. This included:

  Safety performance. If there were any lost-time accidents, then none of the £12500 would be paid in that period. If there were some minor incidents, the payment would be reduced.

  Environmental performance. If there were any major incidents, then no incentive would be paid for that period, while minor incidents would reduce the payment.

  Service quality. This applied to the quality and timeliness of the contractor's production of drawings, safety plans and approvals.

The purpose of these negative fee-at-risk incentives was to make the contractor, which was used to working on a risk-free hourly fee basis, stop and think before spending the client's money when a compensation event occurred, for instance by not 'buying acceleration' from the price-based suppliers and subcontractors.

The contract also included the following features:

- There was a time bonus of £10000 per day for every day that the asset was operational ahead of its late October deadline, up to a maximum of 30 days. This was because, from late September onwards, electricity prices from the grid start to rise.
- Finally, if the client's project budget of £57 million was exceeded, then the maximum that would paid as any sort of bonus, including the fee-at-risk element and time bonus, was capped at £500000. The extra £200000 fee-at-risk and other potential payments were therefore conditional upon the project coming in on or under budget.
- In addition, some low damages for poor performance of the final asset were specified as the contractor refused to enter a contract without exclusive remedies to minimize its potential exposure. These were not really considered part of the incentive mechanism by either party.

From the client's perspective, project costs were reduced and, in this context, the incentive plan can be seen as a success as this was the principal objective of the incentive scheme. I understand that savings of around £2 million were made on the contractor's target. However, it was not working as well as hoped for a number of reasons:

- As any bonus that would be paid out under the contract was accounted for in the contractor's project ledger, rather than the individual design departments', there was little incentive for them, as individual cost and profit centres, to spend more of their own money to reduce overall contract costs.
- The contractor was used to working on an hourly fee basis, so all hours traditionally had to be accounted for. Under the fixed-price part of the target cost contract, each department budgeted on the number of hours worked for design, procurement, etc. Consequently, if any department worked more hours than planned and was not receiving any benefit from doing so, it was motivated to reclaim that extra expense as a compensation event, which adjusted the target.
- The client company still had elements of the old mindset and refused to disclose during the project, despite it not being likely at any point, whether the budget of £57 million was due to be exceeded or not. Consequently, despite significant savings being forecast on the contract target cost, the contractor had ongoing suspicions that the £57 million project budget was going to be exceeded, in which case any bonus would be capped at £500 000. This was not the intention of the client, but it further reinforced the culture of claiming for any additional hours worked, as they would not be recovered through the incentive mechanisms.
- The incentive plan could have been drafted with more clarity to state that any savings under the contract would be paid up to the point at which the project budget was hit, which was the intention of the client. With hindsight, the client thought the incentive plan should have been drafted to state that any over-run on the project budget would reduce the incentive payment to the contractor and not obliterate it!

From the contractor's project manager's perspective:

- There was a general presumption that the fee-at-risk element would be paid if the project manager performed as expected. Consequently, and in particularly with regard to the £100 000 service bonus, the monetary figure was not significant, but was seen as an attention grabber if not awarded, which would draw senior management's attention to the project.

- In reality, the lump sum for design was too low. Consequently, the motivation was not to spend more internally on design, procurement, etc. to search out cost reductions, which would reduce the costs within the target and therefore increase the contractor's profit, but more 'if we do not sort this out now, it will hurt us later in construction'. This was not helped by the client's engineers fiddling with the design just prior to construction.
- The use of the conditional incentive on the project budget, whereby the maximum incentive that could be paid was limited to £500000 if the budget was exceeded, did have some effect in avoiding loading of project costs on to the client's budget.
- However, the lack of knowledge of the total project budget stopped the contractor helping the client and hindered the partnering process, because the contractor could not contribute to the areas of project outside its contract, even though it potentially was in its interests to do so.

From both perspectives the contract could have been drafted with more clarity in two respects:

- The contract was not clear about who would gain from any interest payments that the contractor would receive if payments on the 'S' curve ran ahead of the actual costs incurred by it. At the time of the interviews, it was estimated by the client that this could be up to £0.5 million, partly as a result of savings achieved, but partly because subcontract packages off the critical path were being let later.
- Within the contractor's target cost was some contingency money which would be shared if risks did not occur. However, it was not clear which risks were included within the contract as contingency and which were compensation events that would adjust the target.

Both of these ongoing contractual discussions undermined the relationship.

My conclusion is that the incentive scheme was a success as it reduced project costs, which was the prime objective of the client. However, with hindsight, its operation could have been improved by:

- Greater clarity of drafting of the contract, in terms of expressing the incentives, risk allocation and ownership of interest on cash flow.
- Changes to the contractor's internal organization and accounting procedures outside the core project team, as its departmental structure did not stimulate its employees to contribute fully to reducing costs.

- Greater openness by the client in communicating its forecast of project out-turn cost would have helped the relationship.
- Using a multiplier or percentage reduction on the contractor's total bonus should project costs exceed £57 million, rather than a conditional gatepost. If project costs had become closer to the £57 million, then the £500 000 cap on the contractor's fee and bonuses would have caused serious relationship problems when good co-operative behaviour was most needed. This would be especially so if the contractor's costs were significantly below target.
- In terms of producing open behaviours, the 'service' incentive was not sufficient or properly structured to produce the changes desired by the client. There was a feeling, with which I would agree, that the total payment should either have been increased or dropped altogether. It was also felt that the incentive mechanism should have been structured to reward changed behaviour and better than expected service, rather than just what should be expected.

10.7 Indirect incentives

This book has so far concentrated on direct financial incentives to the contractor or consultant and the 'carrot' of repeat order business as the main motivators to stimulate improved performance, however that is defined, by contractors or consultants. For completeness, other incentives are briefly considered in this section. These are improved cash flow, enhanced reputation and bonus flow-down. These can be used on top of other financial incentive mechanisms.

10.7.1 Improved cash flow

Incentives for improving cash flow can take three forms: shorter payment periods, advanced payments and size of retention.

- More frequent payment, for instance every 2 weeks instead of every 4 weeks or monthly, and faster payment once the amount due has been certified, is likely to make a contract more attractive to a contractor, particularly smaller firms.[1]
- A straw poll of contractors I carried out suggests that roughly 1% of project costs are spent on financing. Clients can generally borrow more cheaply than contractors. All other things being equal, it therefore makes financial sense for the client to take the majority of financing costs. Traditionally, an advance payment may be made when the contractor has to make a significant investment before doing any of the physical work, for example mobilizing in a remote location. Instead, an advance payment could be

made to stimulate greater investment in the project before any physical work is done. As some leverage is lost by the client, it is suggested that this only be employed in a long-term or repeat relationship with a contractor that the client trusts, rather than on a one-off project.

> Howard and Bell[1] report a case in which 20% of the construction manager's fee was paid up-front and that contractor's management team gave the whole project greater and more immediate attention.

- Ashley and Workman[2] briefly reported that, in some instances, the size of the retention had been linked to the schedule status of the project: a retention of 15% if the project was forecast to be late, 10% if it was on time and 5% if ahead of time. If the schedule status of the project determines the size of the retention, then, although there is a genuine incentive to speed up the progress of the work on site, there is also an incentive to programme optimistically. If I was the client's project manager, I would prefer accuracy rather than optimism.

10.7.2 Enhanced reputation

Smith et al.[3] labelled pride and profit as the contractor's main motivations. Although cash flow ensures survival of the business in the short term and profit is certainly desirable on a project-by-project basis, it could be argued that, for a contractor to grow and expand beyond its existing base of clients, a good reputation is needed. High-visibility or flagship projects will enhance a contractor's reputation provided it performs well and achieves the project objectives. Poor performance may detract from it. Making a project a high-visibility one provides the contractor with the incentive to put in a competitive bid and to do a good job once the contract has been won. Signing up to best practice schemes, such as the Movement for Innovation, can help to publicize achievements.

10.7.3 Bonus flow-down

I have identified from the literature three categories of bonus flow-down incentives: payments to subcontractors; periodic worker incentives; and contractor staff incentives.

Payments to subcontractors

In the modern construction environment, it is the norm for much of the work to be either subcontracted or, under the construction management approach, let to specialist works contractors. While the main contractor is responsible for co-ordinating the others, the potential exists for significant savings in time and cost or increases in performance in use to originate from these subcontractors or works contractors. It therefore makes sense to offer them incentives on performance.

The concept and practice of project alliancing, in which the additional profit of the individual contractors is tied to the success of the overall project and not to each individual contract, has been covered in some detail in section 9.2. This concept can be moved down a contractual level to the subcontractors. If this is to be done, then sufficient incentive must be included in the contract with the main contractor to finance worthwhile incentives in these subcontracts, yet leave enough to motivate the main contractor. For instance, if a 20% share of any cost savings is thought to be sufficient to motivate the main contractor and the subcontractors, then the contractor should be allocated 40% of any cost savings, half of which is to be passed down to subcontractors. To make sure this happens, it will have to be written into the main contract as an obligation of the contractor to let the subcontracts with this provision written in.

Periodic worker incentives

Labour productivity can obviously have an effect on out-turn cost. To reward good productivity, a base level has to be established. This suggests that incentives tied to productivity have to be for work for which reliable historic data exist, and this will tend to be for maintenance or repetitive work, for example tunnelling. It is suggested that worker incentives are paid on a regular basis, so that the reward is fairly immediate and can be related to performance.

The danger of using incentives based only on productivity is that the workers are encouraged to pursue productivity at the expense of quality and/or safety. Three suggestions to maintain the quality aspect are:

- The increase in the amount of incentive can diminish as productivity increases so that excessive productivity is not rewarded. Ultimately, a cap can be put on the amount of incentive paid per unit time.
- Any hours spent on reworking or correcting defects can be included in the productivity measure.
- A monthly bonus pool can be created, the size of which depends on the amount of work completed that month, and this is distributed to the workers. The cost of any rework, including materials and supervision, is deducted from this pool.

One way to avoid workers ignoring safety aspects is to have a 'gatepost', which means that no productivity bonus is paid if an accident of a certain sort happens. The danger with this approach is that individual workers can come under pressure from colleagues not to report accidents or near misses. One client in the UK found that a worker carried on with his job, despite missing the end of a finger, which had been hidden in a plastic bag! If near misses and minor accidents are not reported, the figures are misleading and the causes of accidents or near misses are not addressed. Consequently, safety, in the longer term, is reduced! If workers are rewarded for cumulative safety performance, rather than safety performance over a fixed timescale, that is by milestone determination, the pressure not to report incidents becomes even greater!

Any worker incentives can be either paid directly by the client or written into the contract with the contractor.

Contractor staff incentives

The principle behind contractor staff incentives is an extension of the principle behind contractor incentives: the contractor's site team's motivation is aligned with the client's so that it makes decisions which are in both its own and the client's best interests. As with worker incentives, staff incentives can either be paid directly by the client or written into the contract with the contractor. Three strategies, which can be combined, are summarized here:

- The contractor's site team is rewarded for any savings in cost prior to the contractor receiving any of the incentive. Howard and Bell[1] report a case in which the client described the contractor's site team as being 'driven' to achieve the client's cost goals. However, contractors would argue that they are first in line to lose money, so they should be first in line to receive money.
- Individual staff incentives are tied to individual performance. The normal strategy would be that the proportion of the staff incentive paid to an individual is related to his or her position and therefore influence on the end of project objectives. When process incentives are used, a matrix can be developed that relates individual performance to its impact on the measures used for the contractor's evaluation. In practice, Howard and Bell[1] found that considerable time was spent both developing and administering the incentive programme. It may also promote individual performance at the expense of team performance. For this reason, it is suggested that only part of the staff incentive is tied to individual performance, or the size of the individual bonus is moderated by team performance in some way.
- Incentives are partially or wholly banked until the end of the project, with payment again being partially or wholly conditional on end of project objectives being achieved. This would be to avoid an overemphasis on short-term results or false reporting. Reasons for adopting this strategy could be to encourage an emphasis on the end of project objectives or to retain key staff until the end of the project. This could be appropriate in times of relative boom in the construction industry.

10.8 Conclusion

This chapter has introduced five different multi-incentive mechanisms that can be used to blend the different types of incentives introduced in Chapter 6 of this book. In the same way as individual types of incentives can be combined by these multi-incentive mechanisms, so can these mechanisms be combined to form an incentive plan. However, readers are reminded that, when putting one together, it must be done intelligently to produce a balanced incentive, so that the contractor puts the same emphasis on the achievement of different project objectives as the client. The considerations discussed in Chapter 5 are relevant here. These mechanisms are like tools: the skill is not just in using them, but in using them well. Several different types of indirect incentives have also been discussed for the sake of completeness.

> **Review question 1** Refer back to the preview question at the start of this chapter. What details that you needed to know do you now know? What more do you need to know? How and when will you find this out?

> **Review question 2** For a project with which you have either recently been involved or are just about to be involved use the incentive mechanisms outlined in this section to develop as detailed a multi-incentive plan as is useful for you to capture the learning from this and other chapters.

Review question 3   Look at the indirect incentives in section 10.7. What reasons are there for using them in the type of projects with which you are involved, including subcontracts? What reasons are there against using them?

Type	Reasons for	Reasons against

Now draw a learning map.

References

1. Howard W. E. and Bell L. C. *Innovative strategies for contractor compensation.* CII, Austin, Texas, January 1998, Construction Industry Institute Research Report 114-11.
2. Ashley D. B. and Workman B. W. *Incentives in construction contracts.* CII, Austin, Texas, April 1986, Construction Industry Institute Source Document 8.
3. Smith S. E. *et al.* Contractual relationships in construction. *J. Constr. Div. ASCE,* Dec. 1975, **101**, 907–21.

The following report and paper have also been drawn upon for this chapter. Credit is thereby given:

Blyth A. H. Design of incentive contracts, basic principles. *Aeronaut. J.,* 1969, **73**, 119–24.
Perry J. G. *et al. Target and cost reimbursable contracts: Part A: A study of their use and implications; Part B: Management and financial implications.* CIRIA, London, 1982, CIRIA Report 85.

11. Summary and conclusions

This chapter provides a summary of each chapter, before drawing out the common themes of the book and principal conclusions. It can be viewed as an executive summary of the book.

Throughout this book I have used accelerated learning techniques, where possible, to enhance learning and understanding by:

- highlighting key points in bold
- quoting other authors
- illustrating the points made with both diagrams and real-life examples
- asking questions that stimulate the reader both to set outcomes before reading each chapter and to reflect on what has been written afterwards.

Preview question   What are your desired outcomes from reading this chapter?

Chapter 1 gave an overview of each chapter of the book. I also stated the reasons behind my interest in the topic of construction procurement and the reasons for writing this book: principally, my belief that, for partnering to survive and prosper, it needs to be based on a sound commercial and contractual base. The development of this book is a combination of the following influences:

- academic research: a worldwide literature review and my own applied research of projects in the UK
- consultancy and facilitation of workshops to develop the procurement strategy and approach on both individual projects and strategic alliances
- experience of training people in procurement strategy, sometimes developing the procurement strategy for real projects at the same time.

Chapter 2 gave some background on the development of partnering in the UK, concluding that 'partnering' is a concept with many different definitions and ways of being implemented. **Partnering is not, therefore, a procurement route, but encompasses a whole spectrum of approaches at both the procurement and the project implementation stages.** I then presented a model *for* partnering. This is illustrated again in Fig. 11.1, with the addition of various partnering processes and tools which have been explored in the book to varying levels of detail.

I argued that **the central purpose of procurement is to align objectives, so that all participants are motivated to work together for the project's success, rather than only their individual organization's objectives**. The chapter then concluded that partnering as a concept is not appropriate in all circumstances, and that **the extent to which organizations partner and the investment they make in it is dependent upon the benefits that will gained from working together.** This is principally dependent on project complexity, risk and size, as well as the period of time over which the relationship will last.

Chapter 3 looked at the concepts and process of procurement, as well as outlining various processes that feed into the procurement process. Before deciding on the procurement strategy, for each project and organization

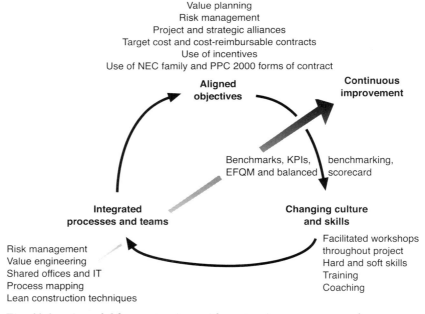

Fig. 11.1. A model for *partnering, with partnering processes and procurement tools*

(including the contractors, consultants and suppliers) the following **information** should be gained, understood and taken into account:

- objectives
- risks and opportunities
- constraints
- capabilities or strengths and weaknesses
- cultural factors.

The value planning phase of value management (to define objectives) and risk management processes feed into this stage. Both of these processes are outlined as a procurement tool in Appendix 1.

Following this 'information' phase, the **'best-fit' procurement route** is chosen. This may not be a commonly used partnering route, such as a target cost contract or project alliance, but a more conventional route. This is why conventional procurement routes are considered in Chapter 4. From this the **contract breakdown structure** can be developed for the project, so that the work content and risk in each contract package matches the capabilities or strengths and weaknesses of likely parties to the project.

The next stage is to **choose the payment terms** and **select the most appropriate conditions of contract for each individual contract package**. The payment terms include matching risk and opportunities with incentives. This could include:

- particularly in price-based contracts, the development of an incentive plan to place greater emphasis on the achievement of certain of the client's objectives
- the allocation of risk between the parties either within the contract or as a client's risk, paid for if it occurs
- in a target cost contract or project alliance, the development of the share profile, which governs the share of the parties' pain and gain.

With respect to selecting the most appropriate conditions of contract, I have a bias for the NEC family of contracts as, in my opinion, it is the most flexible group of contracts in existence. In addition, its principles of clarity and simplicity, and especially of stimulating good project management, encourage parties to work together on a day-to-day basis with more rigour than other forms of contract. A brief overview of the flexibility of the NEC family of contracts is given in Appendix 3.

The next stage is **the selection process**. As well as considering cost, the selection process and questions asked should be designed to pre-qualify both those eligible to do the work, in terms of technical ability, past experience, etc., and those most suitable, in terms of cultural fit, commitment to partnering, continuous improvement, etc. A procurement tool on 'selecting contractors by value' expands on this process in Appendix 4.

Throughout all these phases, the allocation and sharing of risk is central. I revisited **the principles of risk allocation and** extended and clarified them to include **risk sharing,** as is the case in target cost contracts and project alliances. These principles are:

Principle 1. The extent to which the consequences of a risk are allocated to a party should take into account the overall effect on that party's business, both positive and negative.

Principle 2. Risk, both positive and negative, should be allocated to a party in proportion to the extent to which it can influence the likelihood of that risk occurring.

Principle 3. Negative risk should be allocated to a party in proportion to the extent to which it can minimize the consequences if that risk occurs, with, all things being equal, the second principle taking priority.

Principle 4. For minor risks, clarity of allocation should take priority over the other principles, with a tendency towards allocating these risks to the contracting party, especially when those risks are likely to occur frequently.

Before awarding the contract, and ideally in between each stage, the client should **ask 'what if?' questions, taking account of all participants' viewpoints**, to ensure that the parties will still remain motivated to work together in different scenarios that may affect the project. This involves thinking through the second-, third- and even fourth-order effects of risk allocation, incentives, etc. from all perspectives. This is often the part that is missing in projects that do not achieve their objectives.

The final stages are **awarding, communicating, implementing and monitoring**, which lead to **feedback and continuous improvement**, of both the procurement process and the project participants, through measuring their performance, both quantitatively using benchmarks and qualitatively by benchmarking. This is both a check on whether the objectives are being, or have been, achieved and a means to continuous improvement. A procurement tool in Appendix 6 gives the bones of benchmarks and benchmarking. Throughout the process there is some **reiteration** as an issue may come up later in the process or project, which makes it desirable to revisit earlier decisions.

Chapter 4 started by considering different conventional procurement routes, which include the traditional client or consultant design followed by contractor build; contractor design routes; the preferred contractor approach; management approaches, such as construction management and management contracting; and engineer, procure and construct (EPC) approaches. For each route, what it is, its advantages and disadvantages and when to use it were discussed. Each is appropriate in the right circumstances. However, **to varying degrees, each conventional procurement route also has some characteristics that make it unsuitable for 'full' partnering.**

That chapter then went on to review different priced- or output-based payment mechanisms. In these forms of payment a contractor or consultant is paid per unit or item of output. This could be by means of bills of quantities, method-related bills of quantities, a schedule of rates, a lump sum, milestones or activity schedules. Each of these is reviewed. However, **a fundamental deficiency of all price-based payment mechanisms is that the contractor's costs are hidden from the client. At best this reduces the effectiveness of various partnering processes**, such as value engineering and risk management. **At worst, it leads to contractual 'gamesmanship', which acts against and undermines the partnering ethos.**

Chapter 5 discussed concepts and process for the intelligent use of incentives. However, it started by suggesting that the purpose of an incentive is to more *closely* align the motivations of the contractor, consultant or supplier to those of the client. To do this, incentive plans have to be carefully and intelligently thought through to avoid misalignment of objectives. To do this, the designer of an incentive plan has to take into account various concepts, which are, in summary:

- Each project is unique, so the incentive plan has to be unique to be effective.
- Define and weight the project objectives.
- Balance the incentive plan, so that:
  - rewards to the contractor for pursuing different objectives match the value added and weighting of the client's objectives
  - rewards to the contractor take into account risk and who has influence over it.
- Start with a realistic base from which improved performance is rewarded.
- Develop measures of performance that accurately reflect the objectives.
- Use a combination of positive and negative incentives, with the greater monetary emphasis on the positive incentive/bonus payments.
- To ensure alignment, at the very least consult with the other party when developing the incentive plan. This also promotes realism, understanding and joint ownership.
- On longer-term projects, consider the use of intermediate or milestone incentives, which are a mix of objective and subjective measures.
- If using qualitative measures, then off-site determination by more senior client staff is recommended, but only in consultation with both the site team and the contractor.
- Despite the above deliberations, the end result should be as simple an incentive plan as is necessary to align motivations.
- Communicate the objectives and the incentive plan to all personnel involved or associated with the project.

Chapter 6 identified and gave guidance on the design and use of specific incentive mechanisms to enhance value generally and to improve objective measures of performance. I use the value management definition of **'value'**,

which is functionality divided by whole-life costs. These mechanisms would predominantly be used with conventional procurement routes, such as those discussed in Chapter 4, to place greater emphasis on one or more objectives than the procurement route would do on its own.

I differentiated between incentive clauses to stimulate reduced capital costs and reduced whole-life costs. The former are often inaccurately referred to as value engineering clauses, which is more appropriate for the latter. I also presented original thinking on designing **incentive clauses to enhance the value by increasing the functionality of the asset, rather than by reducing whole-life costs** as is normally the case.

The chapter then discussed the use of **incentive clauses to stimulate improvements in specific measures of performance apart from cost**. These were, in order:

- Measures to stimulate improved performance that translates directly into increased revenue or reduced operating costs. An example would be reduced energy consumption in kilowatt hours.
- Measures to stimulate improved performance that does not translate directly into commercial benefits, which may be appropriate if the drivers for the project are, for instance, improved public image or the need to satisfy and perhaps exceed legal requirements. Reducing pollution from a factory, for instance, might satisfy both criteria.
- Different types of time incentives.
- Incentives for quality, as measured by conformance to specification.

Whether bonuses or damages are specified, **for all of the above incentive clauses, which focus on end of project performance, four criteria were identified for their successful implementation.** These are:

(a) The contractor has control over or, at the very least, a strong influence over the level of performance attained. A consequence of this is that for the incentive to remain valid there needs to be a method of adjusting the required level of performance, particularly for breaches of contract by the client if damages are specified.
(b) The unit of performance can be measured relatively objectively and correctly reflects what the client really wants in terms of improved performance.
(c) The inputs into the process or test conditions are clearly specified.
(d) These inputs or test conditions can be controlled.

The chapter then went on to explore:

- Process incentives, which are used to improve how the work is done, in the belief that improved process leads to improved end results. These are generally suitable for projects in which the end objectives and/or risks are ill-defined, unknown or subject to change. To attach incentives to end of project objectives may be counter-productive as participants could start to focus on defensive behaviour, rather than working together. Projects of this type are likely to be let under a cost-based contract, if not a pure cost-reimbursable contract.

- Incentives to stimulate improved health and safety performance. I argued that **health and safety incentives for end of project performance, as measured in number of incidents, may be counter-productive in the medium to long term. If incentives are to be used, they should focus on improving the health and safety processes, which leads to improved results.**

Chapter 7 considered cost-reimbursable contracts in some detail. In their pure form, cost-reimbursable contracts are rarely used. However, both target cost contracts and project alliances are cost-based contracts, so key implementation points which apply to cost-reimbursable contracts also apply to these procurement routes. The **seven key implementation points** identified were:

(a) Use them in the right circumstances: for projects that are either time or quality/performance driven, subject to high risk, scarce supply and/or with a contractor with which there is an existing relationship of trust. In these cases collaborative working — partnering — will increase the likelihood of success.

(b) The client, its consultants and the contractor need to understand how costs are built up under the contract prior to signing it, and to make any adjustments necessary, taking into account how the contractor builds up costs in practice. This is because it affects motivations, transparency and administration during the contract.

(c) The client is more involved in the *management*, as opposed to the administration, of the contract compared with price-based contracts, and staffs the project with sufficient numbers of suitably skilled people with the right attitude and authority to partner.

(d) More specifically, cost-based contracts are staffed with adequate numbers of financial management staff and those put forward and selected should have a proactive focus and financial skills. Additionally, they need to have good interpersonal skills to preserve and improve the relationship when hard decisions and negotiations take place.

(e) Consider when it is most appropriate to reimburse the contractor its costs plus fee: before, when or after the contractor has paid out costs.

(f) Specify and/or agree audit requirements up-front and how these will be implemented.

(g) Ensure that a good financial management system is in place and that it is operated by well-trained, high-quality staff who understand the system.

I consider the most important of these points to be *(a), (c)* and *(g)*. I fleshed out point *(g)*, the ideal requirements for a good financial management system, in greater detail than in any other literature I am aware of. This is because without such a system, the effectiveness of partnering processes, such as joint value engineering, risk management and up-to-date monitoring, forecasting and 'real-time' decision making, is reduced.

Chapter 8 explored target cost contracts. Traditionally, these have been used in less extreme circumstances than pure cost-reimbursable contracts. There are two main reasons that make target cost contracts particularly appropriate for partnering:

- The **open book accounting leads to transparency of cost**. This both enables partnering processes to be more effective and reduces any argument over adjustments to the target, compared with adjustments to the prices under price-based contracts.
- The **sharing of risk and reward creates an alignment of motivations**, being the commercial driver to partner.

Boundary conditions for the use of target cost contracts were established compared with pure cost-reimbursable contracts and price-based procurement routes.

As well as those covered for cost-reimbursable contracts, **additional key implementation points for target cost contracts were identified.** These are:

(a) The existing literature emphasizes the importance of **an accurate target**. By exploring the components of the target — base costs, risk allowances and the fee — this book was more explicit in stating that the client should satisfy itself with the realism of the overall target:
  (i) Evaluate and confirm the realism of the actual cost component of the target (the base estimate).
  (ii) Identify, agree contingencies for and clearly allocate specified risks within or outside the target in accordance with the principles of risk allocation and sharing
  (iii) Only agree a level of fee that is consistent with the returns the contractor would earn under a price-based contract, especially when the fee is expressed as a percentage of actual costs incurred.
  A range of 'what if?' scenarios for out-turn actual cost compared with the original and adjusted target should be generated to, at the very least, inform the selection of the contractor.
(b) The client should **think intelligently about the setting of the share fractions that make up the share profile** as this affects the risk included within the target and the motivations of the parties once it is awarded. The five-zone model for setting the share fractions that make up a share profile in a target cost contract was presented. The circumstances, effects

on motivations and consequences of different share fractions in each of the five zones were explored. Despite there being five zones, our general advice is to have as few share fractions as possible within any share profile.

(c) **Decide when and how any over-run of the target is paid to or back from the contractor.** This becomes relevant only if there is a cost over-run relative to the target, when it becomes very relevant, particularly on large projects.

(d) **Calculate and agree any change in the target** as soon as possible after an event that causes an upward adjustment, and ideally before, because failure to do so may mean that the contract effectively reverts to a cost-reimbursable contract, losing the benefit of aligned objectives.

Finally in this chapter, what is meant by the terms **guaranteed maximum price** (GMP) and **prime contracting** was explored. Both of these are based around target cost contracts, although the latter incorporates many other partnering and procurement concepts and processes.

Chapter 9 explored alliances, both project specific and strategic. The characteristics common to both of these types of alliances were described, when it was appropriate to use each type was identified and their key implementation points, particularly those relating to procurement aspects, were stated. Project alliances are suitable for use on large, complex and risky projects, in which innovation is needed to produce the step changes in results that are needed. The defining characteristic is that they share risk and reward among the participants. Consequently, it could be argued that the key implementation point, after selection of the right participants, is that the incentive plan is so designed that each party makes more profit by saving project costs through co-operation with the others than by increasing the price paid by the client under its individual contract.

Strategic alliances are used if the client has a portfolio of difficult-to-scope work of a similar type which can be let over a number of years. Continuous improvement is more gradual.

Common themes of both approaches are the importance of selecting the right partner that is appropriate for the client and its project(s) and creating — and in strategic alliances maintaining — commercial motivation and cultural change. Both of these require client involvement, leadership and investment to drive them, and the same requirements apply to the alliance partners. Any investment, in business terms, has to achieve payback and a return in terms of reduced time and cost of projects and better completed assets. **Both project and strategic alliances require a large investment but, equally, can produce a large return.** As project alliances can be viewed as a development of target cost contracts and the method of delivering a project within a strategic alliance is often through a target cost contract or project alliance, the key implementation points which were identified in the previous chapters also apply.

Chapter 10 identified and explained five mechanisms for combining individual incentives to stimulate performance to meet two or more project objectives. The individual incentives were explored in Chapter 6, while the considerations outlined in Chapter 5 are relevant for their intelligent and successful use. A danger of all multi-incentive plans is that the client, in trying to be clever, produces too complex a plan, which may actually stimulate a contractor to pursue objectives in an unbalanced or counter-productive way. **The greater the level of trust between the parties and the longer the potential relationship, then the less the need for complex incentive plans.** Several indirect incentive mechanisms were described for completeness.

Chapter 11 has so far summarized the findings of each chapter. What has this book offered the reader? In general, **it presents new thinking and greater specificity, in terms of level of detail, than other available literature**. More specifically, it does the following:

- It introduces the concept that there is a spectrum of partnering and that the method is situational. In general, the further along the spectrum the partners are, the greater the investment needed to make partnering work, but the greater the rewards. Investment therefore has to be balanced against potential returns.

- A new model *for* partnering is presented, which, from feedback in my training seminars, appears to make sense to practitioners and gives a framework for the development of partnering between organizations.

- It offers a process for developing procurement strategy, which also identifies the key considerations to be taken into account. Again, from testing it in training seminars and procurement strategy workshops, it appears to be useful to practitioners.

- The principles of risk allocation are clarified and extended to cover risk allocation and sharing, as is the case in target cost contracts and project alliances.

- It also offers a process for developing a balanced incentive plan. The new thinking is that, to be balanced, what is important is that the relative profit for the contractor on each incentive reflects the weighting of the client's objectives and *not* that an individual incentive reflects the value to the client of that objective being achieved.

- Furthermore, in relation to the above, the results of the value planning phase of value management are integrated into the process of developing a balanced incentive plan.

- It describes the development of an incentive mechanism to enhance value by rewarding increased functionality as opposed to just reduced cost.

- It explicitly states the seven key implementation points for cost-reimbursable contracts, which also apply to all cost-based contracts.

- It goes into a greater level of detail than does other published literature to describe the ideal capabilities of a cost-based financial management system.
- It breaks down the need to assess the accuracy of the target under target cost contracts into the need to assess the realism of the components: the base costs, the risk contingency and the fee.
- It presents the development of the five-zone model for setting the share profile in a target cost contract.
- It explains the common characteristics of project and strategic alliances and identifies their key implementation points.
- It presents for the first time in UK literature various different mechanisms for combined or multi-incentive plans.

I am sufficiently aware to recognize that **the level of detail in some sections of text may be too great for the general reader on procurement.** This is one of the reasons why key points have been highlighted in bold so that the flavour and key considerations can be absorbed. **However, when faced with a specific situation — for instance, when defining the specification for a financial management system or setting a share profile — the detail is now available.**

To summarize, in Chapter 2, I presented the spectrum of partnering, developed through my work with Margett. This is reprinted here (Fig. 11.2). Essentially, there is a range of ways in which participants can partner and a range of procurement routes that can be taken to provide the commercial and contractual alignment for cultural change and integrated processes to occur.

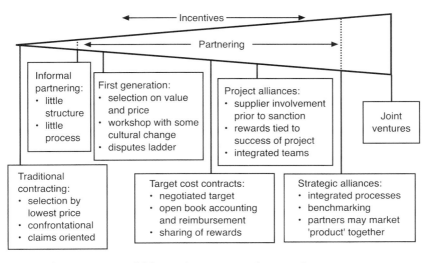

Fig. 11.2. Broome and Margett's spectrum of partnering

Their use is situational and how they are implemented will and should vary from client to client, project to project and over time, as both the industry and individual participants develop. As you travel along the spectrum, greater investment is needed to make partnering relationships work, yet the rewards are also greater. Partnering, and the rewards it brings, is not just about 'being nice', but has to be based on a sound procurement base for the partners to thrive and prosper.

It is my aspiration that this book will provoke thought and is, above all, useful to the practitioner in travelling down the partnering road, whether presenting a high-level concept or a practical specific. Whether I have succeeded is for the reader to decide. **However, I actively seek feedback, both positive and negative, on what is written here and its application in practice.**

I can be contacted with feedback or for consultancy, training and facilitation on 07970 428 929 or by e-mail at Info@jb-project-consulting.co.uk

Review question 1 If reading this chapter as an executive summary, that is before reading the rest of this book, briefly review this chapter identifying what would be useful for you to have more detail about.

Review question 2 What do you agree with in this chapter and book? What do you disagree with? What has been left out? And what do you think should have been said (instead)?

Review question 3 If you have read this book and this chapter, list the concepts and processes that could be useful to you in practice. What specifically could you or your company do differently to turn these into actions on a daily, weekly, monthly or project-to-project basis?

Especially if you have drawn learning maps for each chapter: draw out a learning map to summarize what you have learnt from reading this book.

Appendix 1. Procurement tool 1: The concept of value in value management and the value planning process

This section briefly defines what value is and gives an overview of the value management process, before describing in greater detail the first phase of value management: value planning.

A1.1 The concept of value

In a value management context, 'value' is defined as:[1,2]

$$\text{value} = \frac{\text{functionality}}{\text{whole-life cost}}$$

Therefore, to increase 'value', you either increase the functionality, for example improve the working conditions of office workers to make the office a more pleasant place to work, or decrease the whole-life costs, whether capital, maintenance or other operating costs.

A1.2 Overview of value management

Put simply, the first phase of value management — value planning — concentrates on defining what functionality means to the project stakeholders. This enables outline options for fulfilling this 'functionality' to be generated and the best-value option selected. The second phase — value engineering — concentrates on decreasing life cycle costs while maintaining the defined functionality. How these phases fit together is illustrated in Fig. A1.1.

The various stages within VP1, VP2 and VE are termed the 'job plan'. The value analysis/review stage (VA) is not considered here, although it is part of the process of continuous improvement and could be included as a process for benchmarking (see Appendix 6).

The approach is workshop based, particularly in the early stages, so that all major stakeholders can express their objectives and views, understand others' and then form a consensus both on the end of project objectives and on how, in overview, they can be achieved.

Value management		
Value planning	Value engineering	Value analysis/ review

Concept	Feasibility and outline design	Detailed design	Construction	Post-construction
VP1: Identify need, define objectives and constraints	VP2: Identify, evaluate and select broad approach/ outline scheme design	VE: Identify functional components of project and take out unnecessary life cycle costs while fulfilling these functions		VA: Analyse the completed project and/or review the process to provide feedback for future projects

Fig. A1.1. An overview of the value management process (developed from reference 3)

A1.3 The value planning process

The value planning phase can be divided into two phases — VP1 and VP2 — both of which centre around a workshop approach.

A1.3.1 Value planning phase 1 (VP1)

VP1, at concept, has the following purposes:[1]

- to ensure that there is a need for the project
- to gain understanding, consensus and agreement over the specific project objectives
- to state clearly the value for money criteria
- to provide useful ideas about possible options
- to ensure that the decision-making process is accountable.

In addition, the principal constraints — what has to be done and what cannot be done — are usually identified in the workshop. VP1 takes place in a workshop environment, usually with a professional facilitator orchestrating the process, which consists of the following stages:

Stage 1: Information

Each key stakeholder gives a brief statement describing the need for the project and its key assumptions and constraints. Other participants can ask clarifying and challenging questions at the end of each statement, with the focus being on understanding. A general discussion then follows, from which the facilitator should aim to gain consensus and agreement over the key objectives and constraints, which are then summarized.

Stage 2: Structuring of objectives

The objectives are then structured into a value hierarchy by means of a 'means to an end' analysis, which is illustrated by the development of a value tree. This is simply illustrated in Fig. A1.2 for a new factory. Several drafts may be necessary, and the whole process of developing the value tree together encourages understanding and consensus among the participants. The end result is a value tree with a set of lower-order attributes from which different proposals can be developed.

Note the 'How' and 'Why' at the top. The diagram is developed from left to right by asking: 'How is a good factory achieved?' One of the answers is 'By having good working conditions'. 'How is this achieved?' One of the answers is 'By having good air'. The check on the logic is to work back from right to left, asking: 'Why is this important?'. For example, 'Why is good air important?' 'To provide good working conditions', etc. Also, in practice, there would be discussion on what, for instance, 'good air' meant precisely, which would be captured in the workshop records.

Stage 3: Speculation

Ideas are generated for ways of fulfilling these objectives, usually by brainstorming. In effect, we are asking how the lower-order objectives could be achieved. For instance, 'How is this good air achieved?'. The emphasis is

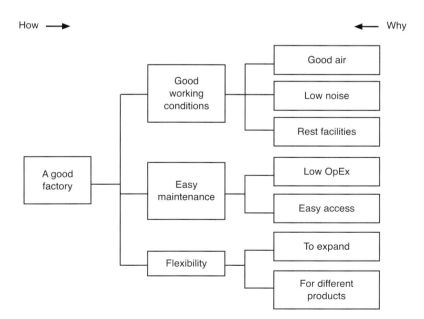

Fig. A1.2. Example of a value tree

on the quantity and diversity of ideas generated, with no evaluation. As they are being generated, each idea is given a number and a recorder often records these ideas on a spreadsheet.

Stage 4: Evaluation

This stage marks a switch from the creative thinking of the previous phase to analytical thinking. Unless it is self-evident, the person who generated the idea is asked briefly to explain, in a sentence or two, what was meant. Each idea is then categorized with a number or label such as:

- red flag: discard idea
- amber flag: not worth proceeding with at the moment but may have an application
- green flag: good idea with potential for implementation.

If there is disagreement among participants, then the facilitator should promote and allow discussion in order to gain consensus. The ideas worth considering are then grouped together into alternative proposals by the participants. Some of the ideas will be mutually exclusive and some will support each other, providing synergy when combined, while others will stand alone. The net result should be a number of outline proposals which can be taken forward to the next stage.

Stage 5: Development

The outline proposals are developed and costed up on a whole-life basis for evaluation in VP2. Often this is done outside the workshop by different groups working on different proposals. To ensure consistency, the alternative scenarios should be priced up by the same cost consultant. The facilitator should send out a pack summarizing the workshop, so that there is a common and independent record of it.

A1.3.2 *Value planning phase 2 (VP2)*

VP2, at feasibility, has the following purposes:[1]

- to verify that the project objectives and constraints are still valid
- to ensure that the outline proposal is chosen in accordance with the value for money criteria
- to achieve group consensus in favour of a single option
- to secure value improvements in the chosen design option
- to ensure that the decision-making proposal is accountable.

The results of VP1, including the developed outline proposals, are brought to the VP2 workshop. As with the first workshop, a pack is normally sent out to participants prior to the workshop. The 'job plan' for VP2 has seven stages.

Stage 1: Information

The facilitator gives a summary of the project objectives and any developments since those identified in VP1 and then does likewise for assumptions and constraints. Clarification and challenges are again allowed and any revisions are noted.

Stage 2: Structuring of objectives

A revised value tree is presented to take account of any revisions to objectives. This revision is done by:

- simplifying it by taking out lower-order attributes which do not directly influence the choice of proposal
- ensuring that no attributes measure the same thing
- taking out fundamental attributes, or minimum criteria, which have to be met, for example those related to safety, but which will not affect the choice of design.

Although capital budget and maximum timescale might be an issue, it is suggested that these are not part of the value tree but are expressed as constraints or minimum criteria. It is also strongly advised that whole-life costs are not considered at this stage.

Stage 3: Assignment of importance weighting

Moving from left to right of the value tree, each attribute is assigned an importance weighting before moving on to the next level of that branch. The total of each column should add up to 1 (Fig. A1.3). To gain the scores in the final column, you multiply out along each branch.

Note how the second-order attribute of 'easy maintenance' has been taken out from Fig. A1.2, and note, in particular, the removal of 'low OpEx' (low operating expenditure). This is because low OpEx will be in the whole-life costs, so it would be 'double counted' when calculating value.

Stage 4: Evaluation

The purpose of this stage is to evaluate each proposal, developed from VP1, against the weighted value tree. This involves each design proposal being introduced and explained before being marked for each attribute. However, before evaluating each proposal, the scoring system for each attribute should be determined.

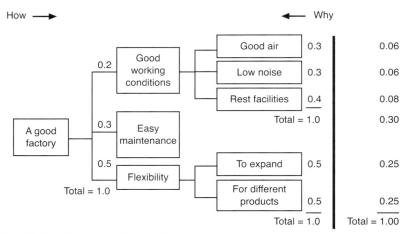

Fig. A1.3.   *Example of a weighted value tree*

It is worthwhile considering how subjective measures are weighted. Green[4] recommends 'Subjective attributes are measured on an arbitrary scale of 0–100, where 0 represents the minimum acceptable standard and 100 the maximum which is achievable. For attributes which can be assessed objectively it is necessary to convert the measurements so that they are also represented on a 0–100 scale.' He points out that these measures need not be linear.

The facilitator should be attempting to gain consensus, so majority voting does not apply and any significant discrepancies in people's thinking should be explored. The scores are then averaged and normalized against 100. Once the evaluation is complete, the results can be fed into a matrix and a 'functionality' score given on a scale of 0 to 100 for each proposal.

Stage 5: Sensitivity analysis

The purpose of this stage is to test the sensitivity of the previous stage to any variation in both the weighting given to different attributes and the scores given to each of the different proposals. Therefore, areas to focus on are those that have a large impact on the overall functionality score, that is a large weighting, and/or those on which there was difficulty in reaching consensus. In any case, it is also worthwhile revisiting the proposals that were considered earlier in the evaluation phase to ensure that participants' scoring has not changed as a result of any change in perceptions during the evaluation phase.

Stage 6: Cost/value reconciliation

Strictly speaking, this should be termed a functionality/whole-life cost reconciliation, in which the functionality score for each proposal is divided by the estimated life cycle cost (from stage 5 of VP1) to give the best-value proposal, which becomes the selected option for further development.

Stage 7: Value improvement

The purpose of this stage is to further improve the value of the selected option. This is done in two ways:

- Good ideas from discarded proposals are discussed and included in the new selected proposal if appropriate.
- Areas of concern are noted and a list of ideas on how they may be alleviated is generated, possibly by brainstorming, and then evaluated for further development and inclusion in the scheme and/or detailed design. This is an obvious area in which risk management techniques may be introduced (see Procurement tool 2: Risk management).

A1.4 Outcome, output (performance), input (technical) and method specifications

Value planning can be used to define the way in which a project is defined in the contract documents. Let us take the example of 'a successful new-build road project' in which the route is prescribed. How is this achieved?

- One of the components could be free-flowing traffic. This is an outcome and a measure could be developed with a payment against this. In fact, on one private finance initiative (PFI) road project, the speed of traffic not falling below a stated minimum is one of the parameters on which the consortium is paid. How is free-flowing traffic achieved?
- One way is to ensure that there are no puddles, expressed perhaps as maximum depth of water lying on the road. This is an output, or performance, specification. How is this achieved?
- One of the ways to achieve this is to specify, and possibly design, drains at regular intervals. This is a technical specification. How is this achieved?
- One of the ways could be by describing how the contractor will install each drain. This is a method specification.

You should be able to follow the logic of this by working back upwards from the last bullet asking the 'why?' question. Using a value tree helps to define the project both because it is a means of generating ways of fulfilling project objectives and because it avoids describing something at two levels. An example of this could be the client designing the drains, yet making payment to the contractor partially dependent on the amount of water lying on the road.

The danger of doing both is that the contractor can then say that the reason for not achieving the performance specification is that the client designed the technical specification. Therefore, the contractor, with some justification, does not have control. **As a generalization, a well-written specification never mixes up the outcome, output, input and method specifications for the same element of work.**

References

1. Connaughton J. N. and Green S. D. *Value management in construction: a client's guide*. CIRIA, London, 1996, CIRIA Special Publication 129.
2. The Institution of Civil Engineers. *ICE design and practice guides: creating value in engineering*. Thomas Telford, London, 1996.
3. Pianas D. *Value management in UK practice and awareness in Greece*. The University of Birmingham, Birmingham, MSc dissertation, 2001.
4. Green S. D. *A SMART methodology for value management*. Downloaded from website www.rdg.ac.uk/-kcsgrest/hkivm2.htm, July 2001.

Appendix 2. Procurement tool 2: Risk management

I define a 'risk' as a source of uncertainty in achieving defined objectives, with the level of uncertainty associated with an individual risk being a combination of the likelihood and impact of its occurrence on those objectives. This means that, to identify a risk, the project objectives have first to be identified! Hence, it may be useful to carry out a value planning exercise, as outlined in Appendix 1.

I define risk management as a structured process for identifying and evaluating risks before developing and implementing actions to reduce the likelihood and/or impact of their occurrence. I consider risk management to have five principal stages:

- *Stage 1: define the scope of the study.* For instance, if it is a £100 million plus project, it may worthwhile taking the time and expense to use a computer software package to model the risk profile and how it changes in the light of the actions that you decide to take (the garbage in, garbage out maxim still applies though). If it is a £0.25 million project, then an informal morning workshop may be more appropriate. The stages of a project at which risk will be revisited can also be determined.
- *Stage 2: identify risk.* This can be through brainstorming, using generic and specific checklists of risks and reference to previous projects and/or technical experts.
- *Stage 3: assess or analyse risk.* This is the stage at which the risks from the previous stage are assessed in terms of likelihood of occurrence and their potential impact. Usually, a number is assigned to each risk, ranking it in terms of both likelihood and impact. These numbers are then multiplied together or plotted on a grid. A very simple grid and ranking system is shown in Fig. A2.1. Note that high, medium and low impact and likelihood are quantified in terms of time and cost. The scores are then multiplied together to gain an overall mark. Each specific risk can be numbered and then placed not only in a box on the grid, but where workshop participants feel it should be within the box compared with other risks.
- *Stage 4: response planning.* This is considered in greater detail below. However, depending on the responses developed, the risk profile of the project can be redefined by returning to stage 3. For instance, the impact and likelihood of the risk after the response strategies have been

I = Impact

High = 3 I > £10k or 1 week	3 Hi/Lo	6 Hi/Me	9 Hi/Hi
Medium = 2 £2k or 1 day < I < £10k or 7 days	2 Me/Lo	4 Me/Me	6 Me/Hi
Low = 1 I < £2k or 1 day	1 Lo/Lo	2 Lo/Me	3 Lo/Hi
	Low = 1 L < 1 in every 5 years	Medium = 2 1 in 5 years < L < 1 in 6 months	High = 3 L > 1 in every 6 months

L =
Likelihood

Fig. A2.1.   Example of a weighted value tree

implemented can be replotted on the grid for comparison. An assessment can then be made of whether the effort and expenditure is worthwhile in terms of the reduced likelihood and/or impact of the risk.

- *Stage 5: response implementation.* This is where the risk management process often falls down. A risk register is the 'deliverable' from the risk management workshop. This has all the identified risks listed and ranked in it. Next to each risk are proactive actions to reduce the likelihood of the risk occurring and next to that reactive actions if it does occur. The problem is that often nobody makes use of this information! From talking to practitioners, the trick is to take the principal risks and assign specific risks to different individuals, making management of these risks part of their job description. Additionally, the risk register is periodically reviewed and updated, so that risks are deleted when the time for their occurrence has passed and assigned to individuals as the time for occurrence approaches. That way, while risk is the responsibility of everybody, specific risks are always the responsibility of somebody. Someone within a project team has to take responsibility for allocating specific risks to specific individuals at the appropriate time in the life of the project.

The literature[1-4] states that there are four **risk responses** — avoidance, reduction, absorption and transfer — which often intermingle. As a framework for developing responses, in my opinion, the strategies for each risk should be considered in the following order:

- Can the risk be *avoided* by undertaking the project or part of the project in a different way? For example, at a high level, if the purpose is to generate electricity and the risk of nuclear contamination is considered to be too great, then alternative means of generation are considered. In extreme cases, this may mean not undertaking the project at all.

- *Reduction* means that measures are taken either to reduce the likelihood of the risk occurring or to minimize the consequences if it does. The former usually means spending some money to gain greater certainty. For both this and the above point, the question of value for money has to be addressed. For instance, is it worth spending £20 000 to avoid a risk that has a 1 in 5 likelihood of occurring and, if it does, would have an impact of £100 000 ? A risk-averse client may say 'yes' whereas another may say 'no': this is why the 'cultural factors' need to be considered (**s**ee section 3.4).
- *Absorption* means that allowance is made for the consequences of the risk for one of the following reasons:
  - because the risk may still occur despite proactive actions to reduce that likelihood;
  - to allow for the cost of defined measures taken to minimize the consequences once it has occurred and/or
  - because it will still have an impact on budget and programme despite the steps taken in the two points above.
- *Transfer* means that it is decided who best to allocate the risk to. One needs to consider who is best placed to take the necessary avoidance or reduction measures and who is best placed to absorb the consequences. So, while in the early stages of a project detailed measures may not have been drawn up, some consideration of the above is needed before a risk is allocated. Once these steps have been taken, the risk needs to be allocated or shared in accordance with the principles for risk allocation and sharing. These are central to procurement strategy and are stated in section 3.5.

References

1. Simon P. *et al.* (eds). *Project risk analysis and management (PRAM) guide*. The APM Group, High Wycombe, UK, 1997.
2. The Institution of Civil Engineers and the Faculty and Institute of Actuaries. *Risk analysis and management for projects (RAMP)*. Thomas Telford, London, 1998.
3. Godfrey P. S. *Control of risk: a guide to the systematic management of risk from construction*. CIRIA, London, 1996, CIRIA Special Publication 125.
4. Chapman C. and Ward S. *Project risk management: processes, techniques and insights*. John Wiley and Sons, Chichester, UK, 1997.

Appendix 3. Procurement tool 3: The NEC family of contracts

The NEC (originally standing for New Engineering Contract, but the full name is now quietly being dropped as nothing can be 'new' for ever) is a family of integrated contracts. All members of the family have three objectives compared with traditional forms of contract:

- greater flexibility
- greater clarity and simplicity
- a stimulus to good (project) management.

The first objective is what this procurement toolbox will concentrate on as it is most relevant to procurement. The current family has several members:

- The NEC Engineering and Construction Contract was the first member of the family and is the main form for any construction and heavy engineering contract.
- The NEC Engineering and Construction Subcontract is virtually a back-to-back subcontract with the above for use with principal subcontractors.
- The NEC Engineering and Construction Short Contract is for low-risk, low-complexity contracts.
- The NEC Engineering and Construction Short Subcontract is for use as a subcontract to the main contract on low-risk, low-complexity subcontracts.
- The NEC Professional Services Contract is for professional services such as design or management. In fact, it can be used for any type of professional services, which need not be construction related. With the modifications suggested in its Guidance Notes, this can be amended to be a design subcontract to the construction contract.
- The NEC Partnering Agreement is for use as an 'add on' set of clauses to the above contracts and with other partners' contracts to form a project or strategic alliance.
- The NEC Adjudicator's Contract is a tripartite contract for situations in which an adjudicator is needed.

To come are:

- the NEC Supply and Install Contract, which is for projects in which most of the work is done off site but some installation work may be needed on site

- the NEC Term Maintenance Contract

With the exception of the Adjudicator's Contract and the Partnering Agreement, each member of the family has almost the same nine core sections, with the clauses within each section being predominantly in the same order and much of the text being identical. Once you become familiar with one contract, you therefore automatically become familiar with the others.

The main contract — the NEC Engineering and Construction Contract — has six main options, which determine how the contractor is paid and, indirectly, the degree of risk on the contractor and the ease with which the client can exert control. The options are:

(a) A: Priced contract with activity schedule
(b) B: Priced contract with bill of quantities
(c) C: Target contract with activity schedule
(d) D: Target contract with bills of quantities
(e) E: Cost-reimbursable contract
(f) F: Management contract

These option clauses account for only 10–15% of the text of the contract, so 85–90% of the text stays the same whatever option is used. The NEC Engineering and Construction Subcontract does not have option F. The NEC Professional Services Contract has the equivalent of options A, C and E with an additional option G: Term contract. Each of these contracts has secondary options that allow the client much more scope for fine tuning the contract to its requirements without writing additional clauses: the client just selects the appropriate secondary clauses.

Other aspects of flexibility in the main contract include:

- Any extent of contractor design can be accommodated from nothing to detailed design, to functional or performance specifications, or any combination of these.
- It is intended to be multidisciplinary and its successful use on at least £40 billion pounds' worth of construction and heavy engineering suggests that it is.
- It is as international as any other contract and, as well as being used in the UK, has been used in contracts in Asia, Australia, the USA, Africa and mainland Europe.
- It allows for any balance of client or contractor certification of quality.

By referencing the Works Information (or drawings and specification) for detailed testing and/or submission requirements and using *italics* for items stated in the Contract Data (the equivalent of an expanded appendix) it allows the client to further fine tune the contract to its specific requirements without modifying the conditions of contract.

Further reading

All members of the NEC family, together with their guidance notes, are available from Thomas Telford, London.

For a legal commentary on the NEC, I would recommend:

McInnis J. A. *The New Engineering Contract: a legal commentary*. Thomas Telford, London, 2001.

For a text on how it complements and has been used within partnering arrangements, I would recommend:

Bennett J. and Baird A. *NEC and partnering: the guide to building winning teams*. Thomas Telford, London, 2001.

For a text on how to use it and its key implementation points, I would recommend my own book:

Broome J. C. *The NEC Engineering and Construction Contract: a user's guide*. Thomas Telford, London, 1999.

For a comparison with other conditions of contract I would recommend:

Forward F. (ed.) *The NEC compared and contrasted*. Thomas Telford, London, 2002.

Appendix 4. Procurement tool 4: Selecting contractors by value

A4.1 The original process

The initial method outlined in this procurement tool is drawn from the CIRIA publication *Selecting contractors by value*.[1] For greater detail on this method, readers are referred to this publication. This methodology can just as easily be applied to the selection of consultants and suppliers, which other publications consider.[2] An overview of the method used for selecting contractors is given below:

(a) Define what value means to the client and weight the points of definition. The value planning phase of value management, as outlined in Appendix 1, is the ideal tool for doing this.

(b) Identify opportunities for contractors to add value to the project, which could include the management of risk. This feeds into the development of the procurement strategy.

(c) Draw up questions which, when asked, probe a contractor's ability to contribute to the project. This can include pre-qualification criteria, method of construction, partnering and technical experience, proposals for managing the project, etc. In projects with any significant amount of contractor design, it would also include an evaluation of how well the outline design fulfils the client's functional and whole-life cost criteria. In terms of a value tree, as illustrated in Fig. A1.2 in Appendix 1, this means extending it rightwards with the 'how?' question being 'how can contractors contribute to the objectives?'

While drawing up these criteria, develop a range of 'model answers' for each question, which give some basis for marking the question. This in turn might impact on the question asked. Each question is weighted to the extent to which its answer contributes to the client's objectives.

Sir Michael Latham,[3] in his report *Constructing the team*, suggests that 'clients should choose their contractor based on value for money with proper weightings of selection criteria, rather than automatically accepting the lowest tender.'

(d) Obtain information from tendering contractors, which is done by asking them to fill in and respond to the 'quality' questionnaire developed in the previous point.

(e) This 'quality' submission is then evaluated and scored, usually by a committee, against the pre-defined criteria. The scores are multiplied by the question weighting to give an overall 'quality' score, which is then combined with the tendered price to give an overall mark for each tendering contractor.

A4.2 Criticisms and responses

This method does have advantages and, for the first time, took issues apart from the tender price into account after pre-qualification when selecting contractors and consultants. However, having been commonly used for a number of years now, some deficiencies are starting to emerge, which can make it a relatively superficial exercise that takes up considerable management and administrative time. For instance:

- My impression, from having worked with clients, as well as from giving workshops or training to consultants and contractors, is that the questions asked in the submissions often bear little correlation to how the contractor or consultant can contribute to the achievement of the client's objectives. This is because the objective-setting process of the client is not feeding into the selection process.

- Contractors new to the process have used consultants to help develop their 'quality' submissions. Indeed, clients have often been able to spot the same wording in submissions by different contractors because they have been prepared by the same consultant.

- Contractors now have standard submissions which they know score highly, although they do refine and tailor them to the project and client. As a result, it is not unusual for all contractors' 'quality' submissions to be scored to within 5% of each other. Even if the 'quality' criteria account for half of the basis for selection, they therefore affect the overall score by only 2.5%. As the variation in tendered prices is usually much greater, this means that price is still the predominant factor in selecting a contractor.

- Contractors may 'talk the talk' and even mean it at a high level. However, at the implementation level, all too often personnel may not even be aware of what has been said in the submission.

As a result of these issues, particularly the last point, clients are responding in a number of ways:

- Statements made in the submission about how contractors will collaborate with the client, put in place processes, use certain key individuals, select or use certain subcontractors, etc. are increasingly being incorporated into the contract and made a contractual obligation.

- Repeat order clients are using benchmarks from other contracts by the same contractor to monitor its performance. This is particularly so when selecting contractors or consultants for strategic partnerships. If a claim is made that cannot be justified by past performance, the contractor is marked down compared with the score it would have obtained had it been honest.
- Clients are using a number of mechanisms to substantiate what is said by contractors. As well as formal interviews, they are also contacting other clients and visiting sites and offices informally, interviewing staff and asking, for instance, to see training records of individual employees to check that statements made in the submission are true.

Sir Michael Latham has four questions for clients to ask the people who come to these interviews:

(a) *'Who is here?'* If it is the marketing people and not the people who will actually run the contract, he suggests giving them a cup of tea before politely sending them away!

(b) *'What have you done to prepare for partnering?'* What he would be looking for here is training, workshops, inductions for new staff, periodic reinforcement and comments on what they do with people who are not suited to a partnering way of working.

(c) If it is a main contractor, *'What do you do about subcontractors?'* Do they, for instance, select on the basis of lowest price or do they have frameworks in existence? Do they include their subcontractors in any workshops?

(d) *'Have you done partnering before?'* If they say they have, what is their definition of partnering? Who was it with and can you have contact details for the client? What were the results? Sir Michael stresses that a 'No' should not be an automatic dismissal as otherwise there will never be any newcomers to partnering. However, a 'No' would mean that more detail is required for the first three questions.

Another aspect, which is increasingly being examined, is the cultural fit of the contractors. The Highways Agency is, for instance, using a model and a set type of questions, developed by the *Advance* consultancy, for eligibility and suitability. Eligibility covers the technical skills and experiences and business processes of the consultancy or contractor and is relatively easy to validate. Suitability relates to the cultural fit with the client and, while harder to 'measure', can still be ascertained.

References

1. Jackson-Robbins A. *Selecting contractors by value*. CIRIA, London, 1998.
2. Construction Industry Board. *Selecting consultants for the team — balancing quality and price*. Thomas Telford, London, 1997.
3. Latham M. *Constructing the team: final report of the government/ industry review of procurement and contractual arrangements in the UK construction industries*. HMSO, London, 1994.

Appendix 5. Procurement tool 5: Value engineering

A5.1 The process

Value engineering has been defined as 'a systematic approach to delivering the required functions at lowest cost without detriment to quality, performance and reliability'.[1] This implies that the required functions have been defined already, for example in the value planning (VP) phase. Although the focus is on reducing cost, ideas may also be found that increase cost, but which offer benefits, that is improved functionality, that either outweigh the extra cost or, while increasing capital costs, reduce overall life cycle costs. The same techniques can be used to reduce project programmes and improve safety. Acting as a facilitator, I have used a similar process to identify and remove non-value adding activities, that is waste, in the construction process.

Like value planning (VP), value engineering is workshop based, although more detailed work will be done outside the workshop. Because it is more concerned with how work is done to achieve the end objectives, the participants are more likely to be the project implementers, rather than the stakeholders in the final product or asset, although some input from them is usually desirable.

In any particular workshop, the stages of value engineering are as follows.

A5.1.1 Stage 1: Information

It is likely that some participants will be new to the project. They therefore need to be briefed on the objectives and constraints of the project so that these are understood and the functionality of the project is not undermined.

The primary aim of this stage is to identify and examine the principal functions that are needed of the main design elements. The selected proposal from VP2 is taken and broken down into design elements. The greatest benefit from a given amount of energy expended is likely to be gained from focusing first on the elements with highest life cycle cost, so these are prioritized. For each significant element the question is asked 'What does it do that contributes to the objectives of the project?' This gives a primary function, which can be broken down into secondary functions, and a task FAST (functional analysis system technique) diagram, similar to a value tree, can be developed. Costs are then put against each function and those that attract the highest costs are an obvious target for subsequent phases of the value engineering study.

A5.1.2   Stage 2: Speculation

For each element, ideas are then generated about how to provide other ways of fulfilling the same function. Brainstorming is commonly used, although other methods can be. The ideas are typically numbered and recorded on a spreadsheet package.

A5.1.3   Stage 3: Evaluation

Ideas are then evaluated. This follows similar principles to those outlined in VP1 stage 4. The ideas that have not been discarded are then grouped into scenarios in much the same way that ideas from VP1 stage 4 are grouped into alternative proposals.

A5.1.4   Stage 4: Development

Each of these scenarios is then developed, perhaps in consultation with external experts, and priced up on a life cycle basis using similar considerations to those outlined in VP1 stage 5.

A5.1.5   Stage 5: Recommendation and briefing

The design option that represents the best value is chosen by the team and justified. Those responsible for implementation of the detailed design and/or construction need not only to be adequately briefed, but also involved in the process.

A5.2 Timing

The question of when to do value engineering workshops arises. The timing of these should coincide with key stages in the project development as they provide the best opportunity for making key decisions before money is unnecessarily expended.[1]

A5.2.1   Scheme design

The earlier the value engineering workshop to refine the proposal selected at the end of VP2 is held in the project life cycle, the greater its impact will be for the same effort. The main thrust of this workshop will be to produce and develop ideas which affect the scheme as a whole. Other ideas that affect only a segment of the works may be noted and developed in subsequent workshops for particular elements.

A5.2.2 Concurrent studies/element design

Particular teams may well only be responsible for particular elements of the scheme, so it may only be worthwhile having smaller workshops for this particular element before detailed design commences. However, these teams need to understand the big picture in terms of both overall objectives and how their part of the scheme fits in with other parts. They also need to address buildability and end user concerns. It is therefore suggested that:

- There is a briefing by someone who has had involvement in the previous phases.
- They have access to information from previous phases that is relevant to them.
- At least one participant who has been involved in previous phases, so is aware of the overall objectives and constraints and the interfaces between different elements, is present.
- At least one participant is from the party or organization that will implement the results of the workshop.
- At least one participant represents the end user or client.

Depending on the size of the team and the element it may only be worthwhile for these to be self-facilitated by someone knowledgeable in value engineering.

A.5.2.3 Contractor's change proposals

Proposals by the contractor under traditional relationships will primarily be focused on taking out capital cost. Any suggestion by the contractor has to be viewed in the light of functionality and increased *whole-life cost* to a client, particularly as savings are often shared. This is a good reason for having incentives to reduce whole-life costs (see section 6.3). I have often heard the view expressed that contractors identify and suggest savings when they start detailed programming for the construction of the element, which has two drawbacks:

- Any savings are fairly small.
- Because of the tight timescales from identification to implementation, the revised designs are often badly thought out and/or poorly detailed. Consequently, additional costs are incurred that nullify any potential savings made. This increases the likelihood of events that may lead to claims both under the construction contract and under the designer's professional indemnity insurance.

A5.2.4 Integrating risk and value management

I have heard of instances in which risk and value management processes have been combined. Often this just means that a risk management workshop is held after a value planning or value engineering workshop. In some instances, the processes are more fully integrated.

As part of a CIRIA research project I was asked to write a paper[2] about the potential for integrating risk and value management. Briefly, my main conclusions were:

- An initial risk management workshop to identify and assess, in a broad-brush manner, the general project risks should be held at the end of the VP1 workshop. These identified risks could then be taken into account when developing the options to take into the VP2 workshop.
- For each of the options taken to the VP2 workshop, option-specific risks should be identified. These risks, and the ones identified at the end of the VP1, should then be assessed for each of the options to give a spread of risk for each option. These could be plotted for comparison in a number of ways depending on the size of the project. For example, on small to medium projects, each option could have its own risk grid (see Fig. A2.1), so that people have a visual idea of the 'riskiness' of each option. For a larger project, the statistical spread of whole-life costs outcomes could be plotted. If this is the case, the functionality score for each design option could then be divided by the spread of whole-life costs to give a plot of likely out-turn 'values' for each design option.
- Once the best-value option has been chosen, risk management and value engineering can be combined into one procedure. Essentially, this is because risks identified under risk management could be considered the opposite of opportunities identified under value engineering. Both processes have an identification/speculation stage, followed by an assessment/evaluation stage and then a response planning/development stage. There could be a combined risk and opportunity register, which would allow the detailed responses to risks and development of opportunities to be considered holistically, as the project progresses, rather than separately. The combined process would therefore be both more efficient and effective.

References

1. Connaughton J. N. and Green S. D. *Value management in construction: a client's guide*. CIRIA, London 1996, CIRIA Special Publication 129.
2. Broome J. C. Literature review and discussion document for integrating value and risk management for PPP/PFI projects. Unpublished paper, November 2001.

Appendix 6. Procurement tool 6: Benchmarks and benchmarking

The process of measuring performance is essential for comparing performance of different contractors and consultants, to ensure continuous improvement and as the basis for rewarding performance when using a balanced incentive plan.

Benchmarks are the measures of performance, while benchmarking is the process of comparing performance with others by finding out the more qualitative information behind the figure, which leads to better performance and then applying what can be learnt to your own organization.

A6.1 Benchmarks

There are essentially three stages/types of benchmarks, the characteristics of which are described in Table A6.1. As can be seen, the benchmarks become more subjective and time-consuming to develop, implement and measure on moving from left to right (end of project to process benchmarks). They also become more specific, in terms of both what the organization or project team is doing and their application. This means that the potential for learning from others is greatest when process benchmarks are compared. However, the processes that lead to 'best in class' end of project benchmarks in one type of project may not work in another. When developing benchmarks, it is important to strike a balance between measuring what is important and ease of measurement. You do not want the measuring to detract from the doing. Benchmarks are a means to end. While the final end is to improve performance, their intermediate end is to highlight areas that can be improved.

A6.2 Benchmarking

This is the basis for comparing not only the measures of performance, but also what lies behind them. This, it could be argued, has four levels (Table A6.2), which can use any of the three types of benchmarks described previously.

Table A6.1. An overview of the types of benchmarks and their characteristics

Type of benchmark	End of project	Intermediate	Process
Description	Measures project outcomes in hard data, e.g. actual project duration over forecast at sanction in days. Often referred to as key performance indicators (KPIs)	Measures intermediate targets, which should mean end of project benchmarks are achieved, e.g. percentage activities completed in a month vs. planned	Descriptions of the best-practice processes, which should lead to intermediate and end of project benchmarks being achieved, e.g. the planning process
Type of measure	Quantitative	More quantitative than qualitative	Qualitative, i.e. a description
Ease of assessment	Relatively easy one-off measurements at end of project	Regular measurements, with some subjectivity; more time-consuming	Time-consuming to develop, implement and measure, but high potential rewards

Table A6.2. Types of benchmarking

Type of comparison	With self through time	Within company	External to company but within industry	External to company and industry
Description	Comparing own current performance or process with past performance	Comparing own performance or processes with separate operational unit, e.g. a different major project or division in same company	Comparing same type of company or projects, but with those who are not direct competitors, e.g. a company operating in a different geographical area	Comparing processes and outcomes across industries, e.g. project processes in oil, chemical and construction industries

Appendix 7. Procurement routes and suitable conditions of contract

The table on the following pages matches different procurement routes with sector, pricing mechanism and conditions of contract.

Table A7.1. *Matching procurement routes with sector, pricing mechanism and conditions of contract*

Procurement route	Sector	Pricing mechanism	Conditions of contract
Traditional: design followed by construction	Building	Bills of quantities	JCT '98 Private Contract with Quantities Local Authority Contract with Quantities
		Approximate bill of quantities	JCT '98 Private Contract with Approximate Quantities Local Authority Contract with Approximate Quantities
		Lump sum	JCT '98 Private Contract without Quantities Local Authority Contract without Quantities Minor Works
	Civil engineering	Bills of quantities	*ICE*, 5th, 6th or 7th edn *FIDIC Red Book*, 4th edn
	Building and civil engineering	Bills of quantities	GC Works 1-198 Contract with quantities for Major Works 298 Minor Works
		Lump sum	GC Works 1-298 Contract without quantities for Major Works
	Multidisciplinary	Activity schedules	NEC — option A: Priced contract with activity schedules EC Short Contract
		Bills of quantities	NEC ECC — option B: Priced contract with bills of quantities EC Short Contract

Contractor design	Building	Lump sum	JCT '81 or '98 for Contractor Design
	Civil engineering	Lump sum	ICE Design and Construct 1992
	Building and civil engineering	Lump sum	GC Works 1-398 Single Stage Design and Build
	Mechanical and electrical engineering	Lump sum	*FIDIC Yellow Book*, 3rd edn; GC Works 398 for Mechanical and Electrical Works
	Process	Lump sum	*IChemE Red Book* (used for works with large civil engineering content)
	Multidisciplinary	Lump sum	FIDIC for Design, Build and Turnkey (*Orange Book*)
		Lump sum	GC Works 498 for Building, Civil Engineering, Mechanical and Electrical Works
		Activity schedules	NEC ECC option A: Priced contract with activity schedules
Preferred contractor: design and build	Multidisciplinary	Activity schedules	NEC ECC Option A: Priced contract with activity schedules
	Building and civil engineering.	Lump sum (payable as a percentage)	GC Works 1-599 Two Stage Design and Build
Management contracting	Building	Lump sum fee to MC; reimbursed cost of works subcontractors	JCT '98 Management Contract
	Multidisciplinary	Reimbursed cost of works subcontractors; management contractor's costs paid as a percentage of what is due to works subcontractors	NEC ECC option F: Management Contract
Construction management	Building	Variable both to construction manager and works subcontractors	Bespoke agreement between Client and CM; any JCT form as appropriate
	Multidisciplinary	subcontractors	NEC Professional Services Contract for Construction Management; NEC ECC: any option or NEC ECSC as appropriate

Procurement route	Sector	Pricing mechanism	Conditions of contract
Engineer, procure and construct (EPC)	Multidisciplinary	Reimbursed cost of works subcontractors	FIDIC conditions for EPC Turnkey Projects
Cost reimbursable	Multidisciplinary	Cost plus percentage fee	NEC Option E: Cost reimbursable contract
	Chemical, but often used in civil engineering	Cost plus fee	*IChemE Green Book*
Target cost	Multidisciplinary	Cost plus percentage fee plus pain/gain share vs. target	NEC option C: Target contract with activity schedule
		Cost plus percentage fee plus pain/gain share vs. target with target adjusted for changes in quantity	NEC option C: Target contract with bills of quantitities
	Chemical, but often used in civil engineering	Cost plus fee plus pain/gain share vs. target	*IChemE Green Book*, but with additional clauses for target and pain/gain share
Project alliances	Multidisciplinary	Extra payments against stated KPIs shared in stated proportions by alliance members	NEC Partnering Agreement clauses added on to existing NEC contracts between client and suppliers
	Building, but has been used in civil engineering	Cost savings or over-run split amongst alliance memebers	PPC 2000

ECC, Engineering and Construction Contract; ECSC, Engineering and Construction Subcontract; FIDIC, Fédération International des Ingénieurs et Conseils; GC, General Conditions; ICE, Institution of Civil Engineers; IChemE, Institution of Chemical Engineers; JCT, Joint Contracts Tribunal; PPC, Project Partnering Contract.

Index

Index

Index

Index

Index